MW00837495

Clay and Clay Minerals

Edited by Gustavo Morari Do Nascimento

Published in London, United Kingdom

IntechOpen

Supporting open minds since 2005

Clay and Clay Minerals
http://dx.doi.org/10.5772/intechopen.95640
Edited by Gustavo Morari Do Nascimento

Contributors
Sylvie Rossignol, Ameni Gharzouni, Clement Alize, Meng Fu, Zepeng Zhang, Rui Jiang, Hongbao Liu, Chandra Mohan, Neeraj Kumari, César Pedrajas Nieto-Márquez, Rafael Talero Morales, Carlos Hernando Aramburo Varela, Luiz Felipe Pinho, Hayat Benmoussa, Maryam Achik, Boutaina Moumni, Abdellah Oulmekki, Abdelhamid Touache, Álvaro Gil González, Francisco Guitián Rivera, Dolores Eliche Quesada, Antonia Infantes-Molina, Olga Kizinievič, Cochiran Pereira dos Santos, Adriana de Jesus Santos, Uche Ekpunobi, Ihueze Christopher Chukwutoo, Philomena Igbokwe, Azubike Ekpunobi, Happiness Obiora-Ilouno, Chijioke Onu, Sunday Agbo, Samuel Ezennaya, Uzochukwu Onuigbo, Ifenyinwa Tabugbo, Emma Amalu, Arit Etukudoh, Caius Onu, Tanushree Choudhury, Aicha Kourim, Moulay Abderrahmane Malouki, Aicha Ziouche, Murugesan Manikkampatti Palanisamy, Gustavo Morari Do Nascimento, Akilamudhan Palaniappan, Venkata Ratnam Myneni, Kannan Kandasamy, Minar Mohamed Lebbai, Padmapriya Veerappan

First published in London, United Kingdom, 2021 by IntechOpen
IntechOpen is the global imprint of INTECHOPEN LIMITED, registered in England and Wales, registration number: 11086078, 5 Princes Gate Court, London, SW7 2QJ, United Kingdom
Printed in Croatia

British Library Cataloguing-in-Publication Data
A catalogue record for this book is available from the British Library

Additional hard and PDF copies can be obtained from orders@intechopen.com

Clay and Clay Minerals
Edited by Gustavo Morari Do Nascimento
p. cm.
Print ISBN 978-1-83969-563-6
Online ISBN 978-1-83969-564-3
eBook (PDF) ISBN 978-1-83969-565-0

Meet the editor

Dr. Gustavo Morari do Nascimento is a professor at the Federal University of ABC, Brazil. He obtained a Ph.D. from the University of São Paulo (USP), Brazil, in 2004. Since completing a postdoctorate at Massachusetts Institute of Technology (MIT), USA, in 2008, Dr. Morari do Nascimento has been working with carbon allotropes, conducting polymers, and conducting polymer-clay nanocomposites. His current research focuses on molecular characterization of chemically modified carbon nanostructured materials with molecular magnets and organic chalcogenide compounds by using FT-Raman spectroscopy, resonance Raman, surface-enhanced Raman spectroscopy (SERS), resonance Raman imaging, and X-ray absorption techniques at the Brazilian Synchrotron Light Laboratory.

Contents

Preface

The synthesis and study of clays and clay minerals are some of the widest fields of research in materials science and technology. Characterization and application of many derived clay materials with different polymers and organic and biological molecules are attracting great interest from scientists and researchers, especially with the emergence of nanotechnology. The catalytic behavior of some clay surfaces can change the properties of adsorbed or intercalated molecules. Theoretical approaches using ab initio, quantum chemical, and Monte Carlo calculations combined with new spectroscopic techniques are expanding the knowledge of clay properties. New two-dimensional materials based on clays and clay minerals are attracting attention for their outstanding properties that make them useful as hosts or supporting matrixes in applications such as pharmaceuticals, tissue engineering, environmental remediation, biosensors, filtration, wound dressings, drug delivery, enzyme immobilization, 3D printing, and more. This book is a comprehensive overview of clay science and technology, focusing on synthesis, characterization, simulation, and applications. It is divided into two parts: "Clay Properties and Characterization" and "Clay Properties and Applications."

The first section of the book includes chapters dealing with fundamental properties of clays, their related materials, and characterization techniques.

Chapter 1 reviews studies related to polymer–clay materials with emphasis on the use of molecular and vibrational spectroscopies in the characterization of conducting polymer-clay nanocomposites.

Chapter 2 reviews fundamental concepts related to clay structure and properties. It also discusses reasons to use clay in hybrid materials.

Chapter 3 focuses on the thermodynamics and kinetics of removing copper (II) and methyl orange from an aqueous solution using natural clay and its composites.

Chapter 4 presents the chemical, mineralogical, and rheological characterization of samples from four clay deposits before and after fractionation. These raw clays are used in the production of ceramic tiles, bricks, blocks, and artisanal pieces in Sergipe, Brazil, for possible use in high value-added products such as cosmetics and pharmaceuticals.

Chapter 5 examines one-dimensional natural clay decorated with magnetic nanoparticles of Fe3O4. The material is well characterized by different physical-chemical techniques. The chapter shows that the functionalization of one-dimensional clay minerals has potential applications in display devices, photonic switches, and other applications.

The second section of the book includes chapters dealing with applications of clays and their related materials.

Chapter 6 discusses the use of bentonite clay in the recovery of copper metal atoms from printed circuit boards (from electronic waste). The recovery process is optimized by several parameters, and this chapter proposes an eco-friendly way to recover copper ions with no environmental issues.

Chapter 7 examines the effect of the addition of two types of wastes on the technological properties of fired brick-based yellow clay. The test results indicate that the addition of wastes to clay bricks improves their technological properties and highlights the possibility of waste reuse in a safe and sustainable way.

Chapter 8 discusses the thermal behavior of geopolymers, which can be changed by clay and alkali compositions. The chapter shows that geopolymers can be used as fire-resistant materials.

Chapter 9 reviews the thermal activation of clays to produce an extraordinarily high-quality supplementary cementitious material (SCM) based on the contents of its hydraulic factors: reactive silica (SiO_2r^-) and reactive alumina ($Al_2O_3r^-$). The production process and the optimization of its use in the new types of cement offer better performance, features, and durability.

Chapter 10 considers the production of electric porcelain insulators utilizing local raw materials from developing countries. The raw materials used include feldspar, quartz/silica, and kaolin. The chapter concludes that standard and acceptable electric porcelain insulators can be produced from local raw materials.

Chapter 11 discusses the physical-chemical characterization of titania-pillared clay hybrid membranes. The developed membranes can be used to remove heavy metal ions from wastewater, the recovery of which yields maximum benefit. The product presented can best treat textile effluent from the dye industry with concentrations in the range of 50 ppm.

Even though knowledge of the real impact of materials derived from clay on the environment, industrial processes, and human health is still limited, I hope that this book will prove useful for understanding the broad and complex field of clay science and technology. Finally, I would like to thank all the contributing authors as well as the staff at IntechOpen for their efforts and support throughout the publishing process.

Dr. Gustavo Morari do Nascimento
Professor,
Centre for Natural Sciences and Humanities,
Federal University of ABC,
Santo André, Brazil

Section 1

Clay Properties and Characterization

Chapter 1

Introductory Chapter: Polymers and Clays - A Fruitful Combination

Gustavo Morari do Nascimento

1. Introduction

1.1 Clays and clay materials

The synthesis and study of materials based on clays and/or clay minerals with polymers are one of the widest fields of research in materials science and technology. Characterization followed by application of many derived clay materials is a big deal in clay science and technology. **Figure 1A** shows that in 2021, more than 16,000 papers having "clay" and "polymer" as keywords were published since 1998. In addition, **Figure 1B** shows that a group of conducting polymers represents more or less 20% of total polymers studied in composites and/or nanocomposites with clays. In addition, **Figure 2** displays that at least 15 different research fields mainly concentrated on chemistry and polymer sciences, environmental sciences, materials and nanotechnology. These two graphs clearly show that polymer clay-derived materials are one of the focuses in the science of advanced materials. Our group has been dedicated to the preparation and characterization of materials consisting of conducting polymers from polyaniline family with clays [1–11]. Among the different techniques used for structural investigation, resonance Raman spectroscopy and Synchrotron X-ray techniques are the most important for these systems.

The term "clay" was defined as "...a naturally occurring material composed primarily of fine-grained minerals (< 4μm), which is generally plastic at appropriate water contents and will harden with dried or fired" [12–15]. Likewise, the term "clay mineral" can be defined as "...phyllosilicate minerals and minerals which impart plasticity to clay and which harden upon drying or firing." Since the origin of the mineral is not part of the definition, clay mineral (unlike clay) may be synthetic. Hence, analyzing the fine-grained clay particles in detail is only possible by a combination of advanced spectroscopic and microscopic techniques [16]. Clays are aluminosilicates where the aluminum can be replaced by magnesium and iron atoms, resulting in an excess of negative charge that is balanced by alkaline or alkaline earth elements. Each clay has different composition, dehydration properties, structural failure limits, decomposition products, cation exchange capacity (CEC), and other useful properties and economic interests.

Clays layers are formed by tetrahedral (T) and octahedral (O) sheets bonded by oxygen atoms. Unshared oxygen atoms are present in hydroxyl form. Two main arrangements of T and O layers are observed: (1: 1) and (2: 1) (T:O) clays. The (1: 1) group is known as kaolin group, with the general composition of $Al_2Si_2O_5(OH)_5$ and the layer thickness of ~0.7 nm [12–14, 17]. In addition, the second main arrangement (2: 1) is well known as phyllosilicates, where one octahedral sheet is sandwiched between two tetrahedral sheets (2:1) with a total thickness of 0.94 nm. When silicon

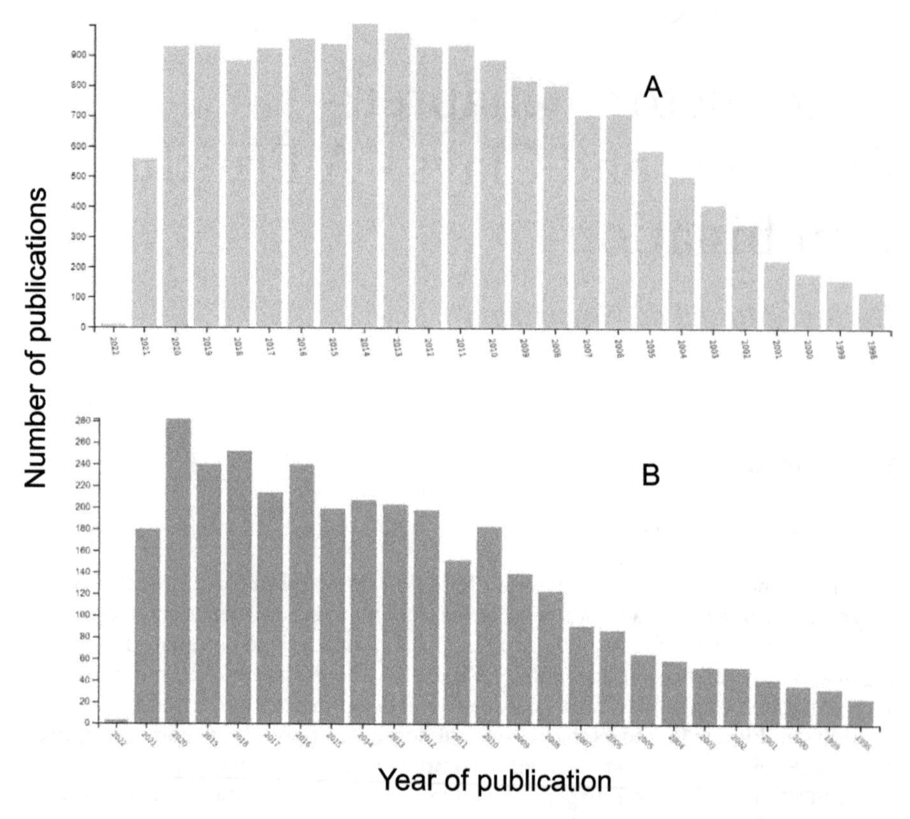

Figure 1.
Number of publications by year for the keywords: A—"clay" and "polymer*" and B—"clay*" and "polymer*" and "conducting*" in the text. The research was done on October 10, 2021, using the web of science database. The total score found are 16.861 and 3.480 papers for graphs a and B, respectively.*

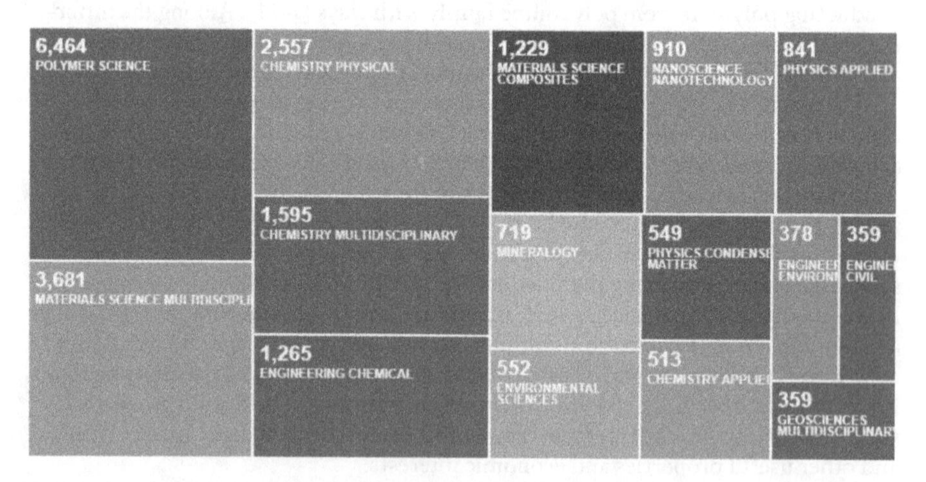

Figure 2.
Number of publications by year having the keywords "clay" and "polymer*" in the text divided by the main research areas or categories. The research was done on October 10, 2021, using the web of science database.*

in tetrahedral sheets is substituted by aluminum, the 2:1 structure is called mica. The negative charge generated by this change is equilibrated by the presence of potassium cations between the layers. Because of the equal size of K^+ cation and the hole created by Si/Al tetrahedral sheets, there is no inter-layer spacing. Hence, no swelling or exfoliation of 2:1 layers is possible. When the aluminum cations in the octahedral sheets are partially substituted by Mg^{2+} or Fe^{2+} cations, the smectite clay group is formed, whose structure consists of a central sheet containing octahedral groups ($MO_4(OH)_2$) bonding to two tetrahedral layers (MO_4) producing layers designated T:O:T [17] (see **Figure 3**). Ions of aluminum, iron and magnesium occupy the octahedral sites, while the centers have tetrahedrons of silicon and aluminum ions.

The T:O:T layers assume a parallel orientation, and the negative electric charge is neutralized by the presence of hydrated positive ions that are in the interlayer region [17]. These clays have high-surface adsorption capacity and catalytic activity in organic reactions. The montmorillonite (MMT) is the most common smectite clay, and the negative charges of the layer arise mainly from substitution of aluminum by magnesium ions in octahedral sites. In addition, the swelling properties, and thermal, chemical and colloidal dispersion stabilities probably are responsible for the extensive use of the MMT clay (ca. 50%) in the polymer clay-derived materials. In this introductory chapter, we will give en passant about the main points about polymers and clays —a fruitful combination.

1.2 Polymer clay materials

A polymer clay material is made by a physical and/or chemical combination of a polymer and synthetic or natural clay. The clay platelets can improve the mechanical, thermal, gas and fire barrier retardancy properties of the polymer. The improvements depend strongly on mechanical and physical dimensions of the clay, the interfacial adhesion between polymer and clay and especially on the aspect ratio of the clay. The aspect ratio of the clay is very important and crucial for many properties in composites, such as electrical, mechanical and thermal properties [18, 19].

Polymer nanocomposite is defined as a composite material in which at least one dimension of at least one component is in the nanometer size scale (< 100 nm) [20]. In recent years, the nanocomposite research area has created efficient and powerful

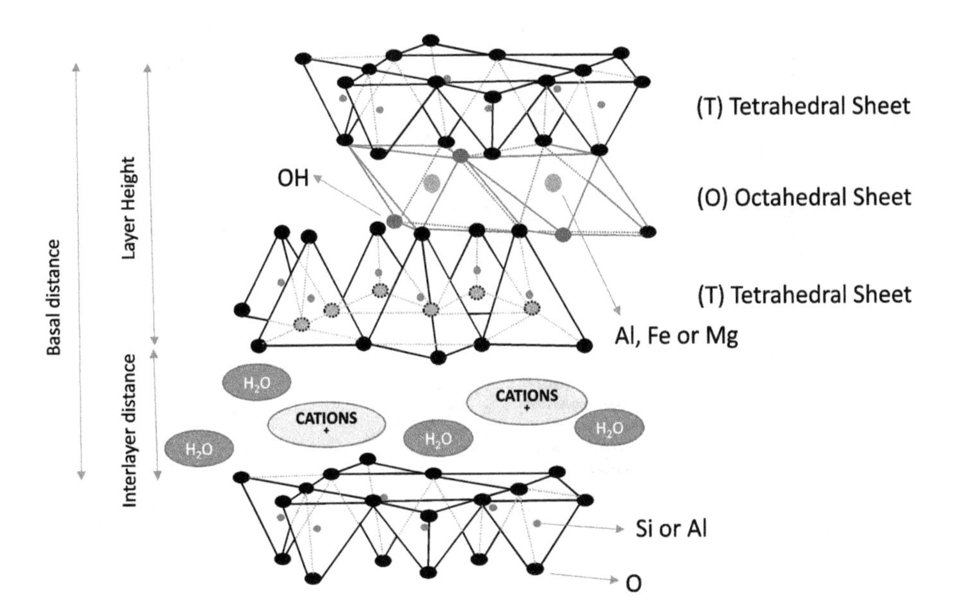

Figure 3.
Schematic representation of montmorillonite clay (MMT).

strategies to upgrade the structural and functional properties of natural and synthetic polymers. Polymer nanocomposites have generated great attention because of superior properties such as strength, toughness and fire resistance far from those of regular micro-composites and comparable with those of metals. The existence of one nanoscale phase tremendously increases the interfacial contact between the polymer and clay. As a consequence, the improvement of the polymer properties, such as mechanical, thermal barrier and flame retardancy, durability and chemical stability, scratch/wear resistance and biodegradability, as well as optical, magnetical and electrical properties, has been observed [21–24]. Recent investigations using continuum mechanics modeling show that the enhancement of nanocomposites properties is highly dependent on the peculiar features of nanofiller material, in particular, its content, aspect ratio and the ratio of filler mechanical properties to those of the matrix [25].

Polymer clay nanocomposites can be made by direct mixture of two aqueous solutions containing the monomer and the clay suspension, respectively (see **Figure 4**), followed by polymerization induced by thermal or light sources or by adding chemical oxidants [26, 27]. Afterward, if the major part of the polymer is produced outside the interlayer space, the resulting compound is named as *Ex situ* nanocomposite. The initial clay concentration can be changed in an aqueous solution in order to completely exfoliate the layers. Hence, the resulting material is known as exfoliated polymer clay nanocomposite. In another route, the monomer is previously intercalated in the interlayer space before the polymerization procedure. Then, the resulting material is known as *in situ* nanocomposite because the major part of the polymeric content is inside the clay interspace (see **Figure 4**). The polymer clay hybrids started with the synthesis of nylon-6-clay hybrid (NCH) produced in 1986 under Toyota Central Research and Development Laboratories. Then, the same strategy was employed in the formation of polymer clay hybrids with various polymeric systems, including epoxies, polyesters, polyimides, nitrile rubber, polypropylene, polyurethanes, polystyrene and

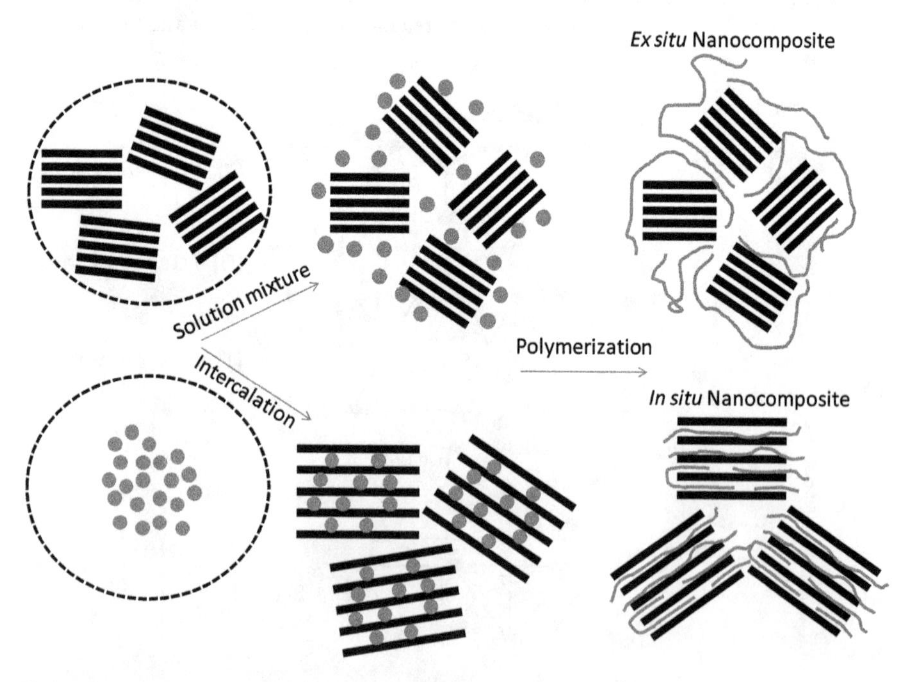

Figure 4.
Schematic representation of two types of preparation of polymer clay nanocomposites.

polysiloxanes. Traditionally, the clay layers must be previously treated with an organic agent to ensure good dispersion of clay layers within the polymer matrix. It is very hard to mix clay layers in most polymer matrices because of their high face-to-face stacking and intrinsic hydrophilic character. These characteristics make most clays incompatible with hydrophobic polymers, and only a few hydrophilic polymers such as poly(ethylene oxide) and poly(vinyl alcohol) can be miscible with clay layers [28]. Modification of clay layers with hydrophobic agents is necessary in order to make clay more compatible with polymers and preclude formation of non-mixed phases.

1.3 Conducting polymer-clay materials

Among the polymers used for production of polymer clay materials are the intrinsically conducting polymers (ICPs). These classes of polymers are conjugated polymers that can be doped by chemical, electrochemical or photochemical processes with an increase of their conductivities (see **Figure 5**). The doping is reversible, and the polymer can return to its original state without major changes in its structure [29–34]. In the doped state, the presence of counter ions stabilizes the doped state. All conductive polymers (and their derivatives), for example, poly(aniline), poly(pyrrole), poly(thiophene)s, poly(*p*-phenylene-vinylene)s, poly(heteroaromatic vinylene) (f, where Y = NH, NR, S, O), among others (see **Figure 5**), may be doped by p (oxidation) or n (reduction) process. Our group has been synthesizing polymer clay nanocomposites formed by poly(aniline) (PANI, see **Figure 6**) and its derivatives with MMT clay for almost two decades [1–11].

The adsorption of aromatic compounds such as aniline on MMT clay was investigated a long time ago, and the clay property to generate colored species by

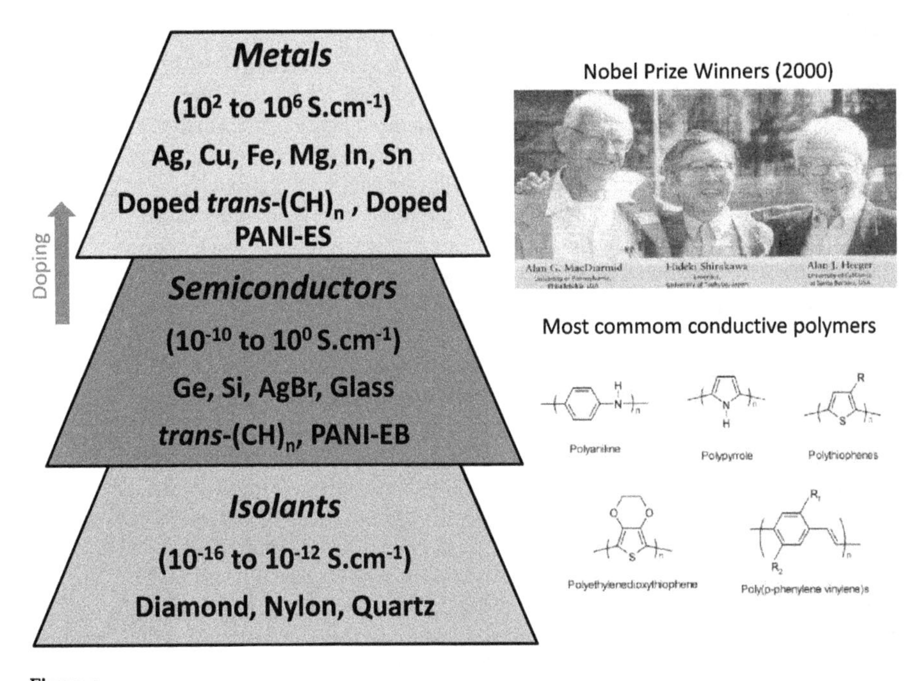

Figure 5.
The Nobel winners in chemistry (Hideki Shirakawa, Alan J. Heeger, and Alan G. MacDiarmid [29–31]) for the discovery and development of conducting polymers and the chemical structures of the most investigated conductive polymers. In addition, the conductivity values for different materials are also displayed in comparison with conducting polymers before and after the doping. The doping produces (the addition of nonstoichiometric chemical species in quantities low ≤10%) dramatic changes in the electronic, optical, electrical, magnetical and structural properties of the polymer.

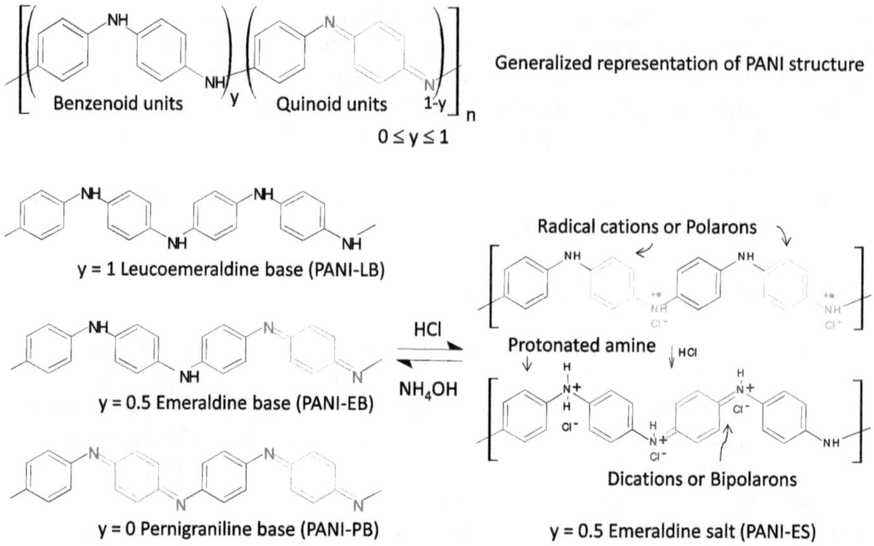

Figure 6.
Representation of PANI structure and its most representative forms.

the adsorption of aromatic amines was on the first experimental observation. The well-known behavior is the blue color generated by the adsorption of benzidine (4,4′-diaminobiphenyl) into clay layers. First, investigations reported that films of MMT containing metal ions become black after immersion in aniline, suggesting the polymerization of the monomer [35–39]. By using resonance Raman spectroscopy (RR), Soma and Soma [40–44] discovered that the adsorption of liquid aniline on Cu^{2+} or Fe^{3+}-MMT causes the formation of the polymer. Soma and Soma suggested that the polymeric structure is equal to that generated electrochemically but with the presence of azo bonds (-N=N-). Another important observation is that intercalated PANI showed FTIR bands at 1568, 1505, 1311 and 1246 cm^{-1} characteristic of the conducting emeraldine state, but they were shifted to higher frequencies to the spectrum of free polymer. According to the authors, this displacement is a consequence of geometric restrictions imposed over the aromatic rings. The intercalation was confirmed by changes in the interlayer distance from 1.47 to 0.36 nm after the polymerization of aniline. Absorption bands were observed at 420 and 800 nm in the UV–vis–NIR spectrum of the material, which are the characteristic of conducting PANI form [45].

In fact, many authors prepared PANI-MMT using ammonium persulphate as an oxidizing agent, and for these authors the electronic spectra and FTIR bands were enough to characterize the PANI in its conductive state (emeraldine salt) [45–55]. However, when our group started to study this material by using resonance Raman spectroscopy (like Soma and Soma one decade earlier [40–44]) together with X-ray absorption techniques, it was revealed that the structure of intercalated PANI into MMT layers is much more complex and different from the free PANI [1–11]. The early stages of the polymerization of intercalated anilinium ions were monitored by *in situ* resonance Raman measurements. It was observed the bands of radical cation of PANI-ES (at 1167, 1318/1339 and 1625 cm^{-1}) and dication (at 1481 and 1582 cm^{-1}) and also bands due to benzidine dication at 1211, 1370, 1455, and 1608 cm^{-1}, confirming that into clay galleries, occur the head-to-tail and also tail-to-tail coupling between the aniline monomers. In the final stages of polymerization, mainly by the resonance Raman data obtained at 632.8 nm, it was confirmed to be a completely new spectrum, whose bands have no similitude with either the radical cation of

PANI-ES or the spectrum of benzidine dication. This result shows that another type of chromophore was formed. At this point, the use of XANES spectroscopy on nitrogen K-edge was fundamental. Through the analysis of several dyes, it was possible to build an extensive data library [11], and by comparative analysis, it was found that the structure of intercalated PANI also has phenazine rings. Combining all spectroscopic data, we have proposed that the best standard compound, having azo group bonded to phenazine- or oxazine-like rings in their structure, was the Janus Green B (JGB). This dye that gives out similar vibrational and electronic signatures to those of the PANI-MMT nanocomposites can be used in the future for simulation of the electronic properties.

2. Conclusion and future remarks

We really think that the polymer clay area has much more to be investigated, but with the employment of new synthetic strategies and the use of advanced spectroscopic techniques. The accumulated experience with PANI-MMT materials revealed the importance of the use of advanced and complementary spectroscopic techniques in order to give a more realistic view of the molecular structure formed in the clay layers. The screening of the electronic and vibrational structure of PANI-MMT through resonance Raman and X-ray absorption spectroscopy has been decisive in the determination of their "real" structure and in the study of the interactions between the clay layers and polymer chains. In fact, by selecting the appropriate laser line, it is possible to study in particular each polymeric segment into polymer backbone. The new Raman instruments can give better Raman imaging of the samples and open the possibility to study inhomogeneity, chemical modifications, and many other aspects of the polymer clay materials. In addition, new Synchrotron light sources will enable us to study changes in these complex materials by *in situ* measurements, resulting in spectral and imaging data. These new data are crucial for better application design and more vast use of materials derived from polymer clays.

Author details

Gustavo Morari do Nascimento
Federal University of ABC, CCNH, Santo André, Brazil

*Address all correspondence to: gustavo.morari@ufabc.edu.br; morari@yahoo.com

References

[1] Do Nascimento GM, Constantino VRL, Temperini MLA. Spectroscopic characterization of a new type of conducting polymer–clay nanocomposite. Macromolecules. 2002;**35**:7535

[2] Do Nascimento GM, Landers R, Constantino VRL, Temperini MLA. Aniline polymerization into montmorillonite clay: A spectroscopic investigation of the intercalated conducting polymer. Macromolecules. 2004;**37**:9373

[3] Do Nascimento GM, Constantino VRL, Temperini MLA. Spectroscopic characterization of doped poly (benzidine) and its nanocomposite with cationic clay. The Journal of Physical Chemistry B. 2004;**108**:5564

[4] Do Nascimento GM, Landers R, Constantino VRL, Temperini MLA. Spectroscopic characterization of polyaniline formed in the presence of montmorillonite clay. Polymer. 2006;**47**:6131

[5] Do Nascimento GM, Barbosa PSM, Constantino VRL, Temperini MLA. Benzidine oxidation on cationic clay surfaces in aqueous suspension monitored by in situ resonance Raman spectroscopy. Colloids and Surfaces A: Physicochemical and Engineering Aspects. 2006;**289**:39

[6] Do Nascimento GM, Padilha ACM, Constantino VRL, Temperini MLA. Oxidation of anilinium ions intercalated in montmorillonite clay by electrochemical route. Colloids and Surfaces A: Physicochemical and Engineering Aspects. 2008;**318**:245

[7] Do Nascimento GM, Temperini MLA. Structure of polyaniline formed in different inorganic porous materials: A spectroscopic study. European Polymer Journal. 2008;**44**:3501

[8] Do Nascimento GM, Temperini MLA. Spectroscopic study of the polymerization of intercalated anilinium ions in different montmorillonite clays. Journal of Molecular Structure. 2011;**1002**:63

[9] Do Nascimento GM. X-ray absorption spectroscopy of nano-structured polyanilines. Chemical Papers. 2013;**67**:933

[10] Do Nascimento GM, Pradie NA. Deprotonation, Raman dispersion and thermal behavior of polyaniline–montmorillonite nanocomposites. Synthetic Metals. 2016;**217**:109

[11] Do Nascimento GM. Structure of clays and polymer–clay composites studied by X-ray absorption spectroscopies. In: Do Nascimento GM, editor. Clays, Clay Minerals and Ceramic Materials Based on Clay Minerals 1st ed. London: InTech; 2016

[12] Bergaya F, Lagaly G. General introduction: Clays, clay minerals, and clay science. In: Bergaya F, Theng BKG, Lagaly G, editors. Handbook of Clay Science. Amsterdam: Elsevier; 2006. pp. 1-18

[13] Hall PL. Clays: Their significance, properties, origins and uses. In: Wilson MJ, editor. A Handbook of Determinative Methods in Clay Mineralogy. Glasgow: Blackie; 1987. pp. 1-25

[14] Guggenheim S, Martin RT. Definition of clay and clay mineral: Joint report of the AIPEA nomenclature and CMS nomenclature committees. Clays and Clay Minerals. 1995;**43**:255

[15] Moore DM, Reynolds RC Jr. X-ray Diffraction and the Identification and Analysis of Clay Minerals. 2nd ed. Oxford: Oxford University Press; 1997

[16] Brown G. Associated minerals. In: Brindley GW, Brown G, editors. Crystal

Structures of Clay Minerals and their X-ray Identification. London: Mineralogy Society; 1980. pp. 361-410

[17] Yariv S. Introduction to organo-clay complexes and interactions. In: Yariv S, Cross H, editors. Organo-Clay Complexes and Interactions. New York: Marcel Dekker, Inc.; 2002

[18] Zhang R, Ni QQ, Natsuki T, Iwamoto M. Mechanical properties of composites filled with SMA particles and short fibers. Composite Structures. 2007;**79**:90

[19] Meneghetti P, Qutubuddin S. Synthesis, thermal properties and applications of polymer-clay nano-composites. Thermochimica Acta. 2006;**442**:74

[20] Hussain F, Hojjati M, Okamoto M, Gorga RE. Review article: Polymer-matrix nanocomposites, processing, manufacturing, and Application: An Overview. Journal of Composite Materials. 2006;**40**(17):1511

[21] Armentano I, Dottori M, Fortunati E, Mattioli S, Kenny JM. Biodegradable polymer matrix nanocomposites for tissue engineering: A review. Polymer Degradation and Stability. 2010;**95**(11):2126

[22] Cosoli P, Scocchi G, Pricl S, Fermaglia M. Many-scale molecular simulation for ABS-MMT nano-composites: Upgrading of industrial scraps. Microporous and Mesoporous Materials. 2008;**107**:169

[23] Ma H, Xu Z, Tong L, Gu A, Fang Z. Studies of ABS-graft-maleic anhydride/clay nanocomposites: Morphologies, thermal stability and flammability properties. Polymer Degradation and Stability. 2006;**91**:2951

[24] Pandey JK, Reddy KR, Kumar AP, Singh RP. An overview on the degradability of polymer nanocomposites. Polymer Degradation and Stability. 2005;**88**:234

[25] Sheng N, Boyce MC, Parks DM, Rutledge GC, Abes JI, Cohen RE. Multiscale micromechanical modeling of polymer/clay nanocomposites and the effective clay particle. Polymer. 2004;**45**:487

[26] LeBaron PC, Wang Z, Pinnavaia TJ. Polymer-layered silicate nanocomposites: An overview. Applied Clay Science. 1999;**15**:11

[27] Thostenson ET, Li C, Chou TW. Nanocomposites in context. Composites Science and Technology. 2005;**65**:491

[28] Pavlidou S, Papaspyrides CD. A review on polymer-layered silicate nanocomposites. Progress in Polymer Science. 2008;**32**:1119

[29] Shirakawa H, Ikeda S. Infrared spectra of poly(acetylene). Polymer Journal. 1971;**2**(2):231

[30] Shirakawa H. The discovery of polyacetylene film: The dawning of an era of conducting polymer (Nobel Lecture). Angewandte Chemie, International Edition. 2001;**40**:2575

[31] MacDiarmid AG. 'Synthetic Metals': A novel role for organic polymers (Nobel Lecture). Angewandte Chemie, International Edition. 2001;**40**:2581

[32] Heeger AJ. Semiconducting and metallic polymers: The fourth generation of polymeric materials (Nobel Lecture). Angewandte Chemie, International Edition. 2001;**40**:2591

[33] MacDiarmid AG, Epstein AJ. The polyanilines: A novel class of conducting polymers. In: Conducting Polymers, Emerging Technologies. New Jersey: Technical Insights Inc.; 1989. p. 27

[34] Do Nascimento GM, Souza MA. Spectroscopy of nanostructured

conducting polymers. In: Eftekhari A, editor. Nanostructured Conducting Polymers. Londres: Wiley and Sons; 2010. pp. 341-375

[35] Yariv S, Michaelian KH. Structure and surface acidity of clay minerals Organo-Clay Complexes and Interactíons; Yariv, S.; Cross, H., Marcel Dekker: New York; 2002. p. 1

[36] Hauser EA, Leggett MB. Color reactions between clays and amines. Journal of the American Chemical Society. 1940;**62**:1811

[37] Yariv S, Heller L, Safer Z. Sorption of aniline by montmorillonite. Israel Journal of Chemistry. 1968;**6**:741

[38] Furukawa T, Brindley GW. Adsorption and oxidation of benzidine and aniline by montmorillonite and hectorite. Clays and Clay Minerals. 1973;**21**:279

[39] Cloos P, Moreale A, Broers C, Badat C. Adsorption and oxidation of aniline and p-chloroaniline by montmorillonite. Clay Minerals. 1979;**14**:307

[40] Soma Y, Soma M. Adsorption of benzidines and anilines on Cu-montmorillonites and Fe-montmorillonites studied by resonance Raman-spectroscopy. Clay Minerals. 1988;**23**:1

[41] Soma Y, Soma M. Chemical-reactions of organic-compounds on clay surfaces. Environmental Health Perspectives. 1989;**83**:205

[42] Soma Y, Soma M, Harada I. Raman-spectroscopic evidence of formation of para-dimethoxybenzene cation on Cu-montmorillonite and Ru-montmorillonite. Chemical Physics Letters. 1983;**94**:475

[43] Soma Y, Soma M, Harada I. The reaction of aromatic-molecules in the interlayer of transition-metal ion-exchanged montmorillonite studied by resonance Raman-spectroscopy. 1. Benzene and para-phenylenes. The Journal of Physical Chemistry A. 1984;**88**:3034

[44] Soma Y, Soma M, Harada I. Reactions of aromatic-molecules in the interlayer of transition-metal ion-exchanged montmorillonite studied by resonance Raman-spectroscopy. 2. 4, 4′-Disubstituted biphenyls. The Journal of Physical Chemistry. 1985;**89**:738

[45] TeC C, Ho SY, Chao KJ. Intercalation of polyaniline in monmorillonite and zeolite. Journal of the Chinese Chemical Society. 1992;**39**:209

[46] Wu Q, Xue Z, Qi Z, Wang F. Synthesis and characterization of PAN/CLAY hybrid with extended chain conformation of polyaniline. Acta Polymerica Sinica. 1999;**10**:551

[47] Wu Q, Xue Z, Qi Z, Hung F. Synthesis and characterization of PAn/clay nanocomposite with extended chain conformation of polyaniline. Polymer. 2000;**41**:2029

[48] Biswas M, Ray SS. Water-dispersible nanocomposites of polyaniline and montmorillonite. Journal of Applied Polymer Science. 2000;**77**:2948

[49] Lee DK, Lee SH, Char K, Kim J. Expansion distribution of basal spacing of the silicate layers in polyaniline/Na+−montmorillonite nanocomposites monitored with X-ray diffraction. Macromolecular Rapid Communications. 2000;**21**:1136

[50] Lee D, Char K, Lee SW, Park YW. Structural changes of polyaniline/montmorillonite nanocomposites and their effects on physical properties. Journal of Materials Chemistry. 2003;**13**:2942

[51] Yeh JM, Liou SJ, Lai CY, Wu PC, Tsai TY. Enhancement of corrosion

protection effect in polyaniline via the formation of polyaniline-clay nano-composite materials. Chemistry of Materials. 2001;**13**:1131

[52] Zeng QH, Wang DZ, Yu AB, Lu GQ. Synthesis of polymer–montmorillonite nanocomposites by in situ intercalative polymerization. Nanotechnology. 2002;**13**:549

[53] Kim BH, Jung JH, Joo J, Kim JW, Choi HJ. Charge transport and structure of nanocomposites of polyaniline and inorganic clay. Journal of the Korean Physical Society. 2000;**36**:366

[54] Kim BH, Jung JH, Kim JW, Choi HJ, Joo J. Effect of dopant and clay on nanocomposites of polyaniline (PAN) intercalated into Na+–montmorillonite (N+-MMT). Synthetic Metals. 2001;**121**: 1311

[55] Kim BH, Jung JH, Kim JW, Choi HJ, Joo J. Physical characterization of polyaniline-Na+–montmorillonite nanocomposite intercalated by emulsion polymerization. Synthetic Metals. 2001;**117**:115

Chapter 2

Basics of Clay Minerals and Their Characteristic Properties

Neeraj Kumari and Chandra Mohan

Abstract

Clay minerals such as kaolinite, smectite, chlorite, micas are main components of raw materials of clay and formed in presence of water. A large number of clays used to form the different structure which completely depends on their mining source. They are known as hydrous phyllosilicate having silica, alumina and water with variable amount of inorganic ions like Mg^{2+}, Na^{+}, Ca^{2+} which are found either in interlayer space or on the planetary surface. Clay minerals are described by presence of two-dimensional sheets, tetrahedral (SiO_4) and octahedral (Al_2O_3). There are different clay minerals which are categorized based on presence of tetrahedral and octahedral layer in their structure like kaolinite (1:1 of tetrahedral and octahedral layers), smectite group of clay minerals (2:1 of tetrahedral and octahedral layers) and chlorite (2:1:1 of tetrahedral, octahedral and octahedral layers). The particle size of clay minerals is <2microns which can be present in form of plastic in presence of water and solidified when dried. The small size and their distinctive crystal structure make clay minerals very special with their unique properties including high cation exchange capacity, swelling behavior, specific surface area, adsorption capacity, etc. which are described in this chapter. Due to all these unique properties, clay minerals are gaining interest in different fields.

Keywords: Clay minerals, cation exchange capacity, swelling capacity, adsorption, tetrahedral

1. Introduction

Georgius Agricola (1494–1555), the founder of geology, was seemingly the first who gave the definition of clay in 1546. It has been modified several times due to which the clay definition raises the questions related of constituents of clay and implicitly which was very important [1]. The latest effort to solve all these issues was done by the Joint Nomenclature Committees (JNCs) of the Association Internationale pour l'Etude des Argiles (AIPEA) and the Clay Minerals Society (CMS). According to these societies, clay, a naturally occurring material, composed mainly of fine-grained minerals, become plastic in presence of water and become hard when dried or fired. By this definition of clay, engineered clays and clay-like materials can be distinguished as clay (fine grained minerals) exhibiting plasticity in presence of water and become hard on drying and firing [2, 3].

1.1 Clay

Clay is a soft, freely bound, fine grained natural rock or earthy material having diameter less than 0.005 mm and composed essentially of clay particles. Based on the standard definition of mineral, clays are mainly inorganic materials except peat, muck, some soils, etc. that contain huge amount of organic/natural materials. The clay particles are formed due to the weathering and erosion of rocks containing soil, ceramic clays, clay shales, glacial clays (including great volume of detrital and transported clays) the mineral group feldspar (known as the 'mother of clay') over vast spans of time. During weathering, the content of feldspar is distorted by hydrolysis process results in formation of clay minerals such as kaolinites (the primary minerals in kaolin clays) and smectite (the primary minerals in bentonite clays). Clay can incorporate with one or more clay minerals even in presence of minute quantities of quartz (SiO_2), metal oxides (Al_2O_3, MgO etc.) and organic matter [4, 5]. The plasticity of clays are due to their particle size, geometry as well as content of water and become hard, stiff, coherent and non: plastic upon drying or firing. Plasticity and hardness are greatly affected by the chemical composition of the material present in the clay. Clays can be molded in any form when they retain water. For example, some species of chlorite and mica are found to be non-plastic while grinding macroscopic flakes even where more than 70% of the material is <2 μm esd (equivalent spherical diameter). Whereas some species of chlorites and micas become plastic on grinding the macroscopic flakes where 3% of the materials is <2 μm esd. Clays are easily molded into a form that they retain when dry, and they become hard and lose their plasticity when subjected to heat

In all definition of clays, the particle size is a key parameter, no generally upper limit is accepted till now. Although clays can be distinguished from other fine-grained soils on the basis of their size difference and mineralogy. The particle sizes of silts (fine-grained soils that do not consist of clay minerals) is larger than clays. Individual clay particles are always smaller than 0.004 mm. The difference between silt and clay varies by discipline. Geologists and soil scientists usually consider a particle size of 2 μm (clays being finer than silts) for the separation, sedimentologists apply 4–5 μm, and colloid chemists use 1 μm [6]. According to Geotechnical engineers, differentiation between silts and clays can be done on the basis of the plastic characteristics of the soil, as measured by the soils' Atterberg limits. The combination of silts, sand and clay (<40%) are called loam [7].

Mostly, geologic clay deposits composed of phyllosilicate minerals having variable amounts of water present in the mineral structure. The clay can appear in different form of colors from white to dull gray or brown to deep orange-red depending on the soil's content [4]. The colloidal suspensions are formed when clays are immersed in water and flocculation occurs when they immersed in saline water.

Clays are divided into two classes:

a. Residual clay: Residual clays are found in the place of origin and formed by surface weathering which give rise to clay in three ways:

   - Chemical decomposition of rocks, such as granite, containing silica and aluminia
   - Solution of rocks, such as limestone, containing clayey impurities, which, being insoluble, are deposited as clay
   - Disintegration and solution of shale [8].

b. Transported clay, also known as sedimentary clay, removed from the place of origin by erosion and deposited in a new and possibly distant position.

1.2 Clay minerals

Clay minerals are the characteristics minerals on the earth found near planetary surface (the surface where the outer crust of the object comes in contact with atmosphere) environment with variable amount of ions like iron, magnesium, alkali metals, alkaline earth metals and other cations. They are considered as important constituents of soil and form by diagenetic and hydrothermal alteration of rocks in presence of water [9]. They are commonly found in fine grained sedimentary rocks such as shale, mudstone and siltstone. Clay minerals act as "chemical sponges" as they have capacity to hold water and dissolved plant nutrients eroded from other minerals due to the presence of some unbalanced electrical charge on their surface [8]. As water is essential for clay minerals formation, therefore, most of the clay minerals are known as hydrous alumino silicate or hydrous aluminum phyllosilicate.

The formation of clay minerals is due to the chemical weathering of rock [9, 10]. The chemical and structural composition of clay minerals is found to be similar to the primary minerals which originate from the crust of earth mainly from igneous or metamorphic rocks. Transformations may occur in ambient conditions. Although some of the most resistant primary minerals such as quartz, micas and feldspar may remain in soils whereas other less resistant primary minerals (pyroxenes, amphiboles) are susceptible to breakdown by weathering, thus forming secondary minerals. The resultant secondary minerals are the formed due to either modification of the primary mineral structure (incongruent reaction) or neoformation through precipitation or recrystallization of dissolved constituents of primary minerals into a more stable structure (congruent reaction). These secondary minerals are most probably defined as phyllosilicates because, as the name suggest (Greek: phyllon, leaf), they exhibit a platy or flaky structure with irregular edges; while one of their most important basic structural units is an extended SiO_4 tetrahedra sheet [11].

As the clay minerals are most important component of the soil, they are usually ultra-fined particles having less than 2 μm sized particles. Clay minerals are found to be the most interesting class of minerals that have attracted substantial worldwide attention and investment in research and development. In 1930, the nature of clay can be defined with advanced development in X-Ray diffraction technology used to investigate the molecular nature of clay particles.

Most of the chemical and physical properties of the soil including swelling - shrinking capacity, cation exchange capacity etc. are due to presence of the clay minerals in soil. Clay minerals are look like micas due to their chemical composition [12].

2. Structure and chemical composition of clay minerals

The properties that define the composition of clay minerals are derived from chemical compounds present in clay minerals, symmetrical arrangement of atoms and ions and the forces that bind them together. The clay minerals are mainly known as the complex silicates of various ions such as aluminum, magnesium and iron [13]. On the basis of the arrangement of these ions, basic crystalline units of the clay minerals are of two types:

a. silicon – oxygen tetrahedron consists of silicon surrounding by four oxygen atoms and unite to form the silica sheet.

b. aluminum or magnesium octahedron consists of aluminum surrounding by six hydroxyl units and combine to form gibbsite sheet (If aluminum is main dominating atom) or brucite sheet (If magnesium is main dominating atom) (**Figure 1**) [14].

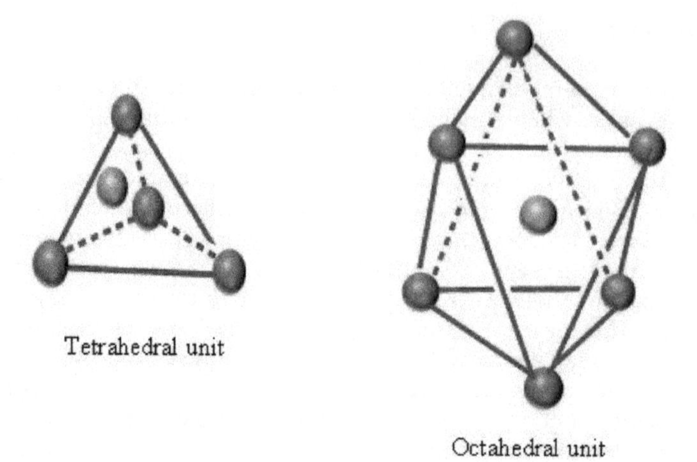

Figure 1.
Structure of tetrahedral and octahedral unit.

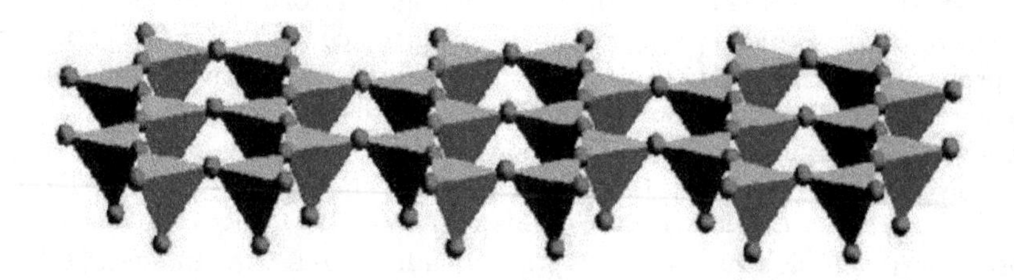

Figure 2.
Arrangement of tetrahedral unit to form the tetrahedral sheet.

2.1 Tetrahedral sheet

The main dominating atom in the tetrahedral sheet is found in form of Si^{4+} cation. The basic building block of tetrahedral sheet is a unit of Si atom surrounded by four oxygen atom known as silica tetrahedra. The tetrahedral sheet is formed by sharing of three oxygen of each tetrahedra with three nearest tetrahedra as shown in **Figure 2**. These oxygen atoms are known as basal oxygen which connect pairs of all tetrahedra together (more or less) in one plane whereas the fourth oxygen atom remain free and form the bond with other polyhedral elements known as apical oxygen. Apical oxygens are all in a separate plane and provide a link between both tetrahedral and the octahedral sheet [15]. As only one apical O is present per tetrahedron therefore, each tetrahedron shares a corner with an octahedron in the octahedral sheet.

The tetrahedral sheet is carrying negative charge due to the isomorphous substitution of Al^{3+} in place of Si^{4+} generating the charge deficiency in tetrahedral sheet. Common tetrahedral cations are Si^{4+}, Al^{3+}, and Fe^{3+}.

2.2 Octahedral sheet

The main dominating atoms in octahedral sheets are Al^{3+} or Mg^{2+} surrounded by six oxygen atoms or hydroxyl group give rise to eight sided building block known as octahedron. Since, octahedral sheet are present in two forms: dioctahedral or trioctahedral sheet.

a. When aluminum having three positive valences present in the octahedral sheet, only two-thirds of the sites are filled so that the charges will be balanced which results in formation of dioctahedral sheet. When magnesium having two positive charge valences is present, all three positions are filled to balance the charge which results in formation of trioctahedral sheet [15]. Therefore, for di – octahedral sheet, Al3+ is the main dominating atom with Al2(OH)6 a unit cell formula and often abbreviated as the stoichiometric equivalent Al(OH)3 where two Al3+ atoms coordinated with six oxygen/or hydroxyl ions

b. In tri – octahedral sheet, Mg2+ is the main dominating atom where three Mg2+ atoms are coordinated with six oxygen/or hydroxyl ions having a unit cell formula of Mg3(OH)6 (also written as Mg(OH)2). Gibbsite or hydrargillite (hydrous aluminum oxide, Al2(OH)6 or Al2O3•3H2O) and brucite (hydrous oxide of magnesium, Mg(OH)2) are the minerals which are generally described in literature on clay chemistry, mineralogy and structure. The octahedral sheet is formed by sharing of two oxygen of each octahedra when various octahedra linked together horizontally (**Figure 3**) [16, 17].

2.3 Isomorphic substitution

The difference in the composition of clay minerals occurs very frequently when substitution of ions takes place within the mineral structure. The substitution of Si^{4+}, Al^{3+}, and Mg^{2+} takes place with other cations with comparable ionic radii in their respective tetrahedral and octahedral sheets due to weathering (**Table 1**). Consequently, in the center of the tetrahedron, replacement of Si^{4+} by Al^{3+} without changing the basic structure of the crystal takes place. Moreover, in octahedron, Al^{3+} and Mg^{2+} cations are replaced by the ions such as $Fe^{3+}/^{2+}$ and Zn^{2+} (ionic radius = 0.074 nm). This process is known as isomorphous substitution where one structural cation is replaced by another of similar size and this kind of replacement signifies the primary cause of both negative and positive charges in clay minerals. For example, the substitution of one Al^{3+} for a Si^{4+} in the tetrahedral unit creates one negative charge. Alternatively, replacement of a lower valence cation by a higher valence (Fe^{2+} by Fe^{3+}) cation results in a gain of one positive charge. The net charge of the clay mineral is determined by after balancing electron loss and gain within the structure. In most soils, the net negative charge exceed by a positive charge after substitution [18].

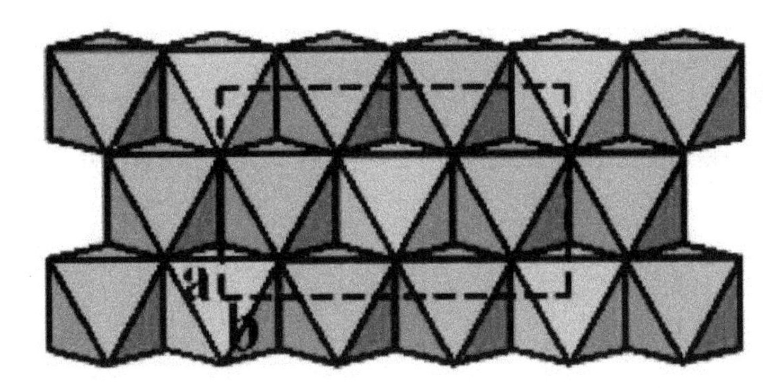

Figure 3.
Arrangement of octahedral unit to form the octahedral sheet.

Cation-exchange capacities and specific surface areas of clay minerals		
mineral	**cation-exchange capacity at pH 7 (milliequivalents per 100 grams)**	**specific surface area (square metres per gram)**
kaolinite	3–15	5–40
halloysite (hydrated)	40–50	1,100*
illite	10–40	10–100
chlorite	10–40	10–55
vermiculite	100–150	760*
smectite	80–120	40–800
palygorskite-sepiolite	3–20	40–180
allophane	30–135	2,200
imogolite	20–30	1,540

**depending on the fraction of internal specific surface area.*

Table 1.
Cation exchange capacity and specific surface area of different clay minerals.

3. Classification of clay minerals

The aluminosilicate layers comprises of the basic structural units of phyllosilicates which is formed by the combination of tetrahedral and octahedral sheets bound by shared oxygen atoms. Both the tetrahedral and octahedral sheets are the main components of phyllosilicates (due to their leaf like or plate like structure, they are known as phyllosilicates) which bound together by sharing of oxygen atoms into different layers. Phyllosilicate are the most common clay minerals consists of Si dominating tetrahedral unit and Al/or Mg dominating octahedral unit which are arranged in to sheet form. Based on number of tetrahedral and octahedral sheets and their arrangement, the phyllosilicates are divided into following categories including layer and chain silicates, sesquioxide and other inorganic minerals:

Clay can be classified depending on the way that the tetrahedral and octahedral sheets are packed into layers. The major groups of clay minerals present in the soil environment include layer and chain silicates, sesquioxides, and other inorganic minerals as shown in **Figure 4** [19].

3.1 Layer silicates

A silicate comprising of planar octahedral layer bound to tetrahedral layer above and below with a distinctive repeating distance between t-o-t layers. These are the primary component of soils and are known as excellent trappers of water held between layers. Minerals within these groups are further categorized into dioctahedral and trioctahedral [11]. On the basis of number and arrangements of tetrahedral and octahedral sheets present in clay, the layer silicate are divided into three categories:

(a) 1:1 type of clay mineral

(b) 2:1 type of clay mineral

(c) 2:1:1 type of clay mineral

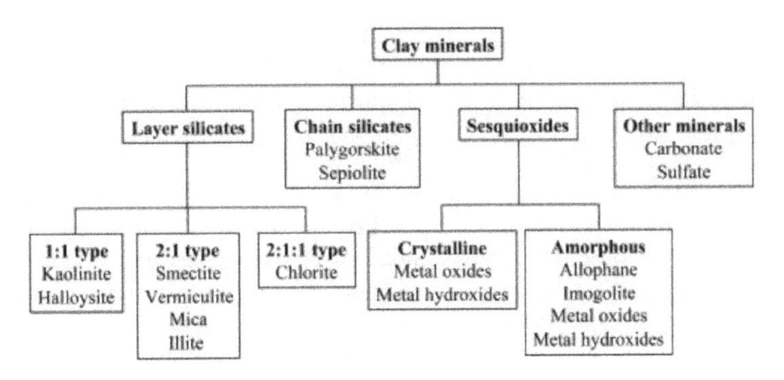

Figure 4.
Classification of clay minerals.

3.1.1 1:1 Layer silicate

Each individual layer is assembled from one tetrahedral (SiO_4) and one octahedral sheet (AlO_6). The sheets are bonded together by sharing of O^{2-} ions. Kaolinite and Halloysite are examples under this category [20].

Kaolinite is a 1:1 clay mineral with chemical formula $Si_4Al_4O_{10}(OH)_8$. The rocks that are found to be rich in Kaolinite are identified as Kaolin or china clay [21]. Kaolinite is derived from the kaolin which is very common and is a corruption of the Chinese Jailing (Pinyin; Wade-Giles romanization Kao-ling), meaning "high ridge," [22]. The chemical weathering of aluminum silicate such as feldspar results in formation of a soft, usually white, earthy mineral (dioctahedral phyllosilicate clay) The dickite and nacrite are rare forms of kaolinite which are chemically similar to kaolinite but amorphous in nature. Kaolinite is found to be electrostatically neutral having triclinic symmetry. The hydrogen bonding is found in between oxygen atoms and hydroxyl ions of the layers that are paired. Since, hydrogen bonding is weak, random movements between the layers are quite common results in lower crystallinity of kaolinite minerals than that of the triclinic kaolinite. The ideal structure of kaolinite has no charge. Hence, the structure of Kaolinite is fixed due to the hydrogen bonding therefore; there is no expansion between the layers or have low shrink-swell capacity when clay is wetted. Kaolinite does not swell in water and have low surface areas and cation exchange capacity (< 1 centimole/kg). Due to the low surface area and little isomorphous substitution, Kaolinite has low capacity to adsorb the ions [15]. Kaolinite composite layers are 7 Å thick and the c-axis/interlayer spacing is also of 7 Å. Dickite and nacrite are polytypic forms of kaolinite consisting of a double 1:1 layer and have monoclinic symmetry. Dickite and nacrite differentiate themselves by different stacking sequences of the two 1:1 silicate layers [23].

The mineral Halloysite having 1:1 layer structure as kaolinite has a single sheet of water molecules between two layers with c-spacing/interlayer spacing 10.1Å which make it different from kaolinite. It is illustrated by its tubular form in contrast to the platy form of kaolinite particles. Dehydration occurs on mild heating of Halloysite and will irreversibly get transformed to kaolinite. Halloysite possesses a hydrated form with a composition of $Al_2Si_2O_5(OH)_4{\cdot}2H_2O$. which irreversibly changes to a dehydrated variety mainly at relatively low temperatures (60° C) or upon being directed to conditions of low relative humidity. The dehydrated form of Halloysite has basal spacing with thickness of a kaolinite layer (approximately 7.2 Å) whereas the basal spacing of hydrated form is about 10.1 Å. The difference of 2.9 Å is due to the thickness of a sheet of water. Consequently, in hydrated form, the layers of halloysite are separated by monomolecular water layers that are lost during dehydration [23].

Serpentine: Serpentine is a group of hydrous magnesium-rich silicate minerals and a common rock-forming mineral having the composition $Mg_3Si_2O_5(OH)_4$ [24]. Serpentine generally appears in three polymorphic forms: chrysotile, a fibrous type used as asbestos; antigorite, a variety exists in either corrugated plates or fibers; and lizardite, a very fine-grained, platy variety. Serpentine is usually grayish, white, or green (due to iron replacing magnesium) but may be yellow (chrysotile) or green-blue (antigorite). The formation of Serpentine takes place below 500°C (930°F) by either addition of water or sometimes silica to various magnesium silicates—e.g., forsterite or enstatite [25]. It usually occurs along the crests and axes of great folds, such as island arcs or Alpine mountain chains. Normal occurrences are in altered peridotites, dunites, or pyroxenites; serpentinite is a rock consisting largely of serpentine.

3.1.2 2:1 Type of clay mineral

Most of the layer silicate clays are commonly found in soils and based on the mica structure in which a single octahedral sheet sandwiched between two tetrahedral sheets and form an individual composite layer as shown in **Figure 5**. Therefore, they are referred as 2:1 layer silicates in which Talc [$Mg_3Si_4O_{10}(OH)_2$] and Pyrophyllite [$Al_2Si_4O_{10}(OH)_2$] signifies the trioctahedral and dioctahedral members. In dioctahedral and trioctahedral layer silicates, two and three octahedral sites are occupied respectively out of the three available sites in the half- unit cell (single Si_4O_{10}) [26].

These types of clay minerals consist of one octahedral layer sandwiched between two tetrahedral layers. They are further characterized into two categories:

A. Expanding clay minerals: Smectite group and Vermiculite

B. Non – expanding clay minerals: illite (mica groups)

A. **Expanding clay minerals:** This group includes mainly smectite group of clay minerals and vermiculite clay mineral. They are known for their interlayer expansion which happens during their swelling behavior when they are wet.

Smectites are mainly based on either trioctahedral 2:1 (talc) or dioctahedral 2:1 (Pyrophyllite) structure and differ from these neutral structures due to the presence of isomorphous substitution in the octahedral or tetrahedral layer. The **Smectite** group of clay minerals are further divided into Saponites (trioctahedral) and Montmorillonite (dioctahedral). Another important member of the Smectite family is **Bentonite**. Bentonite clay is also known as sedimentary clay and has unique property of water retaining.

The most prominent members of this group are Montmorillonite. Beidellite, nontronite, and saponite. The flake-like crystals of smectite (e.g., Montmorillonite) are consisting of an expanding lattice, 2:1 type clay mineral. Each layer is composed an octahedral sheet sandwiched between two tetrahedral (silica) sheets. Slight attraction is found between oxygen atoms present in the bottom tetrahedral sheet of one unit and in the top tetrahedral sheet of another unit. This allows a variable space between layers, which is occupied by exchangeable cations and water. Therefore, the exchangeable cations and water can easily enter the interlayer space resulting in the expansion of layers that may vary from 9.6 Å to 20 Å [14]. In Montmorillonite, magnesium ions are replaced aluminum ions in some sites of octahedral sheet and likewise, some silicon ions in the tetrahedral sheet may be replaced by aluminum ions. This type of replacement is known as isomorphic substitution which give rise

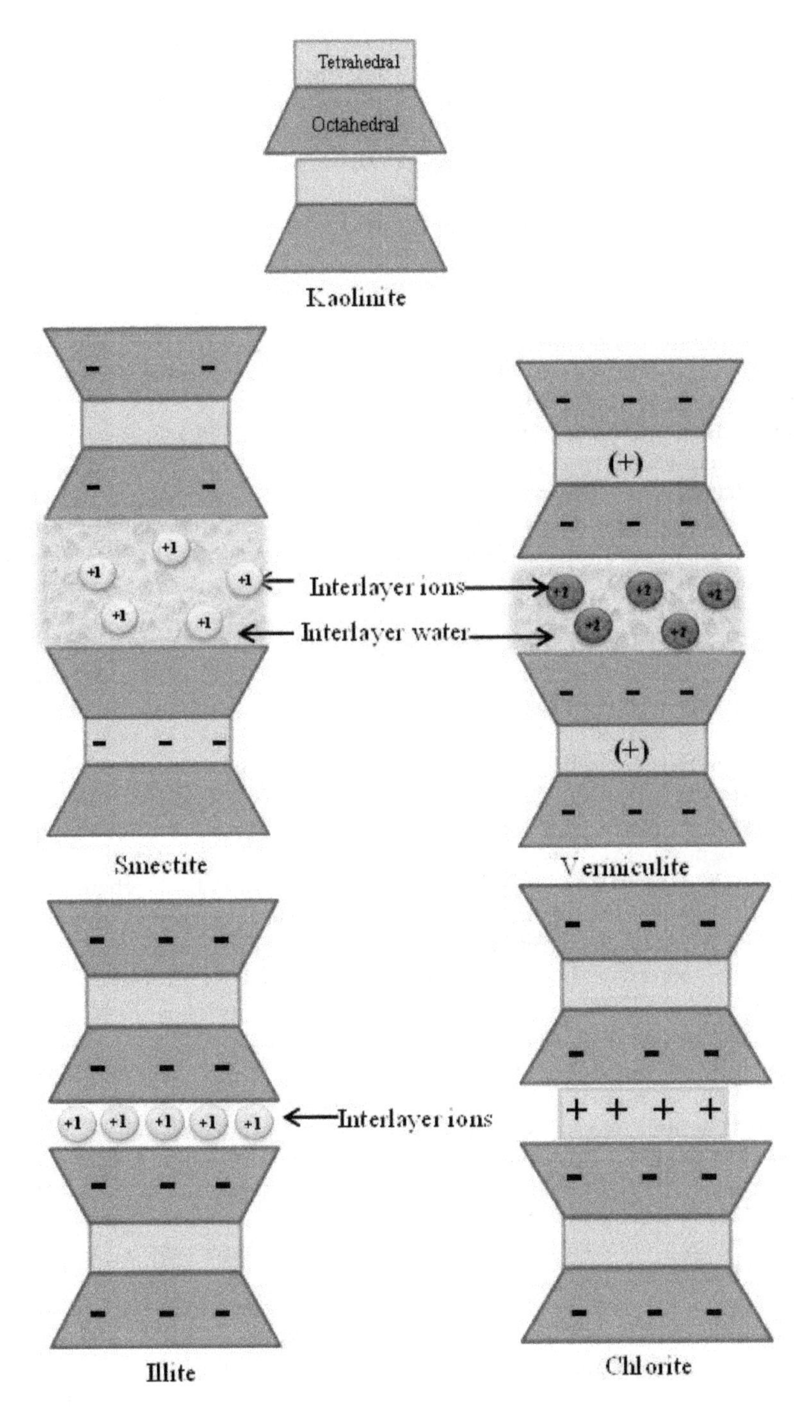

Figure 5.
Different types of clay minerals.

to a negative charge on the surface of clay minerals. The magnitude of the negative charge depends upon the number of substituted atoms/ions. These negative charges of the unit cell are typically balanced by exchangeable hydrated alkali (Li, Na, K, Rb, Cs, Fr) or alkaline earth (Be, Mg, Ca, Sr., Ba, Rd) cations. Therefore, the layer charge density of these minerals is found to be in between 0.2–0.6 per unit formula [27]. The general structural formula of smectite group of clay minerals is $(Na, Ca)_{0.33}(Al,Mg)_2Si_4O_{10}(OH)_2.(H_2O)_n$. The structure, chemical composition, exchangeable ions are responsible for their several unique properties such as high cation exchange capacity, high surface area and high adsorption capacity.

The quantity of cations required to balance the charge deficiency induced by these substitutions is referred to as the cation exchange capacity (CEC). The CEC for Montmorillonite ranges from 80 to 100 milliequivalent per 100 grams. Montmorillonite clays have very poor thermal stability.

These minerals show some prominent characteristics like high cation exchange capacity, swelling and shrinkage capacity. When smectite dominated soils (e.g., Vertisols) undergo dryness, wide cracks commonly appears making the soil difficult to till due to their hardness [28].

Bentonite: Bentonite is an impure form of aluminum phyllosilicate clay consisting 98% of montmorillonite and produced by in-situ divitrification of volcanic ash or by mechanical and chemical weathering of the parent rock, most often in the presence of water. Bentonite was found in the Cretaceous Benton Shale near Rock River, Wyoming (Bentonite, wikipedia). Chemical composition of the unit cell has been represented as $[(Si_{8.0})(Al_{3.02}Mg_{0.50}Ca_{0.06}Fe_{0.18}Ti_{0.02}Na_{0.22})O_{20}(OH)_4]$. It is a versatile mineral due to its platelet structure. The platelet consisting of a tetrahedral silicon oxide layer in which some silicon replaced by trivalent cations sandwiched between two octahedral aluminum oxide layers in which aluminum replaced by divalent cations. The hydroxide group is present on the edge of each platelet results in thixotropic nature [28].

The different types of bentonite are found based on their respective dominant element, such as potassium (K), sodium (Na), calcium (Ca), and aluminum (Al). For industrial purposes, three main classes of bentonite exist: sodium, calcium and potassium bentonite.

Sodium bentonite: Sodium bentonite expands in wet condition where it absorb the water as much as several times its dry mass. Because of its excellent colloidal properties, [29]. It is often used in drilling mud for oil and gas wells and also in boreholes for geotechnical and environmental investigations [30]. Due to its swelling capacity, sodium bentonite is used as a sealant, since it offers a self-sealing, low permeability barrier. Enhancement in some rheological or sealing performance are observed after various surface modifications of sodium bentonite for example, the addition of polymers [31].

Calcium bentonite: Calcium bentonite is considered as a useful adsorbent for ions, fats and oils [32]. It is known as the main active component of fuller's earth, probably one of the earliest industrial cleaning agents. Calcium bentonite can be converted to sodium bentonite (termed sodium beneficiation or sodium activation) by ion exchange process and show many of sodium bentonite's properties. In simple form, add 5–10% of a soluble sodium salt such as sodium carbonate to wet bentonite followed by mixing and allow the mixture to leave for a certain time so that the ion exchange take place. Hence, some properties of sodium-beneficiated calcium bentonite (or sodium-activated bentonite) such as viscosity and fluid loss of suspensions may not be fully comparable to those of natural sodium bentonite [30, 33].

Potassium bentonite: This is also known as potash bentonite or K-bentonite. Potassium bentonite is formed from alteration of volcanic ash and considered as potassium-rich illitic clay.

Vermiculite: Vermiculite also belongs to 2:1 group of clay minerals where one octahedral sheet occurs between two tetrahedral sheets. Most of the Vermiculites are Al dominated showing dioctahedral structure. Vermiculite is known as hydrous phyllosilicate mineral which undergoes substantial expansion when heated results in exfoliation and commercial furnaces can routinely generate this effect. Vermiculite formed by the weathering or hydrothermal modification of biotite or phlogopite [34]. Vermiculite was first described in 1824 in Millbury, Massachusetts. Its name is derived from Latin word, vermiculare, "to breed worms", for the manner in which it exfoliates when heated (Vermiculite,). In Vermiculite clay mineral, tetrahedral sheet is highly negatively charged due to the more substitution of Al^{3+} in place of Si^{4+} results in high layer charge density (in between 0.6–0.8 per unit formula) which is higher than smectite group of clay mineral [35]. The chemical formula of Vermiculite is $(Mg,Fe^{2+},Fe^{3+})_3(SiAl)_4O_{10}(OH)_24H_2O$. The water molecules are present along with Mg^{2+} and other ions in the interlayer space instead of K^+ ion which makes it different from micas. Therefore, both the tetrahedral and octahedral units are joined together tightly rather than driving apart from each other resulting the less expansion of interlayer spacing on wetting [36]. The cation exchange capacity of Vermiculite is very high (100–150 meq/100 g). Vermiculite clays are weathered micas where the potassium ions are replaced by magnesium and iron ions between the molecular sheets [9, 37].

B. **Non-expanding clay minerals:** This group includes mainly Mica (illite) clay mineral which is a secondary form of mineral precipitate. This group is an example of a phyllosilicate, or layered alumino-silicate. Muscovite and biotite are also found in the clay fractions which are also called fine grained Mica. Illite is considered as an modified product of muscovite and feldspar formed from weathering and hydrothermal environments; known as component of sericite. It is commonly found in soil and argillaceous sedimentary rocks as well as in some low grade metamorphic rocks [38]. In illite, the tetrahedral sheet has more negative charge even higher than Vermiculite which is due to the presence of 20% of aluminum atoms in tetrahedral sheet in place of silicon atoms sites having considerable ion (isomorphic) substitution. The charge deficiency is mainly balanced by K^+ ions which are present in the interlayer space and act as bridge between the layers thus preventing the expansion of layers making them non - expanding. Therefore, the interlayer spacing is found to be 10 Å. The chemical formula is $(K,H_3O)(Al,Mg,Fe)_2(Si,Al)_4O_{10}[(OH)_2,(H_2O)]$ [39]. The adsorption capacity, swelling, shrinkage capacity is less than Montmorillonite and Vermiculite but more than Kaolinite interstratified layers are present. The cation-exchange capacity (CEC) of illite is smaller than that of smectite but higher than that of kaolinite, typically around 20–30 meq/100 g [40].

3.1.3 2:1:1 Type of clay mineral

Chlorite is mainly belongs to 2:1:1 silicate group which are basically iron magnesium silicates with some aluminum atoms. The typical chlorite clay crystal composed of 2:1 layers, such as in vermiculites clay mineral alternate with a magnesium dominated tri-octahedral sheet (also known as brucite) giving rise to 2:1:1 ratio. All the octahedral positions in chlorite are occupied by magnesium ions as in the brucite layer [41]. The negative charge of chlorites is less than smectite or vermiculites but about the same as that of fine grained mica. There is no water adsorption between the layers responsible for the non – expanding nature of this crystal. The interlayer spacing is about 14 Å. Chlorites having a muscovite-like silicate layer and an aluminum hydroxide sheet are called donbassite and show the ideal formula of $Al_{4.33}(Si_3Al)O_{10}(OH)_8$ [22]. In many cases, the aluminum ions present in octahedral layer are partially replaced by magnesium ions as in magnesium-rich aluminum dioctahedral chlorites called sudoite. Another type of dioctahedral chlorite is Cookeite in which lithium substitutes for aluminum in the octahedral sheets [15, 42].

3.2 Chain silicates

3.2.1 Palygorskite or attapulgite

Palygorskite is a fibrous magnesium aluminum phyllosilicate having the formula $(Mg,Al)2Si_4O_{10}(OH) \cdot 4(H_2O)$ which mainly found in a type of clay soil in the Southeastern United States. It is one of the types of fuller's earth [43]. The structure of palygorskite consists of extended silicon-oxygen sheets results in the retention of the mineral in the layer silicate family whereas the tetrahedral SiO_4 groups forming silicon-oxygen sheets are oriented in such a manner so that extended lathlike features could be developed which create the fibrous morphology. The chain silicate mineral found in sediments from playa lakes, saline deposits in desert soils and in calcareous material. Attapulgite is one type of palygorskite found in Attapulgus, Ga. For chemical formula and physical properties of attapulgite [44, 45].

3.2.2 Sepiolite

It is also known as Meerschaum, a fibrous hydrated magnesium silicate having chemical formula $Mg_4Si_6O_{15}(OH)_2 \cdot 6H_2O$. It is opaque and white, gray, or cream in color. It may seem like the bones of the cuttlefish Sepia. The name of Sepiolite is derived from cuttlefish Sepia.

The structures of sepiolite and palygorskite are almost similar consisting of narrow strips or ribbons of 2:1 layers that are attached to each other at the corners. One ribbon is attached to the another by inversion of the direction of the apical oxygen atoms of SiO_4 tetrahedrons; in other words, an extended rectangular box comprising of continuous 2:1 layers is enclosed to the nearest boxes at their extended corner edges. Therefore, due to the absence of silicate layers, channels or tunnels occur on the extended sides of the boxes results in the fibrous morphology of the minerals. Since the octahedral sheet is irregular, some of the magnesium ions present in octahedral layer are exposed at the edges and hold on bound water molecules (H_2O). In addition to the bound water molecules, variable amounts of zeolitic/free water (H_2O) are included in the rectangular channels. The width of the ribbons is found to be greater in sepiolite than in palygorskite which is a major difference between these chain silicates. The width of ribbons defines the number of octahedral cation positions per formula unit [5, 46].

3.3 Sesquioxide

Sesquioxide clays are produced from heavy rainfall and leached most of the silica and alumina from alumino – silica clay by leaving less soluble iron oxide (Fe_2O_3), iron hydroxide ($Fe(OH)_3$) and aluminum hydroxide ($Al(OH)_3$). Sesquioxides of iron and aluminum are found in soil. A sesquioxide is an oxide comprising three atoms of oxygen and two another element. For example, aluminum oxide (Al_2O_3) is a sesquioxide. Many sesquioxides contain the metal atom having +3 oxidation state and the oxide ion such as Al_2O_3, La_2O_3 except the alkali metal sesquioxides which contain both peroxide, (O_2^{2-}) and superoxide, (O_2^{-}) ions, e.g., Rb_2O_3 is formulated $[(Rb_+)_4(O_2^{2-})(O^{2-})_2]$ [45]. They are not adhesive in nature and do not swell in presence of water. They have ability to hold large amount of phosphate as they have tendency to hold phosphorous tightly make them unavailable for absorption by plants. They have low CEC. They are found in both crystalline and amorphous form. Crystalline Sesquioxide are either metal oxide or hydroxide whereas amorphous Sesquioxide are Allophane and Imogolite.

A. **Imogolite** is an aluminosilicate having the composition of $SiO_2 \cdot Al_2O_3 \cdot 2.5H_2O$. In 1962, this mineral was discovered in a soil obtained from glassy volcanic ash known as "imogo." Electron-optical observations of imogolite suggest a unique morphological feature with smooth and curved threadlike tubes differing in diameter from 10 to 30 nanometers which can further extend upto several micrometers in length. The shape of imogolite is cylindrical consisting of a modified gibbsite sheet where the hydroxyl of one side of a gibbsite octahedral sheet lose protons which form bond with silicon atoms located at vacant octahedral cation sites of gibbsite. Thus, three oxygen atoms and one hydroxyl present around silicon atom make up an isolated SiO_4 tetrahedron as in orthosilicates which make a planar array on the edge of a gibbsite sheet. Because of shorter bond length between silicon-oxygen bonds than aluminum-oxygen bonds sheet change into curve shape results in a tube like structure with inner and outer diameters of about 6.4 Å and 21.4 Å, respectively, and with all hydroxyls exposed at the surface.

B. **Allophane** are considered as a group of naturally occurring hydrous aluminosilicate minerals. They are not totally amorphous but are short-range (partially) ordered. Allophane are described by the dominance of Si-O-Al bonds where most of the aluminum atoms are tetrahedrally coordinated. Unlike imogolite, the morphology of allophane varies from fine, rounded ring-shaped particles to irregular aggregates which indicates that the ring-shaped particles may be hollow spherules or polyhedrons. Despite their indefinable structure, their chemical compositions surprisingly fall down in a relatively narrow range as the SiO_2:Al_2O_3 ratios are mostly found to be in between 1.0 and 2.0. In general, the SiO_2:Al_2O_3 ratio of allophane is higher than that of imogolite [46].

4. Characteristics of clay minerals

Clay minerals are considered as gift for human beings as they are exploring the clay minerals continuously through research as these are of very low cost, environment friendly, easily available and non – toxic. The clay minerals are so widespread that in the world, there is hardly any country where there are no deposits of one or other kind of clay minerals. In nature, clay minerals are found with certain physical and chemical characteristics due to which these clay minerals play an important role in different fields from research to industries [47]. The clay minerals are a class of rock-forming minerals having porous like sheet structure with different distances between the sheets. The combination of the electrical conductivity of the matrix material and the pore fluid is the electrical conductivity (mS/m) of the porous material. The cation exchange capacity, a number of possible charged ions by the negatively charged surface of clay materials, depends on the number of sheets and the cations located in these structures [48]. Therefore, physical and chemical properties of clay minerals depend significantly on their sheet structure, cation- and anion-exchange capacity and adsorption ability which mainly determines their importance in different applications [49].

4.1 Cation – exchange capacity

The ability of clay minerals to adsorb certain cations/anions and their retention around outside of structural unit depends on positive or negative charge deficiency in their mineral structure.

The exchange of these adsorbed ion takes place with other ions. The quantitative relationship between different reacting ions makes the exchange reaction completely different from simple sorption. Cation-exchange capacity (CEC) is the measurement of number of cations retained on the surface of soil particles [50]. It has been defined as quantity of cations that are available for exchange with other cations at a given pH and usually expressed in milliequivalent/100 gram of dry clay. Negatively charged ions present on the surface of soil particle bind with positively charged ions but allow them to exchange in the surrounding soil water with other positively charged particles results in alteration of chemistry of soil [51]. The various aspects of soil chemistry are affected by CEC. As CEC indicated the soil capacity to retain the nutrients like K^+, NH_4^+, Ca^{2+}, therefore, the soil fertility is measured by CEC. It also indicates the capacity to retain pollutant cations like Pb^{2+}. (CEC Wikipedia) CEC depends on particle size, crystallinity perfection and adsorbed ion therefore for a given mineral, values exist in range rather than single specific capacity. The exchange capacities also depend on pH due to the presence of hydroxyl group on the surface of certain clay minerals like allophane and kaolinite.

The original negative charge layer is either replaced or exchanged by the adsorbed cations. This ability of colloidal particles such as clay minerals to maintain and exchange positively charged ions is important because it governs the mobility of positively charged chemical species both in soils and in general geochemical cycling of cations as shown in **Figure 6** [52]. CEC is a reversible process and normally correlated with clay minerals due to the presence of interlayer exchangeable cations such as smectites. The cation-exchange capacities of the clay minerals is given in the **Table 1.**

There are various cations which do not have same replacing power and not equally replaced under a given set of conditions. For example, calcium will easily replace sodium than sodium will replace calcium. Due to similar size potassium and ammonium ions, they easily fit in the hexagonal cavities of the silicate layer. Vermiculite and vermiculitic minerals preferably and irreversibly adsorb these cations and fix them between the layers. Heavy metal ions such as copper, zinc, and lead are strongly attracted to the negatively charged sites on the surfaces of the 1:1 layer minerals, allophane and imogolite, which are caused by the dissociation of surface hydroxyls of these minerals.

The method used to determine the CEC mainly include the complete exchange of cations by a cationic species like ammonium, Na, K, Co(III) hexamine complex, Ba and Cu(II)ethylene diamine complex. The indirect method to determine CEC mainly involves the exchange of naturally occurring cationic species in clay minerals with organic cations such as alkylammonium. Depending on the method

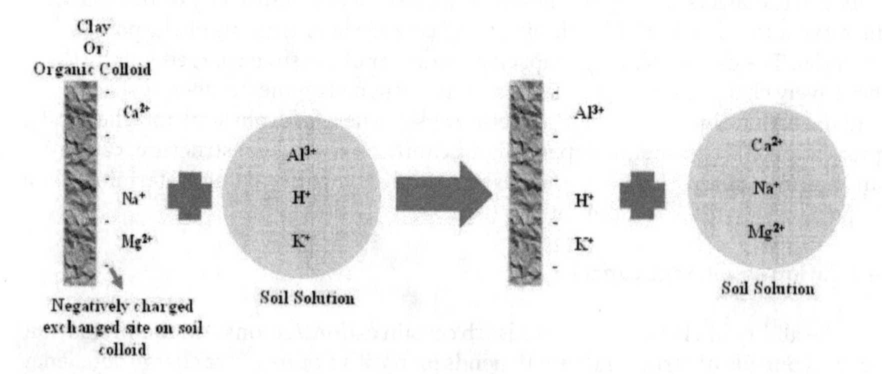

Figure 6.
Clay minerals showing the cation exchange capacity.

used for determining CEC, if the exchanged cations are present in excess, they are removed in subsequent step and the cations retained on the surface of clay are determined.

Methylene blue used for determination of CEC in a rapid qualitative procedure but when compared with other methods, results were not appropriate [53, 54]. Some other complexes like an Ag thiourea complex, Co(III) hexamine complex, and Cu(II) ethylenediamine complex [55–57]. Due to high affinity of clay minerals for these ions, CEC can be determined directly.

There are some other techniques like potentiometric titration, surface tension measurement which are used for determination of CEC. The potentiometric titration used for different types of clay minerals like Colay 90Wyoming bentonite, Na-Montmorillonite and Illite bearing shale whereas surface tension measurement used for Montmorillonite, Kaolinite and Illite [58].

4.2 Swelling capacity

If dry clay minerals are allowed to adsorbed water in a controlled environment, water is added into their interlayer space in more or less discrete forms of layer causing swelling or expansion of the interlayer space. The swelling of interlayer space of clay minerals is due to the hydration energy forces associated with the particles interaction [59]. The swelling clays are prone to large volume change which are related to change in water content. The swelling capacity of clay minerals depends on the following factors:

- The layer charge density of clay minerals
- The type of the interlayer ions whether they are monovalent or divalent.
- The concentration of ions presents in the surrounding solution with clay minerals.
- The amount of water present in the interlayer of clay minerals.
- The quantity and types of minerals i.e. composition of clay minerals

The swelling capacity phenomenon depends on granularity as well as superficial activities of clay itself. Swelling clay minerals are geological type of materials containing the mineral particles more than 50% with less than 2-micron size. The main mineral components of clay minerals are dispersed layer silicate [60]. The swelling properties of clay minerals play an important role in design of structures of light buildings. However, clay minerals/soil are heterogenous in nature; their chemical composition depends on other elements also instead of swelling minerals. There are several mineralogical research which discuss about the swelling and non – swelling clay minerals.

The mobilization of swelling capacity may result stability concerns and foundation threats, tunnels and slopes which required certain assumption and factors like swelling potential which need to be mobilized by applying the swelling pressure. The factors affecting the swelling potential are known as internal factors (cations present in clay minerals and properties of clay minerals) and factors having significant effect on swelling potential are known as external potential (properties of ions and available pore water) [61].

Swelling pressure mainly depends on the average specific surface area, more surface area, more Swelling pressure mainly depends on the average specific surface area, more surface area, more force acting on the surface results in high volume change and high swelling pressure [62]. During the swelling process, deformation of crystal structure in clay minerals takes place results in change in mineral strength and hydraulic conductivity. The structure of clay minerals showing swelling capacity is represented by sheets of SiO_4-tetrahedrons and $Al(OH)_3$-octahedrons which are bonded by oxygen molecules and combined to each other through interlayer having free and exchangeable cations and water molecules with variable thickness and ratio [63]. The clay minerals showing more expansion belongs to 2:1 group of clay minerals with tetrahedrons and octahedrons layers where cations and water molecules are stored in the interlayer spaces [64]. The difference between swelling and non-swelling clay minerals is the size of interlayer space. Greater the interlayer space, more change will be in swelling behavior. The interlayer spacing is measured using X-Ray Diffraction analysis. The swelling clay show more interlayer spacing while non-swelling clay show less interlayer space (**Table 2**). The mechanism of swelling of clay minerals is shown in **Figure 7**. The water molecules attached to the surface of clay minerals which is negatively charged results in hydration during the swelling process for most expandable clay minerals. The hydration is the first step in swelling process. The hydration process results in osmotic swelling where water molecules flow toward interlayer of clay minerals having high ion concentration as there is difference in concentration of ions between the unit layers and in the pore water [64].

S. N.	Clay Mineral	Type	Basal Spacing (Å)	Swelling Potential
01	Kaolinite	1:1	7·2	Almost none
02	Montmorillonite/Bentonite	2:1	9·8–20	High
03	Vermiculite	2:1	10–15	High
04	Mica	2:1	10	Low
05	Chlorite	2:1:1	14	None

Table 2.
Basal spacing of different types of clay minerals on the basis of swelling potential.

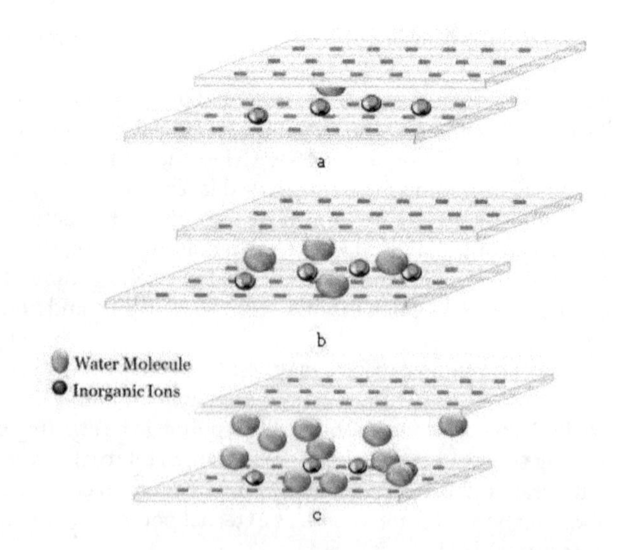

Figure 7.
(a) Non-swelling clay minerals, (b) clay minerals with low swelling capacity and (c) clay minerals with high swelling capacity.

DOI: http://dx.doi.org/10.5772/intechopen.97672

4.3 Surface charge properties

The surface charge of clay minerals affects various chemical properties of clay minerals by varying the quantity of electrical and surface charge density. The surface charge properties play an important role in the formation of organo complexes of clay minerals, migration of ions, swelling and shrinkage. On the basis of difference in surface properties, clay minerals are categorized into two categories:

A. Clay minerals having permanent negative charge: The permanent negative charge in clay minerals occurs due to the isomorphous substitution in the tetrahedral and octahedral layers. This type of charge is also known as structural charge and is pH independent. The negative charges of clay minerals are mainly balanced by the interlayer ions present in the interlayer space of clay minerals. The basal plane of clay minerals are permanently charged through which overall negative charge originated which is measured over pH from 2 to 12 for many clay platelets as shown in **Figure 8**. The edges faces are pH dependent results in anisotropy of clay particles [65]

B. Clay minerals having Variable charge: The charge arises due to the protonation of Si – OH group present on the edges of clay surface. This type of charge is pH dependent. It may either be positive or negative due to the protonation or deprotonation of functional group of clay minerals depending on the pH [65, 66].

The different basal planes such as Kaolinite, gibbsite have different charging properties as the surface charge is affected by salt concentration. In case of edge surface, when hydroxyl group expose to the solution, absorbing or release of protons takes place depending on nature of hydroxyl group and proton concentration in the solution. The most important property related to charge of clay minerals is point of zero charge (pH_0) indicating the condition where the clay minerals carry positive or negative charge. According to Uehara and Gillman, pH_0 is the pH positive and negative charge varies with charge components where these are equal. The surface charge not mainly affects the aggregation of clay particles by also contaminants uptake from the electrolyte solution. The data used to describe the surface charge is collected under the ambient conditions like room temperature and pressure. The behavior of oxide minerals particle can be understood with respect to their charging properties as different crystal planes of a given particle has uniform charge properties. Various crystal faces exposed by the clay platelets show different properties to the surrounding solution results in significant anisotropy [67].

The negative charge present on clay surface is also examined by anion exclusion and cation adsorption in a region near the clay surface known as electrical double layer (EDL). The anion exclusion and electrophoretic mobility can be measured in aqueous dispersion of clay particles indicating the thickness of EDL in terms of several nanometer which completely depend on the ionic strength [68]. The EDL can be conceptually subdivided into a Stern layer containing inner- and outer-sphere surface complexes and a diffuse layer containing ions that interact with the surface through long-range electrostatics [69, 70]. The surface chemistry of clay minerals can now be described by two processes like physisorption and chemisorption of molecules and ions which takes place in the interlayer space and at the edges of the clay mineral layers. For better description of the surface properties, surface electric properties like surface potential and surface charge density are required [71, 72].

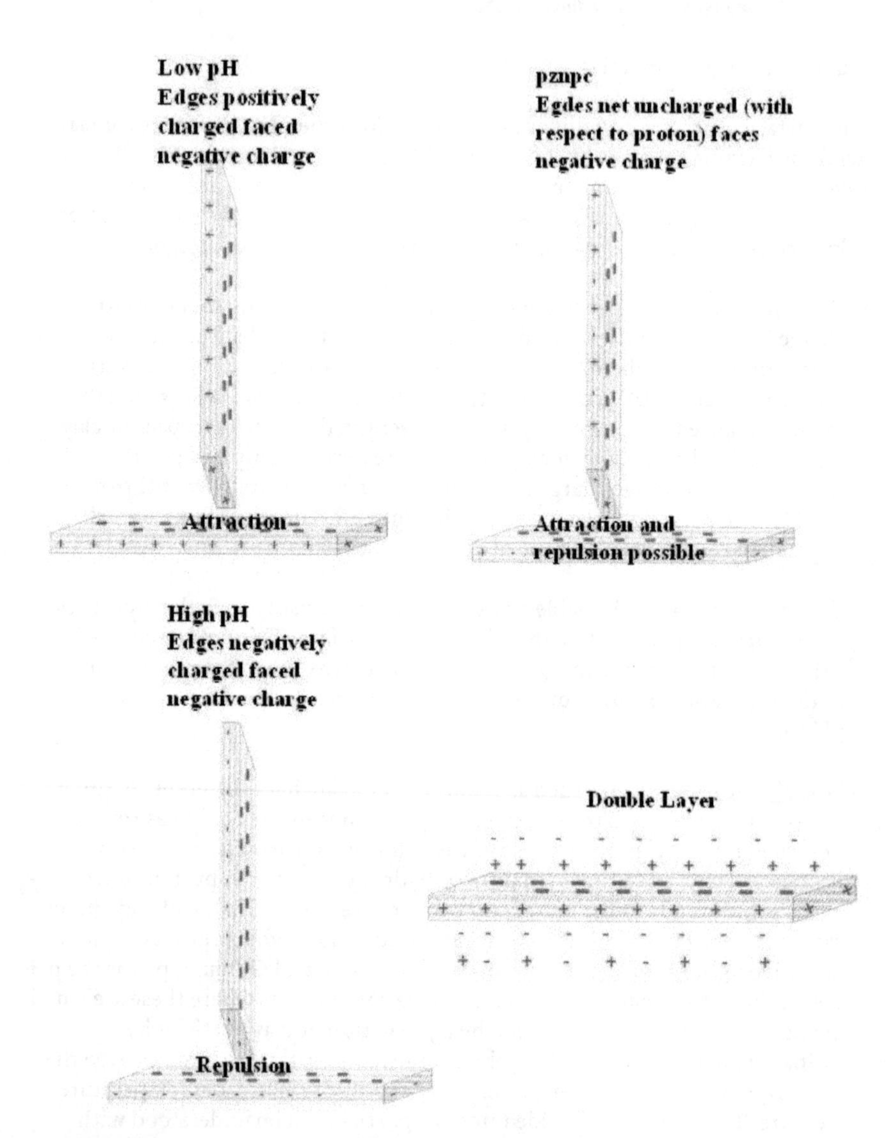

Figure 8.
Surface charge of clay minerals at different pH.

4.4 Adsorptive properties

Clay and clay-based minerals show non-covalent adsorptive behavior through three ways onto various molecules from liquid to gaseous state.

1. Physical adsorption where non-ionic adsorption takes place onto the clay surface (larger surface area compromised in small volumes).

2. Ion exchange adsorption which takes place either through the electrostatic interaction or exchange.

3. Addition of small molecules in pore/cavities and partial or complete elimination of large molecules by the cavities through zeolitic adsorption action [73].

The adsorption capacities of clay minerals depend on various factors. The high adsorption capacities of clay minerals for metal ions, organic matters and other substances are due to large surface area, low permeability, high cation exchange capacities and high retention capabilities. There are some other factors like structure and chemical composition of clay minerals which affects their adsorption capacity. There are different active sites in the clay minerals through which adsorption takes place: i) exchangeable cations (Na^+, K^+, Ca^{2+}); ii) hydroxyls of acidic/basic character (SiOH, SiO(H^+)Al, Al-OH, and OH or Mg-OH); iii) coordinatively unsaturated ions of Al^{3+}, Mg^{2+}, and/or Fe^{3+}; and (iv) oxygen anions O^-. Such active sites present on the surface and the structural elements results in physical adsorption through Vander wall interaction of hydrogen bonding which takes place through the hydroxyl group present on the surface. Secondly, chemisorption also takes place due to the formation of chemical bond formed through stronger interaction between surface and molecules [74, 75].

4.5 Specific surface area (SSA)

Specific surface area (SSA) is defined as the surface area of soil particles per unit mass (or volume) of dry soil. Its unit is in m^2/g or m^2/m^3. The clay minerals show high specific surface area due to the high soil water contaminant interaction results in high reactivity. The reactivity is different for different clay minerals (Kaolinite < Illite < Montmorillonite). The surface area of clay minerals mainly depends on the particle size and shape of the constituents present in clay minerals. As the particle size decreases, the specific surface area increases that can be both internal as well as external. This statement is true in case of the clay minerals which have large fraction of internal surface area such as smectite, vermiculite, sepiolite and palygorskite.

The specific surface area is different for different types of clay minerals. The expanding clay minerals like Montmorillonite and Vermiculite have high specific surface area up to 810 m^2/g (combination of both internal and external surface areas) whereas non-expanding clay minerals like Kaolinite have specific surface area up to 10–70 m^2/g as they show only external surface area due to non-contribution of interlayer surface as shown in **Table 3** [76]. The specific surface area can be increased by treatment of acid activation mainly with inorganic acids.

4.6 Plasticity

Plasticity of clay mineral is one of the important properties. It is the deformation of shape of clay minerals under the influence of finite force. It is defined as property of material which allow it to be repeatedly deformed without rupture

S. N.	Clay Mineral	Type	Specific surface area ($m^2 g^{-1}$)
01	Kaolinite	1:1	5–20
02	Montmorillonite/Bentonite	2:1	700–800
03	Vermiculite	2:1	500–700
04	Mica	2:1	50–200
05	Chlorite	2:1:1	—
06	Sepiolite/palygorskite	2:1	150–900

Table 3.
Specific surface area of different types of clay minerals.

when acted upon by a force sufficient to cause deformation and which allows it to retain its shape after the applied force has been removed. The plasticity of clay minerals is affected by their composition (types of clay minerals, proportion of non-plastic minerals etc.), organic substances, specific surface area, dispersion state of particles, particle size distribution and water characteristics (viscosity and surface tension). The other factors are pressure applied, body temperature and nature of additive used. High plasticity of clay-water system require more force for deformation which occurred to a greater extent without any cracking as compared to clay-water system having low plasticity which easily deform and rupture. The plasticity of clay minerals is related to morphology of clay minerals having platelet like structure which slide over each other after addition of water content. As the water content in clay minerals is increased, plasticity also increased up to maximum depending on nature of clay. Plasticity also known as extrudability, ductility consistency or workability.

When water is added in dry clay, cohesion is increased and tend to maximum after displacing of air from the pores present between clay particles. When water reaches into the pores, formation of high yield strength body takes place results in cracking or rupturing due to the deformation. The minimum quantity of water required to make plastic clay is known as plastic limit. When the water content increases in the clay, it converts into paste where the yield strength gradually reduced. The clay become sticky to fingers. The water content corresponding to this state is known as liquid limit. With further increasing the water content, dispersed form of clay obtained. The difference in water content between these two points is expressed as plasticity index [77, 78].

4.7 Dispersion/flocculation

Dispersion is defined as a system where solid/liquid particles are dispersed into the continuous phase of liquid/solid/gas of different composition. In case of clay minerals, when they are wetted, separation of particles of clay minerals takes place results in formation of dispersion. Are detached. The flocculation is defined as when the particles such as of clay minerals dispersed into the solution, they come in contact and adhere with each other to form clusters, flocks or clumps of larger size (**Figure 9**). The clay dispersion is regulated by repulsive and attractive forces at the surface of charge colloid in electrical double layer. For dispersion of clay particles, there should be balanced between attractive and repulsive forces which is examined by exchangeable cations and ionic strength of the clay solution [79]. The dispersion of clay particles affected by variation in pH. Depending on oxide content and

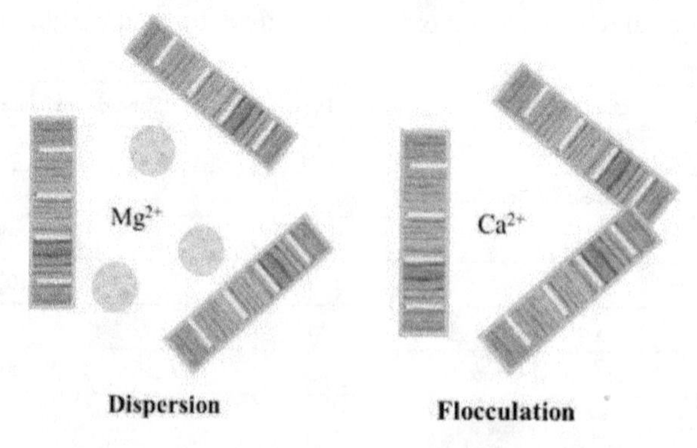

Figure 9.
Dispersion and flocculation in clay minerals.

composition of clay minerals, they exhibit net negative or positive charge at high or low pH.

Suarez et al., (1984) reported that clay dispersion increased with increasing pH at constant sodium adsorption ration and electrolyte concentration for arid-zone clays; kaolinite and smectite [80]. For example, in case of sodium saturated clay, the particle charge depends on protonation of aluminol and silanol group which are affected by pH results in alteration of dispersion/flocculation behavior of clay minerals [81, 82]. The influence of pH plays an important role during the analysis of electrokinetic properties of clay minerals. In case of electrical potential of clay minerals, the effect of pH can be related to amount of variable charge present on external surface of the particles [83].

5. Characterization of clay minerals

At present, identification and characterization of clay minerals can be done in easier way using modern analytical techniques such as Nitrogen Adsorption Isotherm, X-Ray diffraction (XRD), Fourier-Transform Infra-Red (FT-IR), Scanning Electron Microscopy (SEM), Transmission Electron Microscopy (TEM), Zeta potential and Thermal Gravimetric Analysis (TGA). The nitrogen adsorption isotherm used for analyzing the specific surface area, pore volume and pore size distribution by characterizing the porous materials like clay minerals. XRD is mainly used for identification of crystallinity of clay minerals. The characteristic peaks clay minerals like illite, kaolinite, chlorite, smectite etc. can be identified using XRD pattern which further gives information about the interlayer space. The interlayer space is determined using Bragg's equation ($n\lambda = 2d\sin\theta$). For example, the characteristics peak of Montmorillonite is around 6.0° with interlayer spacing of 14.2Å and when this clay mineral is treated with a surfactant/acid, the interlayer spacing will be increased. FT-IR technique is used for identification of functional group like hydroxyl group, Si-O, Al-O group etc. For example The OH stretching vibration band that manifests at 3698.1 cm^{-1}, 3622.6 cm^{-1}, 3411.7 cm^{-1}, 1638.9 cm^{-1}, 1032.2 cm^{-1}, 914.3 cm^{-1} and 799.2 cm^{-1} indicate the presence of kaolinite. Scanning electron microscopy used to study the surface topology of clay minerals such as the size of platelets and their shape mainly describes the surface morphology. SEM does not provide any information about the structure of clay minerals even after modification with surfactant or any acid. Transmission electron microscopy is used for studying microstructure and micromorphology of clay minerals by observing the stacking of layers and interlayer space [84, 85]. Zeta potential mainly used to study the surface charge of clay minerals. Zeta potential holds the information about electric double layer of charged particles whose magnitude is proportional to particle charge adhere on outer surface of clay minerals. Thermo gravimetric analysis used for determination of thermal stability of clay minerals. The curve obtained during analysis at various temperatures indicates the dehydration, dehydroxylation and phase transformation of clay minerals [86].

6. Modification of naturally occurring clay minerals

Naturally occurring clay minerals has mixed cations present on the surface and in interlayer space due to which it is impossible to use clay minerals for certain purposes as surface properties do not allow. Therefore, the interlayer space of clay minerals saturated with desired cations to confer physic-chemical properties which makes them unique for certain applications. Clay minerals are modified to enhance the properties of clay minerals like adsorption capacity, specific surface area, permeability etc. Different ways used to modify the clay minerals like ion exchange using cationic or anionic inorganic/organic complexes, binding of inorganic/organic anions, mainly at edges, reaction with acids, pillaring by different types of poly (hydroxo metal) cations, interlamellar or intraparticle and interparticle polymerization and physical treatments such as lyophilisation, ultrasound, and plasma. Clay minerals can also be modified by pillaring using suitable pillaring agent allowing the layers of clay minerals to open results in their high resistance, high thermal stability, porosity, surface area and basal spacing [87, 88].

A well-known method of ion-exchange is to use alkylammonium ions to make the clay minerals compatible with hydrophobic material in different processes. The natural and synthetic clay minerals can be modified through exchange of interlayer cations using particular organic cations like l-carnitine, spermine, hexadimethrine, tyramine, phenyltrimethylammonium, and hexadecyltrimethylammonium results in development of new types of inorganic–organic hybrid materials. These large organic molecules intercalated in the interlayer of clay minerals results in expansion of interlayer space [89]. The modified clay minerals can be characterized using different analytical techniques like XRD, FT-IR, SEM, TEM etc. as discussed above.

The pillaring of clay minerals is done by cation exchange method where mainly inorganic molecules, hydroxyl polycations of polynuclear metals like Al, Cr, Zn, Ti etc. are introduced into the interlayer of clay minerals [90].

7. Conclusion and outlook

The abundant clay and their minerals are derived from raw materials from small to wide range of composite make them suitable for different environmental application and purposes. They are most common type of sedimentary rock and formed by weathering of these rocks at the earth's surface. They are known as 'chemical sponge' as they can hold water and other inorganic ions results in holding unbalanced charge on their surface due to which some clay minerals are positively charges and some are negatively charged. Due to the presence of water and inorganic ions, clay minerals shows remarkable characteristic which make them unique for different applications. The physico-chemical properties of clay minerals like specific surface area, ion exchange capacity, adsorption capacity, swelling capacity can be enhanced through modification with different organic cation which makes them unique for certain applications like low cost remediation of contaminated water bodies and soil.

DOI: http://dx.doi.org/10.5772/intechopen.97672

Author details

Neeraj Kumari and Chandra Mohan*
SBAS, K. R. Mangalam University, Gurugram, India

*Address all correspondence to: chandra.mohan@krmangalam.edu.in

References

[1] Guggenheim S, Martin RT. Definition of clay and clay mineral: Joint report of the AIPEA nomenclature and CMS nomenclature committees. Clay Minerals. 1995;30:257-259.

[2] Bergaya F, Lagaly G. General introduction: Clays, clay minerals and clay science. Handbook of clay science. 2006;1:1-8. doi:10.1016/s1572-4352(05)01001-9

[3] Guggenheim S, Formoso ML, Galan E, Bish DL. Definition of clay and clay mineral: Joint report of the AIPEA nomenclature and CMS nomenclature committees. Clay and clay minerals. 1995;43:255-256. DOI: 10.1346/CCMN.1995.0430213

[4] What is clay. Science Learning Hub. 2010. Available from https://www.sciencelearn.org.nz/resources/1771-what-is-clay. (Accessed: 2020-06-20)

[5] Augustyn A. Clay, Encyclopedia Britanica. 2020 Available from https://www.britannica.com/science/sand (Accessed: 2020-06-20)

[6] Guggenheim, Stephen; Martin, R. T. (1995), "Definition of clay and clay mineral: Journal report of the AIPEA nomenclature and CMS nomenclature committees", Clays and Clay Minerals, 43 (2): 255-256, doi:10.1346/CCMN.1995.0430213

[7] Clay. Wikipedia, Available from https://en.wikipedia.org/wiki/Clay. (Accessed: 2020-06-20)

[8] Kerr PF. Formation and occurrence of clay minerals. Clays and Clay Minerals. 1952;1: 19-32.

[9] Tong WK. Introduction to Clay Minerals. 2000. Available from https://www.oakton.edu/user/4/billtong/eas100/clays.htm (Accessed on 2020-07-23).

[10] Hillier S. Clay mineralogy. In GV Middleton, MJ Church, M Coniglio, LA Hardie, and FJ Longstaffe eds. Encyclopaedia of sediments and sedimentary rocks: Kluwer Academic; 2003. P. 139-142. DOI: 10.1007/3-540-31079-7_47

[11] Barton CD, Karathanasis, AD. Clay minerals. In: Rattan Lal, comp., ed. Encyclopedia of Soil Science. New York. 2002;187-192.

[12] Klein C, Hurlbut C. Systematic Mineralogy Part IV: Silicates. Manual of Mineralogy, 20th Ed.; John Wiley & Sons: New York, 1985;366-467.

[13] Benjamin K. The Clay Mineral – Structure. 2004. Available from http://www.groundwaterresearch.com.au/reference_files/hydrology_and_the_clay_minerals/structure.htm (Accessed on 2020-07-23)

[14] Guggenheim S. Introduction to the properties of clay mineral. Available from http://www.minsocam.org/msa/Monographs/Mngrph_03/MG003_371-388.pdf

[15] Layer silicate clays – Genesis and classification. Available from http://ecoursesonline.iasri.res.in/Courses/Introduction%20to%20Soil%20Science/SSAC121/Data%20Files/lec15.pdf, (Accessed on 2020-07-30).

[16] Schultz DG. An Introduction to Soil Mineralogy. Dixon JB, Weed SB, In Minerals in Soil Environments, 2nd ed Soil Science Society of America: Madison, WI. 1989;1-34. https://doi.org/10.2136/sssabookser1.2ed.c1

[17] Sarkar B, Singh M, Mandal S, Churchman GJ, Bolan SN. Clay minerals—Organic matter interactions in relation to carbon stabilization in soils. The Future of Soil Carbon. 2018;71-86. doi:10.1016/b978-0-12-811687-6.00003-1

[18] Deer WA, Howie RA, Zussman J. An introduction to the rock-forming minerals. Harlow: Longman. 2nd ed. mineralogical Society of Great Britain and Ireland (2nd ed.). 1992. DOI: https://doi.org/10.1180/DHZ.

[19] Pohl WL. Economic Geology: Principles and Practice: Metals, Minerals, Coal and Hydrocarbons – Introduction to Formation and Sustainable Exploitation of Mineral Deposits. Chichester: Wiley; 2011. p. 331. DOI:10.1002/9781444394870

[20] Schroeder PA. Kaolin. New Georgia Encyclopedia. Available from https://www.britannica.com/science/kaolin. (Accessed on 2020-07-31).

[21] Perry DL. Handbook of Inorganic Compounds. 2nd ed. Boca Raton: Taylor & Francis. 2011.

[22] Grim RE, Kodama H. Clay minerals. Encyclopedia Britannica. Available from https://www.britannica.com/science/clay-mineral (Accessed on 2020-07-31).

[23] Dictionary of Geology – Definitions. Available from https://www.theodora.com/geology/glossarys.html#serpentine (Accessed on 2020-07-31).

[24] The serpentine mineral group. Available from https://www.minerals.net/mineral/serpentine.aspx (Accessed: 2020-07-31).

[25] Serpentine subgroup. Available from https://en.wikipedia.org/wiki/Serpentine_subgroup (Accessed: 2020-07-31).

[26] Anthony JW, Bideaux RA, Bladh K W, Nichols MC Handbook of Mineralogy Volume IV. Mineral Data Publishing, Tucson. 2000;pp 680.

[27] Uddin F. Clays, nanoclays and montmorillonite clay minerals. Metallurgical and Material Transaction. 2008;39:2804-2814.

[28] Murray HH. Structure and composition of clay minerals and their physical and chemical properties. Applied clay mineralogy – occurrence, processing and applications of Kaoline, Bentonite, Polygorskite-Sepiolite and common clays. Haydn H Murray. 2006:7-31. Doi:10.1016/s1572-4352(06)02002-2

[29] Sutherland WM. Wyoming bentonite. 2014. Available from fhttps://www.wsgs.wyo.gov/products/wsgs-2014-bentonite-summary.pdf (Accessed 2020-08-05)

[30] Odom IE. Smectite clay minerals: Properties and uses. Philosophical transactions of the Royal Society a: Mathematical, physical and Engineering Sciences. 1984;311:391. doi:10.1098/rsta.1984.0036. JSTOR 37332.

[31] Hosterman JW, Patterson SH. Bentonite and Fuller's earth resources of the United States. U.S. Geological Survey professional paper 1522. 1992. DOI: https://doi.org/10.3133/pp1522

[32] Theng BKG. Formation and properties of clay polymer complexes. Elsevier. 1979.

[33] Lagaly G. Surface and interlayer reactions: bentonites as adsorbents. Churchman, GJ, Fitzpatrick RW, Eggleton RA (ed). Clays Controlling the Environment. Proceedings of the 10th International Clay Conference, Adelaide, Australia. 1995;137-144p.

[34] Robertson RHS. Fuller's Earth. A History of calcium montmorillonite. Volturna, Press, Hythe, England. 1986;421p

[35] Guynnet D, Gaucher E, Gaboriau H, Pons CH, Clinard C, Norotte V, Didier G. Geosynthetic clay liner interaction with leachate: Correlation between permeability, microstructure, and surface chemistry. Journal of Geotechnical and Geoenvironmental

Engineering. 2005;131:740. doi:10.1061/(ASCE)1090-0241(2005)131:6(740)

[36] Vermiculite, Wikipedia. Available from https://en.wikipedia.org/wiki/Vermiculite. (Accessed 2020-08-10).

[37] Vermiculite. Available from https://rruff.info/doclib/hom/vermiculite.pdf. (Accessed: 2020-08-10).

[38] What is Vermiculite? What is it used for? Available from https://www.greenandvibrant.com/vermiculite (Accessed: 2020-08-29).

[39] Illite group (July, 2020). Available from https://pubs.usgs.gov/of/2001/of01-041/htmldocs/clays/illite.htm, (Accessed: 2020-08-29).

[40] Illite mineral data Available from http://webmineral.com/data/Illite.shtml#.XyAKkJ4zZPY, (Accessed: 2020-08-29).

[41] Illite, (July 2020). Retrieved from https://en.wikipedia.org/wiki/Illite, July 28, 2020.

[42] Swagata P. Six main types of clay minerals. Available from https://www.soilmanagementindia.com/soil-properties/6-main-types-of-clay-minerals/3564, (Accessed: 2020-08-31).

[43] Palygorskite. Wikipedia, Available from https://en.wikipedia.org/wiki/Palygorskite#:~:text=Palygorskite%20or%20attapulgite%20is%20a,the%20types%20of%20fuller's%20earth. (Accessed: 2020-08-31)

[44] Palygorskite. Available from http://www.handbookofmineralogy.com/pdfs/palygorskite.pdf, (Accessed: 2020-09-29).

[45] Rafferty JP. Palygorskite mineral, Available from https://www.britannica.com/science/sepiolite. (Accessed: 2020-10-05)

[46] Wada K. Allophane and Imogolite in minerals in soil environments. Soil Science Society of America. 1989;1:1051-1087.

[47] Kodama H. Clay minerals, Encyclopedia Britannica, Available from https://www.britannica.com/science/clay-mineral/Interstratified-clay-minerals (Accessed: 2020-10-20).

[48] Ugochukwu UC. Characteristics of clay minerals relevant to bioremediation of environmental contaminated system. Modified clay and zeolite nanocomposite material. 2019;219-242. https://doi.org/10.1016/B978-0-12-814617-0.00006-2.

[49] Nadziakiewicza M, Kehoe S, Micek P. Physico-chemical properties of clay minerals and their use as a health promoting feed additive. Animals. 2019;9:714. doi:10.3390/ani9100714.

[50] Schoonheydt R A, Johnston CT. The surface properties of clay minerals. EMU notes mineral. 11:337-373. DOI: https://doi.org/10.1180/EMU-notes.11.10

[51] Verbung K, Baveye P. Hysterisis in the binary exchange of cations on 2:1 clay minerals: A critical review. Clays and Clay Minerals. 1994;42:207-220. DOI: DOI: 10.1346/CCMN.1994.0420211

[52] Kahr G, Madsen ET. Determination of the cation exchange capacity and the surface area of bentonite, illite and kaolinite by methylene blue adsorption. Applied clay science. 1995;9:327-336. DOI: https://doi.org/10.1016/0169-1317(94)00028

[53] Cohen R, Yariv S. Metachromasy in clay minerals. Journal of the chemical society, faraday transaction. 1984;86. DOI: https://doi.org/10.1039/F19848001705

[54] Chabra R, Pleysier J, Cremers A. The measurement of the cation

exchange capacity and exchangeable cations in soils: A new method. Proceedings of the International Clay Conference, 1975;439-449.

[55] Aran D, Maul A, Masfaraud JF. A spectrophotometric measurement of soil cation exchange capacity based on cobaltihexamine chloride absorbance. Sciences. 2008;340:865-871. Doi : 10.1016/j.crte.2008.07.015.

[56] Bergaya E, Vayer M. CEC of clays: Measurement by adsorption of a copper ethylenediamine complex. Applied clay science. 1997;12:275-280. DOI: https://doi.org/10.1016/S0169-1317(97)00012

[57] Chiu YC, Haung LN, Uang CM, Huang JF. Clay minerals by potentiometric titration using divalent cation electrodes. Colloids and Surfaces. 1990;46:327-337 DOI: https://doi.org/10.1016/0166-6622(90)80174-3

[58] Burrafato G, Miano F. Determination of the cation exchange capacity of clays by surface tension measurement. Clay minerals. 1993;28:475-481. DOI: https://doi.org/10.1180/claymin.1993.028.3.10

[59] Karpinski B, Szkodo M. Clay minerals – Mineralogy and phenomenon of clay swelling in oli and gas industry. Advanced in material science. 2015;15:37-55. DOI: https://doi.org/10.1515/adms-2015-0006

[60] Cherif MM, Amal M, Ramdane B. Effect of swelling minerals on geotechnical characteristics of clay soil. MATEC web of conference. 2018;149:02067. DOI: https://doi.org/10.1051/matecconf/201814902067

[61] Brekke TL, Selmer-Olsen R. Stability problems in underground constructions caused by montmorillonite-carrying joints and faults. Engineering geology. 1965;17:3-19. DOI: https://doi.org/10.1016/0013-7952(65)90004-9

[62] Pusch, R. 2012. Environmental soil properties and behaviour, swelling clays, chapter 4. CRC press, Taylor & Francis Group, LLC: Pp.133-161.)

[63] Nilsen B. Cases of instability caused by weakness zones in Norwegian tunnels. Bulletin of Engineering Geology and the Environment. 2011;70: 7-13. DOI: 10.1007/s10064-010-0331-x

[64] Physical properties of soil. Available from http://soils.missouri.edu/tutorial/page8.asp. (Accessed 2021-01-31)

[65] Karak T. Das DK, Singh UK, Maiti D. Influence of pH on soil charge characteristics and Cadmium sorption in some noncontaminated soil of indian subtropics. Scientific World Journal. 2005;5:183 – 194. doi: 10.1100/tsw.2005.26

[66] Moghimi AH, Hamdan J, Shamsuddin J, Samsuri AW, Abtahi A. Physiochemical properties and surface charge characteristics of arid soil in southeastern Iran. Applied and environmental soil science. 2013;2013:1-11. DOI: https://doi.org/10.1155/2013/252861

[67] Preicanin T, Abdelmonem A, Montavon G, Luetzenkirchen J. Charging behavior of clays and clay minerals in aqueous electrolyte solution – Experimental methods for measuring the charge and interpreting the results. In: Gustavo Morari do Nascimento. Clay, Clay minerals and ceramic materials based on clay minerals. DOI: 10.5772/62082.

[68] Sposito G. The diffuse-ion swarm near smectite particles suspended in 1:1 electrolyte solutions: modified Gouy-Chapman theory and quasicrystal formation. In Guen N, Pollastro. Clay Water Interface and Its Rheological Implications. Clay minerals society. 1992;127-156 p.

[69] Henderson D, Boda D. Insights from theory and simulation on the electrical

double layer. Physical chemistry chemical physics. 2009;11:3822-3830. DOI: https://doi.org/10.1039/B815946G

[70] Tournassat C, Bourg, IC, Steefel CI, Bergaya F. Surface properties of clay minerals. Developments in Clay Science. 2015;5-31. doi:10.1016/ b978-0-08-100027-4.00001-2.

[71] Guo Y, Yu X. Characterizing the surface charge of clay minerals with atomic force microscope (AFM). AIMS Material Science. 2017;4:582-593. doi: 10.3934/matersci.2017.3.582

[72] Giese, R. F., & van Oss, C. J. (2002). Colloid and Surface Properties of Clays and Related Minerals (Vol. 105). Boca Raton, FL: CRC Press.

[73] Aboudi Mana SC, Hanafiah MM, Chowdhury AJ. Environmental characteristics of clay and clay based minerals. Geology. Ecology and landscape. 2017;1:155-161. DOI: https://doi.org/10.1080/24749508.2017.1361128

[74] Novikova L, Belchinskaya L. Adsorption of Industrial Pollutants by Natural and Modified Aluminosilicate. Clays, Clay Minerals and Ceramic Materials Based on Clay Minerals. 2016. DOI: 10.5772/61678

[75] Carter DL, Mortland MM, Kemper WD. Specific surface. Methods of soil analysis. Part 1. Physical and mineralogical methods. 2nd ed. soil science Society of America. 1990. DOi: https://doi.org/10.1002/gea.3340050110

[76] Gunal H, Ransom MD. Clay mineralogy, specific surface area and micromorphology of polygenetic soils from eastern Kansas. Archives of Agronomy and Soil Science. 2006;51: 459-468. DOI: https://doi.org/10.1080/03650340500186439

[77] Andrade FA, Al-Qureshi HA, Hotza D. Measuring the plasticity of clays: A review. Applied clay science. 2011;51:1-7. DOI: https://doi.org/10.1016/j.clay.2010.10.028

[78] de Andrade FA, Al-Qureshi HA, Hotza D. Measuring and modeling the plasticity of clays. Materials Research. 2010;13. DOI:http://dx.doi.org/10.1590/ S1516-14392010000300019

[79] Rengasamy P, Olsson KA. Sodicity and soil structure. Australian journal of soil research. 1991;29:935-952. DOI: https://doi.org/10.1071/SR9910935

[80] Suarez DL, Rhodes JD, Lavado R, Grieve CM. Effect of pH on saturated hydraulic conductivity and soil dispersion. Soil Science Society of America Journal.1984;48:50-55. DOI: https://doi.org/10.2136/sssaj1992.03615995005600020014x

[81] Thellier CT, Sposito G, Holtzclaw KM. Proton effects on quaternary cation exchange and flocculation of Silver Hill illite. Soil Science Society of America Journal. 1992;56:427-433. DOI: https://doi.org/10.2136/sssaj1992.03615995005600020014x

[82] Chorom M, Rengasamy P. Dispersion and zeta potential of pure clays as related to net particle charge under varying pH, electrolyte concentration and cation type. European journal of soil science. 1995;46:657-665. DOI: https://doi.org/10.1111/j.1365-2389.1995.tb01362.x

[83] Tirado-Corbala R, Slater BK, Dick WA, Bigham J, McCoy E. Hydrologic properties and leachate nutrient responses of soil columns collected from gypsum-treated fields. Soil and Tillage Research. 2013; 134:232-240. DOI: https://doi.org/10.1016/j.still.2013.08.007

[84] Dong L, Qian T, Peng Y, Peixin D, Junming Z, Yun L, Hongling B, Jieyu Z. Facile sample preparation method allowing TEM characterization of the

stacking structures and interlayer spaces of clay minerals. Applied Clay Science, 2019;171:1-5. https://doi.org/10.1016/j.clay.2019.01.019

[85] Ismadji S, Soetaredjo FE, Ayucitra A. The characterization of clay minerals and adsorption mechanism onto clays. Clay Materials for Environmental Remediation. 2015;93-112. doi:10.1007/978-3-319-16712-1_5

[86] Fosu-Duah EL, Padmanabhan E, Gamez JA. Characteristic zeta potential of selected oligocene-miocene shales from the setap formation, on shore Sarawak-Malaysia. International Journal of Applied Engineering Research. 2017; 12: 6360-6368.

[87] Faiza B, Gerhard L. Surface modification of clay minerals. Applied Clay Science, 2001;19:1-3

[88] Celis R, Trigo C, Facenda G, Hermosin MDC, Cornejo J. Selective modification of clay minerals for the adsorption of herbicides widely used in olive groves. Journal of Agricultural and Food Chemistry. 2007;55(16):6650-6658. doi:10.1021/jf070709q

[89] Sarkar B, Rusmin R, Ugochukwu UC, Mukhopadhyay R, Manjaiah KM. Modified clay minerals for environmental applications. Modified Clay and Zeolite Nanocomposite Materials, 2019;113-127. doi:10.1016/b978-0-12-814617-0.00003-7

[90] Bergaya F, Aouad A, Mandalia T. Chapter 7.5 pillared clays and clay minerals. Handbook of Clay Science, 2006;393-421. doi:10.1016/s1572-4352(05)01012-3

Chapter 3

Thermodynamic and Kinetic Behaviors of Copper (II) and Methyl Orange (MO) Adsorption on Unmodified and Modified Kaolinite Clay

Aicha Kourim, Moulay Abderrahmane Malouki and Aicha Ziouche

Abstract

In this study, the adsorption of Copper Cu (II) and methyl Orange (MO) from aqueous solution, on Tamanrasset's unmodified and modified Kaolinite clay which as low cost adsorbents, was studied using batch experiments. The adsorption study includes both equilibrium adsorption isotherms, kinetics and thermodynamics study. For the characterization of the adsorbent several properties are determined such as pH, the Specific Surface Area, the Point of Zero Charge and the Cation Exchange Capacity. Indeed, various parameters were investigated such as contact time, initial metal and dye concentration, mass of solid, pH of the solution and temperature. The adsorption process as batch study was investigated under the previews experimental parameters.

Keywords: Adsorption, Kaolinite, Copper, Methyl Orange, Kinetic, Isotherms

1. Introduction

The extensive use of chemicals in developing and developed countries over the last century increased the amount of dyes and heavy metals which is released into surface and underground water through discharges of wastewater produced from metallurgical, mining, chemical, research laboratories, printing paper and battery manufacturing industries [1, 2]. Copper (Cu (II)) is extremely toxic, not biodegradable and it accumulated in living organisms, and may thus pose a threat to human beings. In addition, Copper ions is considered as vital transition metal ion because of its necessity in biological activities of living organism, whereas at certain concentration, it causes serious damages to human health and environment [3–5].

Methyl orange (MO) is an azo soluble dye, shows low biodegradability and is soluble in water hence it is difficult to remove from aqueous solutions by common water purification methods. As other dyes MO is toxic and carcinogenic, posing serious hazards to humans and the environment [6].

Purification of water can be achieved by physicochemical and biological methods. The physicochemical methods include precipitation [7], membrane filtration [8], liquid–liquid extraction [9] reverse osmosis [10], electrolysis or ultrasonic electrolysis [11], electrodialysis [12], electrodeposition [13], ion exchange resins [14], incineration and electrokinetic method [15], flotation [16], flocculation [17], coagulation [18], photocatalysis [19], adsorption and biosorption [20]. Biological process includes biodegradation or bioremediation [21], phycoremediation [22]. Adsorption method is more effective, economic with high potential and low energy consumption specially it has the advantage of the utilization of abundant with low cost adsorbents.

Clay minerals in the soil play the role of a natural scavenger by removing and accumulating pollutants through ion exchange and adsorption process. Generally, these minerals are categorized into Montmorillonite, smectites, Illite and kaolinite [23]. Kaolinite is a harmful charge clay mineral with a soft consistency. It made up of a silicon tetrahedral (T) sheet and an aluminum octahedral (O) sheet which called 1:1layer clay (2 sheets). Kaolinite has considered as an excellent adsorbent clay because of its high specific surface area, high exchange capacity, large potential for ion exchange, surface charges, charge density, chemical and mechanical stability, a variety of surface and structural properties, hydroxyl groups on the edge, silanol groups of crystalline defects or broken surfaces, and Lewis and Brönsted acidity [24–27]. Kaolinite clay also has been widely accepted as low cost abundant adsorbent for the removal of copper and methyl orange from wastewater due to the surface structure and edges. Recently many studies used natural kaolinite [28], other scientists used purified kaolinite in other wise other researchers used organo kaolinite as adsorbents [29]. However, kaolinite in its different geological origins may have variable chemical compositions and structural deformation. Elements such as Fe, Ti, Mn, Mg, and Cr, and impure phases, such as quartz, and Illite, are normally contained in natural kaolinite. Even, a small amount of these impurities may significantly affect the chemical properties of kaolinite. Those researches were carried out with physical or chemical modification of kaolinite in order to enhance the properties of kaolinite and to increase the adsorption capacity.

The aim of this paper is to access the ability of Tamanrasset's kaolinite clay and its derivatives (purified, activated, pillared and modified) to adsorb Cu(II) and MO from aqueous solution. The effect of the contact time, temperature, mass of solid, solution pH and concentration of the adsorbate was studied. The kinetics and factors controlling the adsorption were also studied. Therefore, the physicochemical characteristics of materials were considered such as pH, the specific surface area, the point of zero charge and the cation exchange capacity.

2. Material and methods

2.1 The adsorbate and solution

The adsorbates in this study were copper and methyl orange prepared by dissolving $CuCl_2$, $2H_2O$ and MO into 1000 mL of deionized water to stock solution concentration of 1000 mg/L, the adjustment of pH in the solution was achieved by adding NaOH and HCl 0,1 M are from Sigma-Aldrich. The desirable experimental concentrations of solutions were prepared by diluting the stock solution with distilled water when necessary.

2.2 The adsorbents

2.2.1 Raw clay

The natural clay sample was obtained from Tamanrasset south of Algeria. It was prepared before use by sun drying, then ground into fin particles and sieved to a particle size of 300 μm after that, it was stored in a desiccator for late experimental use.

2.2.2 Purified clay

The clay was purified with the purpose of removing all crystalline phases and organic matter according to the procedure described by Robert and Tessier in order to obtain 2 micrometers clay fractions intercalated with sodium ions (Clay-Na) [30].

2.2.3 Activated clay

The chemical activated clay was carried out by adding 50 g of raw clay to 500 ml of sulfuric acid 1.5 M and refluxing at 110°C for 4 h. The resulting clay suspension was then rapidly quenched by adding 500 ml of ice water. After cooling the sample was washed several times with distilled water until neutral pH, then filtered, dried in oven and calcined at 500°C for 4 hours [31, 32].

2.2.4 Pillared clay

The pillaring solution was prepared by the slow addition of NaOH 0.225 M to a 0.5 M solution of $AlCl_3$ at room temperature, until a molar ratio of OH/Al = 1.8 was reached. The pillaring of Clay-Na by polycation of aluminum is carried out according to the conventional procedure (cationic exchange with a heat treatment) [33].

2.2.5 Clay-CTAB

In 500 ml Buchner, 10 g of purified clay was added to 250 ml of CTAB solution 0.02 M, the mixture was stirring at room temperature for 24 h. Then, the suspension was filtered and washed several times until the negative test of Br-. The CTAB-Clay was dried at 105°C for one hour, ground and stored in sterile glass box [34, 35].

2.3 Physicochemical characteristics of adsorbents

2.3.1 The pH of adsorbent

Ten grams of crushed kaolinite was stirred in 75 ml of deionized water in a beaker over the night then it filtered. The pH was measured by a glass electrode (pH METER HI2210) [36].

2.3.2 The specific surface area

Sear's method was chosen to estimate the surface areas of clay adsorbents [37]. 0.5 g of each clay was acidified with 0.1 M HCl to a pH 3–3,5. The volume was made up to 50 ml with distilled water after addition of 10 g of NaCl. The titration was carried out with standard 0.1 M NaOH buffer solution from pH 4 to pH 9. The volume, V, required to raise the pH from 4 to 9 was noted and the surface area was computed from the following equation:

$$S(m^2/g) = 32V - 25 \quad (1)$$

2.3.3 The point of zero charge

The point of zero chare or pHPzc is point where the net charge of the material equal to 0. The PZC war determined by the pH drift method [38, 39].

2.3.4 The cation exchange capacity

The CEC of materials was calculated by methylene blue method [40].

2.4 Bath equilibrium studies

Bath experiments were performed in asset of 250 mL Erlenmeyer flasks that contain a volume of 100 mL in each flask of fixed initial concentrations of metal and dye solutions. The flasks were kept in a thermostated water bath (Wise bath® eed Back Control Digital Timer Function, Laboratory Instruments) shaker at a constant speed of 150 rpm for 360 min (6 h). The sample solutions were filtered at equilibrium to determine the residual concentrations. The amount of adsorbate adsorbed at the equilibrium condition, q_e (mg/g), was calculated by the following Equations [41]:

$$q_e = \frac{(C_0 - C_e)V}{W} \quad (2)$$

Were C_0 and C_e are the initial and equilibrium metal and dye concentrations (mg/L), respectively. V is the volume of solution (L) and W is the mass of adsorbent used (g).

The concentration of Cu(II) before and after adsorption was determined by a flam atomic absorption spectrometry (Analyst 700 Perkin Elmer Atomic Absorption Spectrometer) and the concentration of MO was determined by UV–Visible spectrometry (M209T Spectronic Camspec).

2.5 Kinetics studies

The kinetic experiments, adsorption capacity of Cu (II) and MO at time t, q_t (mg/g), was calculated as follows:

$$q_t = \frac{(C_0 - C_t)V}{W} \quad (3)$$

Were C_t (mg/L) is the concentration of copper/Methyl orange at any time t (min).

3. Results and discussion

3.1 Characterization of adsorbents

3.1.1 pH and the point of zero charge

The surface of kaolinite has a net positive surface charge at pH < PZC, whereas at pH > PZC, it has a negative surface charge. The PZC value or natural kaolinite was8.9 this value indicates that the adsorption of copper and methyl orange by untreated kaolinite will occur at pH ≥ 8.9.

3.1.2 Surface area

The specific surface area of 5 to 25 m^2/g for the untreated kaolinite clay. The specific surface area of natural, purified, activated, pillared, and CTAB kaolinite are measured as 25.4, 36.7, 30.14, 42.1 and 43.15 m^2/g, respectively. The specific surface area increased up to 30.1 for activated clay. Such the high value of specific area is not achieved in the present work by treatment with 1.5 M H_2SO_4 acid. The chemical modification opens up the edge of the platelets and as consequence, the surface area and the pore diameter increase too.

3.1.3 Cation exchange capacity

The kaolinite used in the present work had CEC of 5.92 meq/100 g as measured by methylene blue method. Kaolinite as other clay minerals contain both Brönsted and Lewis acid cites associated respectively with the interlamellar region and the edge sites.

The ions exchange capacity of kaolinite is attributed to the structural defects, broken bonds and structural hydroxyl transfers. Chemical modifications increase the total number of exchange sites. The results obtained are summarized in **Table 1**.

3.2 Bath studies

3.2.1 Effect of adsorbent dose

The adsorbent dose is an important parameter too because it determines the capacity of adsorbent for a given initial concentration of metal solution.

Figure 1a and **b** showed that the amount adsorbed q_e decrease with the increase of adsorbent dosage. This is due to the increase in surface area and hence more available adsorption sites competing for the same number of initial ion concentration [42].

3.2.2 Effect of time contact and initial concentration

Equilibrium time is an important parameter in the studies of wastewater treatment. The adsorption of Cu^{2+} onto clay (0,08 g of raw, purified and pillared clay, 0.1 g of activated clay and 0.06 of modified CTAB clay) at various initial concentrations (5, 25, 50, and 100mg/L), and in the case of methyl orange the dosage of modified and unmodified clay was 0.1 g at various initial concentrations (5, 20, and 35 mg/L) was studied as a function of contact time in order to determine the necessary adsorption equilibrium time.

Figure 2a and **b** shows the effects of contact time and initial concentration on the adsorption of copper and methyl orange into raw clay. We notice that the adsorption is rapid at the initial stages during 10–50 minutes. This is due to the fast

Properties	pH	Point of Zero Charge	Specific Surface Area (m^2/g)	Cation Exchange Capacity (meq/100 g)
Raw clay	7.44	8.9	25.4	5.95
Purified Clay	9.83	3.5	36.7	11.82
Activated Clay	3.40	7.5	30.14	13.75
Pillared Clay	5.43	5.1	42.1	13.05
Clay-CTAB	1.6	3.25	43.15	12.18

Table 1.
Physicochemical properties of adsorbents.

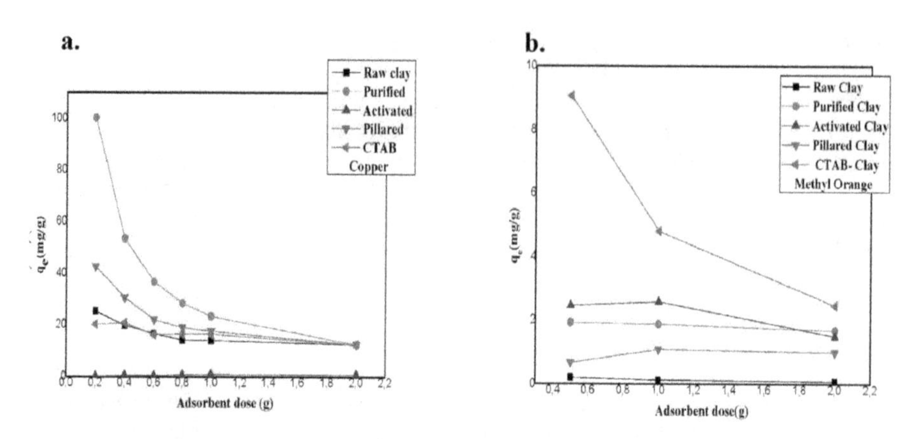

Figure 1.
Effect of adsorbent dose on the amount adsorbed onto copper and methyl orange.

that there were a large number of vacant sites for metal on the external surface of clay particles. Then it's gradually decreases with the progress of adsorption until the equilibrium is reached because of the active sites saturation of the adsorbent [43, 44]. As shown in **Figure 2**, the contact time for the Cu(II) and MO to reach equilibrium was 50 min and 60 min, respectively.

The **Table 2** below shows the adsorption capacity of adsorbed at the equilibrium (q_e) increased with an increase in the initial concentrations.

3.2.3 Effect of pH on the amount adsorbed

pH is the most important environmental factors influencing not only site dissociation, but also the solution chemistry and in the efficiency of adsorption [45], it effects both the dye structure and the surface on the adsorbent. As seen in **Figure 3** the sorption capacity of copper increased whenever pH of the solution increases. While, the adsorption amount of methyl orange onto the clay increases as pH is lowered from 11 to 2, confirmed that the initial solution pH is a key adsorption parameter that strongly affects metal and dye adsorption because of the decreased positive charges on the adsorbent surface with an increased pH. The pH of the solution also affects the solubility and species of adsorbate, the adsorbents, and the degree of ionization of the adsorbate [46–48].

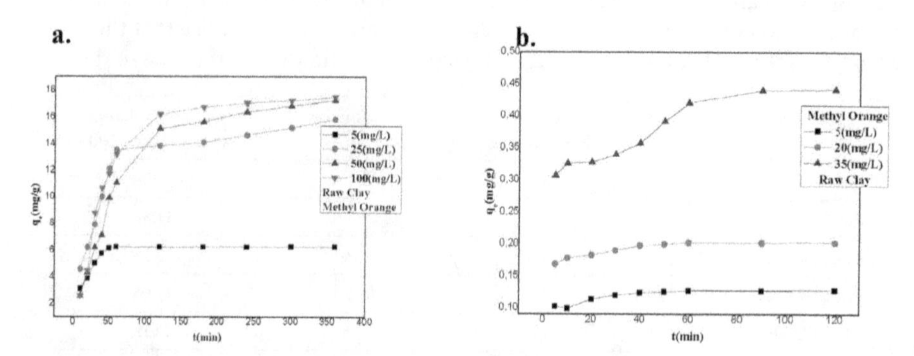

Figure 2.
Effect of initial concentration and contact time.

Clay		Natural	Modified			
			Purified	Activated	Pillared	Clay-CTAB
Cu(II)	q_e(mg/g)	6.25–20.91	6.25–27.65	0.39–1.17	6.25–24.47	8.33–30.31
MO		0.126–0.423	1.879–2.835	2.599–5.672	1.083–3.591	4.804–10.447

Table 2.
The amount adsorbed.

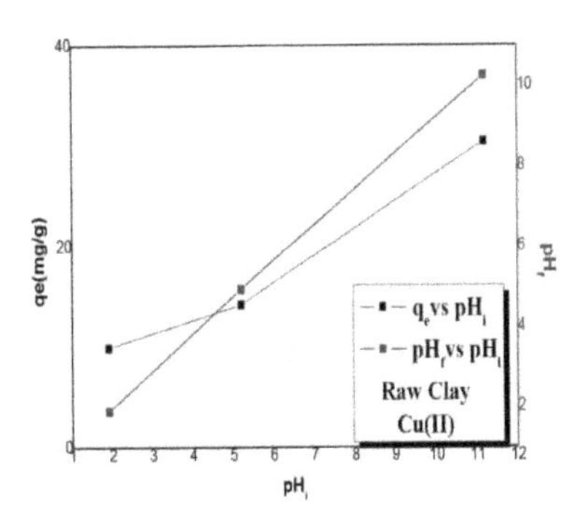

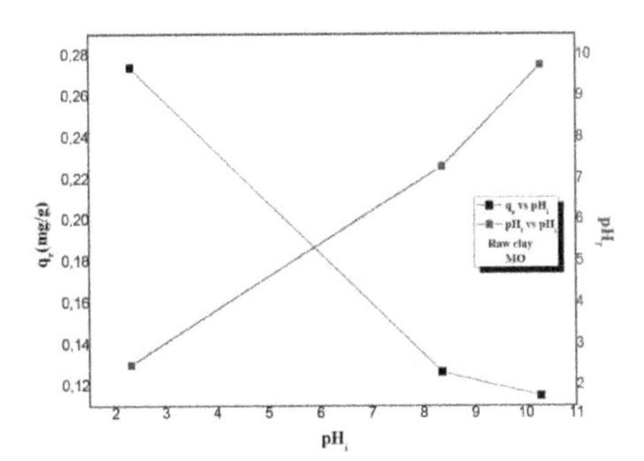

Figure 3.
Effect of pH.

3.2.4 Effect of temperature on the amount of adsorption

Because temperature is an important parameter for adsorption process and bath adsorption studies were carried out at different temperatures and concentrations of Cu(II) ions and MO dye. The amount of sorption increasing with increasing temperature witch indicates that the nature of this adsorption is a chemical sorption [42]. Whereas, the adsorption capacity of MO onto raw and activated kaolinite decrease whenever temperature increase, as shown if **Figure 4**, indicating possibilities of reversible adsorption process [49].

3.3 Kinetic studies

Two kinetic models fitted this adsorption process very well as explained below [50, 51].

3.3.1 Pseudo-first order kinetic model

The pseudo first-order kinetic model is expressed as:

$$log\left(q_e - q_t\right) = log\, q_e - \left(\frac{k_1}{2.303}\right)t \quad (4)$$

Where $\mathbf{q_t}$ is the amount adsorbed (mg/g) at time t (sec) and $\mathbf{k_1}$ is the pseudo-first order constant (s^{-1}) and calculated by linear regression of log(q_e-q_t) versus t plot.

3.3.2 Pseudo-second order kinetic model

The pseudo second-order kinetic model is given as:

$$\left(\frac{t}{q_t}\right) = \left(\frac{t}{q_e}\right) + \left(\frac{1}{k_2 q_e^2}\right) \quad (5)$$

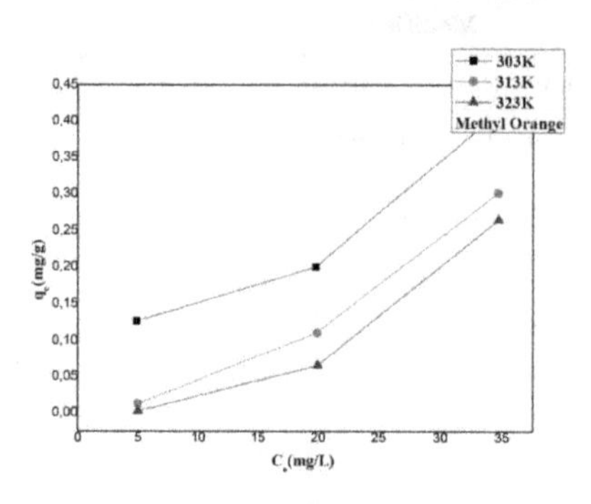

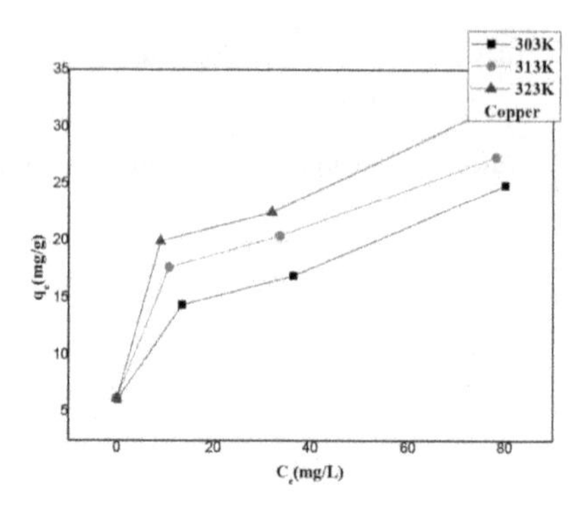

Figure 4.
Effect of varying temperatures on the amount adsorbed.

Where, $\mathbf{k_2}$ is the pseudo second order rate constant (g.mg^{-1}.s^{-1}) and can be calculated by linear regression of $\frac{t}{q_t}$ versus **t** plot. The adsorption kinetics constants and the correlation coefficient values R^2 are summarized in **Tables 3** and **4**: The values of the correlation coefficient R^2 of the pseudo-second order model are significantly higher than those of the pseudo-first model.

3.4 Adsorption isotherms

The adsorption isotherm of Cu^{2+} and MO was checked whether it fits the Langmuir and Freundlich isotherms (**Table 5**).

Adsorbent	C_0 (mg/L)	$q_{e,exp}$ (mg/g)	Pseudo-first order			Pseudo-second order		
			k_1 (min^{-1})	$q_{e,cal}$ (mg/g)	R^2	k_2 (g/mg. min)	$q_{e,cal}$ (mg/g)	R^2
Raw Clay	5	6.25	0.032	1.199	0.7	0.0248	6.0402	0.999
	25	16.58	0.006	8.452	0.859	0.0022	16.667	0.996
	50	20.91	0.004	15.066	0.869	0.00074	20.833	0.991
	100	20.12	0.005	12.022	0.797	0.0011	20.06	0.986
Purified Clay	5	6.25	0.044	0.473	0.847	0.0418	6.36	0.999
	25	27.65	0.006	12.82	0.902	0.0017	27.77	0.999
	50	25.98	0.005	11.22	0.709	0.0017	26.31	0.996
	100	21.97	0.006	8.709	0.837	0.0025	22.22	0.998
Activated Clay	5	0.6	0.093	58.88	0.664	0.00141	1.597	−0.039
	25	1.17	0.009	0.807	0.935	0.0192	1.1331	0.985
	50	0.39	0.017	0.364	0.843	0.0291	0.487	0.957
	100	0.4	0.11	0.22	0.734	0.055	0.447	0.991
Pillared Clay	5	6.25	0.221	29.51	0.954	0.1560	6.28	0.999
	25	24.47	0.008	5.49	0.906	0.00578	24.5	0.999
	50	16.45	0.008	6.025	0.863	0.00403	16.66	0.998
	100	23.53	0.006	7.58	0.828	0.00347	23.809	0.997

Adsorbent	C_0 (mg/L)	$q_{e,exp}$ (mg/g)	Pseudo-first order			Pseudo-second order		
			k_1 (min^{-1})	$q_{e,cal}$ (mg/g)	R^2	k_2 (g/mg. min)	$q_{e,cal}$ (mg/g)	R^2
Clay-CTAB	5	8.33	0.061	6.29	0.971	0.03868	8.474	0.999
	25	30.31	0.007	7.07	0.797	0.00471	30.303	0.998
	50	22.13	0.007	7.102	0.797	0.0074	16.66	0.997
	100	29.18	0.005	17.37	0.881	0.0013	23.809	0.997

Table 3.
Kinetic parameters for the adsorption of Cu(II) onto adsorbents at different initial concentrations.

Adsorbent	C_0 (mg/L)	$q_{e, exp}$ (mg/g)	Pseudo-first order			Pseudo-second order		
			k_1 (min^{-1})	$q_{e, cal}$ (mg/g)	R^2	k_2 (g/mg. min)	$q_{e, cal}$ (mg/g)	R^2
Raw Clay	5	0.128	$6.44*10^{-4}$	1.048	0.575	3.322	0.130	0.999
	20	0.202	$5.25*10^{-4}$	1.243	0.575	2.888	0.205	0.999
	35	0.425	$2.9*10^{-4}$	1.354	0.877	0.354	0.464	0.992
Purified Clay	5	2.003	0.230	10.125	0.641	0.037	2.213	0.996
	20	2.2075	0.027	11.015	0.606	0.041	2.49	0.996
	35	2.921	0.039	36.332	0.613	0.024	3.359	0.992
Activated Clay	5	2.710	0.042	71.186	0.687	0.011	3.745	0.912
	20	2.705	0.045	61.446	0.685	0.014	3.773	0.952
	35	6.1002	0.101	$2.741*10^4$	0.719	0.004	8.849	0.913
Pillared Clay	5	1.123	0.015	4.027	0.734	0.059	1.307	0.995
	20	2.210	0.033	27.542	0.755	0.018	2.808	0.970
	35	3.825	0.773	$2.2*10^3$	0.824	0.004	9.208	0.659
Clay-CTAB	5	5	0.078	$2*10^3$	0.787	0.008	6.45	0.996
	20	8.231	0.146	$1*10^7$	0.926	0.002	15.339	0.982
	35	15.206	0.249	$2.5*10^{12}$	0.926	0.001	22.029	0.987

Table 4.
Kinetic parameters for the adsorption of MO onto adsorbents at different initial concentrations.

The Langmuir isotherm theory assumes that the adsorption is single-layer and takes place at homogenous sites specific to the adsorbent. The equation of Langmuir isotherm model is given as:

$$\frac{C_e}{q_e} = \frac{1}{K_L\, q_{max}} + \frac{C_e}{q_{max}} \tag{6}$$

and the Freundlich isotherm assumes that the adsorption is multi-layer and that the surface of the adsorbent heterogeneous [52]:

$$ln\, q_e = ln\, K_F + \frac{1}{n}\, ln\, C_e \tag{7}$$

Where K_L Langmuir isotherm constant (L/mg), n is the degree of non-linearity and K_F is Freundlich isotherm constant (mg1–1/n L1/ng).

	Temperature (K)	Langmuir			Freundlich		
		q_{max} (mg/g)	K_L (L/mg)	R^2	K_F ($mg^{-11/n}/gL^{1/n}$)	1/n	R^2
Copper							
Kaolinite	303	3.099	8.338	0.918	154.88	0.203	0.957
	313	5.366	5.22	0.962	275.42	0.182	0.988
	323	31.86	1.002	0.954	293.764	0.214	0.985
Purified Kaolinite	303	10.64	2.479	0.992	279.25	0.198	0.979
	313	287.35	0.094	0.998	411.14	0.184	0.934
	323	55.55	0.497	0.998	542	0.188	0.872
Activated Kaolinite	303	0.069	18.184	0.984	0.0064	0.53	0.848
	313	0.117	18.512	0.677	0.071	0.406	0.471
	323	0.184	10.725	0.759	0.238	0.284	0.223
Pillared Kaolinite	303	5.714	4.023	0.9124	326.58	0.139	0.776
	313	7.535	3.359	0.937	311.17	0.18	0.704
	323	12.73	2.366	0.979	505.824	0.172	0.922
Kaolinite-CTAB	303	11.83	0.25	0.9725	475.33	0.175	0.83
	313	18.94	1.712	0.987	734.51	0.157	0.885
	323	32.53	1.142	0.996	855.066	0.185	0.899
Methyl Orange							
Kaolinite	303	0.0229	28.411	0.0551	0.049	0.548	0.738
	313	0.0023	44.934	0.821	$8.85*10^{-4}$	1.633	0.998
	323	0.00051	33.140	0.652	$5.80*10^{-5}$	2.363	0.999
Purified Kaolinite	303	0.794	5.452	0.943	1.322	0.297	0.965
	313	1.166	5.074	0.993	1.364	0.404	0.912
	323	1.112	5.483	0.957	1.729	0.320	0.987
Activated Kaolinite	303	2.293	2.760	0.988	2.013	0.336	0.841
	313	1.007	6.129	0.948	1.116	0.478	0.818
	323	0.364	21.803	0.986	0.477	0.680	0.973
Pillared Kaolinite	303	0.264	20.148	0.440	0.496	0.538	0.874
	313	0.550	6.993	0.652	1.485	0.194	0.101
	323	2.364	1.726	0.970	2.773	0.084	0.584
Kaolinite-CTAB	303	3.144	3.495	0.720	5.636	0.125	0.297
	313	4.016	3.188	0.773	6.295	0.140	0.48
	323	6.756	2.766	0.697	10.280	0.083	0.535

Table 5.
Adsorption isotherms of copper onto kaolinite clay.

The data show that Langmuir model is more suitable to describe the adsorption reaction of copper and methyl orange on modified kaolinite and it is better fitted to Freundlich isotherm model onto natural clay with experimental data with higher R^2 values. So it's surface mono-layer adsorption and the adsorption sites are homogeneous.

	ΔH° (KJ.mol^{-1})	ΔS° (KJ.mol^{-1})	ΔG°(KJ.mol^{-1})		
			303 K	313 K	323 K
Copper Cu (II)					
Raw Clay	−4.164	0.015	−5.681	−5.695	−8.322
Purified Clay	−0.068	0.0032	−6.942	−8.841	−7.4
Activated Clay	—	—	—	—	—
Pillared Clay	−2.801	0.012	−6.833	−7.901	−8.788
Clay-CTAB	−2.976	0.013	−7.263	−8.399	−9.34
Methyl Orange					
Raw Clay	6454.238	49.531	−8553.66	−9048.97	2769285
Purified Clay	162.425	14.139	−4121.69	−4263.08	1331469
Activated Clay	82099.03	278.510	−2289.5	−5074.6	821607.5
Pillared Clay	−97702.93	−297.451	−7575.28	−4600.77	2349112
Clay-CTAB	−9293.706	−20.406	.31110.69	−2906.63	995458.5

Table 6.
Thermodynamics parameters at different temperatures.

3.5 The thermodynamic studies

The thermodynamic parameters **ΔG°, ΔH°** and **ΔS°** are computed from the plots on ln K_L vs. 1/T, and are better described by following Equations [53]:

$$\ln K_L = \frac{\Delta S}{R} - \frac{\Delta H}{RT} \tag{8}$$

$$\Delta G = \Delta H - T\Delta S \tag{9}$$

Where, **R** is The gas constant 8.314*10^3 (KJ/mol. K), **T** is temperature (K) and $\mathbf{K_L}$ known as the distribution coefficient of the adsorbate, is equal to C_e/q_e(L/g) (**Table 6**).

4. Conclusion

The thermodynamics and kinetic study of the removal of copper (II) and methyl orange from aqueous solution using natural clay and its composites has been investigated in this work. The adsorption process showed that purified and CTAB clays were effective in the uptake of copper and methyl orange from aqueous solutions until 34.12 mg/g and 15.78 mg/g, respectively. Whereas, activated and pillared kaolinite are not efficient adsorbent for the removal of Cu(II) and methyl orange, respectively; with amount of adsorption less than 2 mg/g. The amounts of Cu^{2+} and MO were found to vary with pH and the dose of adsorbent. The adsorption data conformed to Langmuir model, and its fitted to pseudo first order and pseudo second order. However, pseudo second order best described for the adsorption process. The determined negative free energy changes ΔG° and positive entropy ΔS ° indicated the feasibility and spontaneous nature of the adsorption process. The negative value of enthalpy change ΔH° suggests that the adsorption process is exothermic, while, the interactions are entotermic accompanied by increase in entropy and Gibbs energy.

Author details

Aicha Kourim[1*], Moulay Abderrahmane Malouki[2] and Aicha Ziouche[3]

1 Department of Material Sciences, University of Tamanrasset, Algeria

2 Sciences and Environment Research Laboratory, University of Tamanrasset, Algeria

3 Research Center in Industrial Technologies CRTI, Algiers, Algeria

*Address all correspondence to: aichakourim@gmail.com

References

[1] A. Bogusz, P. Oleszczuk and R. Dobrowlski, "Application of laboratory prepared and commercially available biochars to adsorption of cadmium, copper and zinc ions frow water," Bioresource Technology, pp. 196, 540-549 doi: 10.1016/j. biortech.2015.08.006, 2015.

[2] X. Yan, Y. Wan, Y. Zheng, F. He, Z. Yu, J. Huang, H. Wang, Y. S. Ok, Y. Jiang and B. Gao, "Surface functional groups of carbon-based adsorbents and their roles in the removal of heavy metals from aqueous solutions: A critical review," Chemical Engineering Journal, vol. 366, pp. 608-621, 2019.

[3] Taty-Costodess, H. Fauduet, C. Porte and A. Delacroixs, "Removal of Cd(II) and P(II) ions from aqueous solutions by adsorption onto sawdust of pinus sylvestris," J Hazard Master, pp. 105 (1-3): 121-142, 2003.

[4] Wang, Y. Pan, P. Cai, T. Guo and H. Xiao, "Single and binary adsorption of heavy metal ions from aqueous solutions using sugarcane cellulose-based adsorbent," Bioresource Technology, pp. 241, 482-490 doi: 10.1016/j. biortech.2017.05.162, 2017.

[5] Y. Zhou, Y. He, Y. Xiang, S. Meng, X. Lui, J. Yu, J. Yang, J. Zhang, P. Qin and L. Luo, "Single and simultaneous adsorption of pefloxacin and Cu(II) ions from aqueous solutions by oxidized multiwalled carbon nanotube," Science of the Total Environment, vol. 646, pp. 29-36, 2019.

[6] Y. Tang, J. Tian, T. Malkoske, W. Le and B. Chen, "Facile ultrasonic synthesis of novel zinc sulfide/carbon nanotubecoaxial nanocables for enhanced photodegradation of methyl orange," J. Mater Sci., no. 52, pp. 1581-1589, 2017.

[7] G. M. Worrall, J. T. Buswell, C. A. English, M. G. Hetherington and G. D. W. Smith, "A study of the precipitation of copper particles in a ferrite matrix," Journal of Nuclear Materials, vol. 148, pp. 107-114, 1987.

[8] R. S. Juang and M. N. Chen, "Removal of Copper (II) Chelates of EDTA and NTA from Dilute Aqueous Solutions by Membrane Filtration," Ind. Eng. Chem. Res, vol. 36, no. 1, pp. 179-186, 1997.

[9] G. T. Wei, J. C. Chen and Z. Yang, "Studies on Liquid/Liquid Extraction of Copper Ion with Room Temperature Ionic Liquid," Journal of the Chinese Chemical Society, vol. 50, pp. 1123-1130, 2003.

[10] T. Bakalár, M. Búgel and L. Gajdošová, "Heavy metal removal using reverse osmosis," Acta Montanistica Slovaca, vol. 3, pp. 250-253, 2009.

[11] R. Farooq, Y. Wang, F. Lin, S. F. Shaukat, J. Donalson and A. J. Chouhdary, "Effect of ultrasound on the removal of copper from the model solutions for copper electrolysis process," Water Research, vol. 36, no. 12, pp. 3165-3169, 2002.

[12] F. S. Eberhard and I. Hamawand, "Selective Electrodialysis for Copper Removal from Brackish Water and Coal Seam Gas Water," International Journal of Environmental Research, vol. 11, pp. 1-11, 2017.

[13] A. Kuleyin and H. Erikli-Uysal, "Recovery of Copper Ions from Industrial Wastewater by Electrodeposition," International Journal of ELECTROCHEMICAL SCIENCE, vol. 15, pp. 1474-1485, 2020.

[14] R. K. Misra, S. K. Jain and P. K. Khatri, "Iminodiacetic acid functionalized cation exchange resin for adsorptive removal of Cr(VI), Cd(II), Ni(II) and Pb(II) from their aqueous

solutions," Journal of Hazardous Materials, vol. 185, pp. 1508-1512, 2011.

[15] T. Huang, L. Liu, S. Wu and S. Zhang, "Research on a closed-loop method that enhances the electrokinetic removal of heavy metals from municipal solid waste incineration fly ashes," Chem. Pap., vol. 73, pp. 3053-3065, 2019.

[16] E. A. Deliyanni, G. Z. Kyzas and K. A. Matis, "Various flotation techniques for metal ions removal," Journal of Molecular Liquids, vol. 225, pp. 260-264, 2017.

[17] G. K. G. C. Barros, R. P. F. Mel and E. L. B. Neto, "Removal of copper ions using sodium hexadecanoate by ionic flocculation," Separation and Purification Technology, vol. 200, pp. 294-299, 2018.

[18] X. Tang, H. Zheng, H. Teng, Y. Sun, J. Guo, W. Xie, Q. Yang and W. Chen, "Chemical coagulation process for the removal of heavy metals from water: a review," Desalination and Water Treatment, vol. 57, no. 4, pp. 1733-1748, 2016.

[19] L. Clarizia, M. RaceLuca, L. Onotri, I. Somma, N. Fiorentino, R. Andreozzi and R. Marotta, "Removal of Copper, Iron and Zinc from Soil Washing Effluents Containing Ethylenediaminedisuccinic Acid as Chelating Agent Through Sunlight Driven Nano-TiO2-Based Photocatalytic Processes," Nanotechnologies for Environmental Remediation, pp. 239-253, 2017.

[20] J. B. Dulla, M. R. Tamana, S. Boddu, K. Pulipati and K. Srirama, "Biosorption of copper(II) onto spent biomass of Gelidiella acerosa (brown marine algae): optimization and kinetic studies," Appl. Water Sci., vol. 56, no. 10, 2020.

[21] F. Akhtar, K. M. Archana, V. G. Krishnaswamy and R. Rajagopal, "Remediation of heavy metals (Cr, Zn) using physical, chemical," SN Applied Sciences, vol. 267, no. 2, 2020.

[22] S. Ahmad, A. Pandey, V. Pathak, V. Tyagi and R. Kothari, "Phycoremediation: Algae as Eco-friendly Tools for the Removal of Heavy Metals from Wastewaters," in Bioremediation of Industrial Waste for Environmental Safety, 2020, pp. 53-76.

[23] S. E. Bailey, T. J. Olin, M. R. Bricka and D. D. Adrian, "A review of potentially low- cost sorbents for heavy metals," Water Research, vol. 33, no. 11, pp. 2469-2479, 1999.

[24] H. H. Murray, "Applied clay mineralogy today and tomorrow," Clay Minerals, no. 34, pp. 39-49, 1999.

[25] T. J. Rong and J. Xiao, "The catalytic cracking activity of the Kaolin group minerals," Materials Letters, no. 57, pp. 297-301, 2002.

[26] V. Vimonses, S. Lei, B. Jin, W. K. Chow and C. Saint, "Adsorption of congo red by three Australian kaolins," Applied Clay Science, vol. 43, no. 3-4, pp. 465-472, 2009.

[27] X. Lui, X. Lu, M. Sprik, J. Cheng, E. J. Meijer and R. Wang, "Acidity of edge surface sites of montmorillonite and kaolinite," Geohimica et Cosmochimica Acta, vol. 117, pp. 180-190, 2013.

[28] J. Won, X. Wirth and S. E. Bums, "An experimental study of cotransport of heavy metals with kaolinite colloids," Journal of Hazardous Materials, no. 373, pp. 476-482, 2019.

[29] M. O. Omorogie, F. O. Arunbiade, M. O. Alfred, O. T. Olaniyi, T. A. Adewumi, A. A. Bayode, A. E. Ofomaja, E. B. Naidoo, C. P. A. T. A. Okoli and E. I. Unuabonah, "The sequestral capture of fluoride, itrate and phosphate by metal-doped and sulfactant-modified hybrid clay materials," Chem. Pap., vol. 72, no. 2, pp. 409-417, 2018.

[30] M. Robert and D. Tessier, "Méthode de préparation des argiles des sols pour études minéralogiques," Ann. Agrom, pp. 25, 859-882, 1974.

[31] V. Sori, T. Roy, S. Dhara, G. Choudhary, P. Sharma and R. K. Sharma, "On the ivestigation of acid and sulfactant modification of natural clay for photocatalytic water remediation," J Master Sci, pp. 53, 10095-10110, 2018.

[32] A. K. Panda, B. G. Mishra, D. K. Mishra and R. K. Singh, "Effect of sulphuric acid treatment on the physic-chemical characteristics of kaolin clay," *Colloids and Surfaces A : Physicochem.* Eng. Aspects, pp. 363, 98-104, 2010.

[33] D. Nistor, N. D. Miron and I. Siminiceanu, "PREPARATION DES ARGILES PNTEES D'ORIGINE ROUMAINE AVEC DES POLYCATIONS D'ALUMINIUM ET DE FER," *Quatrième Colloque Franco-Roumain de Chimie Appliquée,* pp. VII(3), 1582-540X, 2006.

[34] M. A. Akl, A. M. Youssef and M. M. Al-Awadhi, "Adsorption of Acid Dyes onto Bentonite and Sulfactant-modified Bentonite," J. Anal. Bioanal. Tech., p. 4: 174, 2013.

[35] L.-G. Yan, L.-L. Qin, H.-Q. Yu, S. Li, R.-R. Shan and B. Du, "Adsorption of acid dyes from aqueous solution by CTMAB modified bentonite: Kinetic and isotherm modeling," Journal of Molecular Liquids, pp. 211, 1074-1081, 2015.

[36] W. Keller and K. Matlack, "The pH of clay suspensions in the field and laboratory, and methods of meausurment of their pH," Applied Clay Science, pp. 5, 123-133, 1990.

[37] K. G. Bhattacharyya and S. S. Gupta, "kaolinite, montmorillonite, and thier modified derivatives as adsorbent for removal of Cu (II) from aqueous solution," Separation and Purification Technology, pp. 50,388-397, 2006.

[38] M. V. Lopez-Raman, F. Stoeckli, C. Morino-Castilla and F. Carrasco-Marin, "On the characterization of acidic and basic surface sites on carbons techniques," Carbon, pp. 37: 1215-1221, 1999.

[39] K. M. A. Kifuani, V. P. Noki, D. P. J. Ndelo, W. M. D. Mukana, B. G. Ekoko, L. B. Ilinga and M. J. Mukinayi, "Adsorption de la quinine bichlorohydrate sur un charbon actif peu couteux à base de Bagasse de canne à sucre imprégnée de l'acide phosphorique," *Int. J. Biol. Chem. Sci.,* pp. 6(3): 1337-1359, 2012.

[40] J. Cenens and R. A. Schoonheydt, "VISIBLE SPECTROSCOPY OF METHYLENE BLUE ON HECTORITE, LAPONITEB, AND BARASYMIN AQUEOUS SUSPENSION," *Clays and Clay Minerals,* vol. 36, no. 3, pp. 214-224, 1988.

[41] R. Torres-Caban, C. V. Vega-Olivencia, L. Alamo-Nole, D. Morales-Irizarry, F. Romman-Velazquez and N. Mina-Camilde, "Removal of Copper from Water by Adsorption with Calcium-Algate/Spent-coffe-Grounds Composite Beads," Materials, pp. 12, 395, 2019.

[42] Y. H. Li, B. Xia, Q. S. Zhao, F. Q. Lui and P. Zhang, "Removal of copper ions from aqueous solution by calcium alginate immobilized kaolin," J. Environ. Sci, pp. 23, 404-411, 2011.

[43] S. V. Badmaeva, S. T. Khankhasaeva and E. T. Dashinamzhilova, "Experimental Simulation of Sorption Processes of Heavy Metals on Natural Clay Minerals," in *IOP Conference Serie: Earth and Environmental Science*, 2019.

[44] F. Hamadache, A. Chergui, F. Halet, A. R. Yeddou and B. Nadjemi, "Copper, Zinc and Nickel's removal by bentonite clay: case study in mono and multicomponent systems," *Algerian* Journal of Environmental Science and Technology, pp. 2437-1114, 2019.

[45] R. Msaadi, G. Yilmaz, A. Allushi, S. Hamadi, S. Ammar, M. M. Chehimi and Y. Yagci, "Highly Selective Copper Ion Imprited Clay/Polymer Nanocomposites Prepared by Visible Light Initiated Radical Photopolymerization," Polymers, pp. 11, 286, 2019.

[46] J. T. Nwabanne and P. K. Igbokwe, "The thermodynamic and kinetic behaviors of lead (II) adsorption on Activaed Carbon derived from Palmyra Plam Nut," *International Journal of Applied* , pp. Vol,2 No.3, 2012.

[47] K. Huang, Y. Xia and H. Zhu, "Removal of heavy metal ions from aquous solution by chemically modified mangosteen pericarp," Desalin. Water Treat., pp. 52, 7108-7116, 2014.

[48] P. Pavasant, R. Apiratikul, V. Sungkhum, P. Suthiparinyanont, S. Wattanachira and T. F. Marhaba, "Biosorption of Cu2+, Cd2+, Pb2+, and Zn2+ uzing dried marine green macroalga Caulerpa Lentillifera," Bioresour Technol, pp. 97, 2321-2329, 2006.

[49] A. T. Sdiri, T. Higashi and F. Jamoussi, "Adsorption of copper and zinc onto natural clay in single and binary systems," Int. J. Environ. Sci. Technol, pp. 11, 1081-1092, 2014.

[50] S. Lagergren, "About the theory of so-called adsorption of soluble substances, Kungliga Svenska Vetenskapsakademiens," handlingar, pp. 24: 1-39, 1898.

[51] Y. S. Ho and G. McKay, "Pseudo-second order model for sorption processes," Process Biochemistry, pp. 34: 451-465, 1999.

[52] D. Saha, N. Mirando and A. Levchenko, "Liquid and vapor phase adsorption of BTX in lignin derived activated carbon: Equilibrium and kinetics study," Journal of Cleaner Production, pp. 182, 372-378, 2018.

[53] A. Ozer, F. Tumen and M. Bildik, "Cr (III) Removal from Aqueous Solutions by Depectinated Sugar Beet Pulp," Environment Technology, pp. 18: 9, 893-901, 1997.

Chapter 4

Chemical, Mineralogical, and Rheological Characterization of Regional Clays for Potential Use in Cosmetics and Pharmaceutical Products

Cochiran Pereira dos Santos and Adriana de Jesus Santos

Abstract

Four clay samples from different deposits in the state of Sergipe, Brazil, were fractionated by dispersion and centrifugation for comparative tests with a standard commercial clay used for cosmetic and pharmaceutical purposes. For this, they were characterized by X-ray diffraction, X-ray fluorescence spectroscopy, measurements of cation exchange capacity, oil absorption and viscosity, in addition to particle sizes and plasticity indexes. The objective was to determine the physical and chemical properties of raw clays and the consequent granulometric fractions to evaluate their potential use in products with high added value. After fractionation, the samples showed significant amounts of smectite and kaolinite, which combined with the size, particle distribution, chemical composition, and high adsorption capacity, especially in the PDL and PV samples, make them potentially interesting for applications in pharmaceutical and cosmetic products, they can also be used in spas and esthetic centers for therapeutic purposes based on their softness and cation exchange capacity.

Keywords: clay, clay minerals, ceramics, cosmetics, pharmaceutical use

1. Introduction

Clays have been used as raw material by humanity since antiquity for the manufacture of ceramic objects such as vases, bricks, and tiles and, more recently, in several technological applications, such as paper, paint, in the oil industry, adsorbents in lightening processes in the textile and food industry, catalysis etc., and their applications are strongly dependent on their structure, composition and physical properties [1, 2] (**Figure 1**).

The interest in its use has been gaining strength due to the search for environmentally friendly materials, that do not harm the environment when discarded, the abundance of world reserves and its low cost [3]. The possibility of chemical modification of clays allows the development of its use for different types of technological applications, adding value to this abundant natural resource. Raw clay deposits are rarely pure and most are composed of two or more clay minerals thoroughly

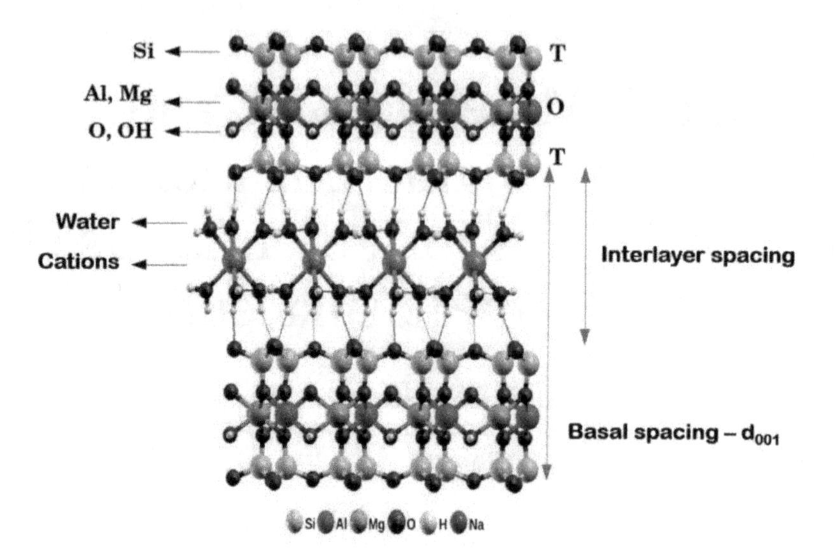

Figure 1.
Typical representation of the structure of a clay.

mixed with one another, and variable amounts of non-clay minerals in the form of associated minerals, amorphous materials, and organic matter [4–7].

Brazil is one of the main world suppliers of clay, and in the state of Sergipe, several clay deposits have been used for decades in the production of ceramic tiles, bricks, blocks, and handmade pieces [8–11]. However, these traditional products have low added value when compared to others, such as pharmaceuticals and cosmetics that use special clays in their composition. Among these clays, the most used industrially and commercially, is bentonite, a plastic clay from the group of smectites with a high content of colloidal matter, which can present varied colors, such as white, gray, yellow and others, depending on its origin and chemical composition [12]. According to [7, 13, 14], the industrial use of a clay in a pharmaceutical and cosmetic industry, is a consequence of the nature and properties of the clay that is an essential component of this clay, as well as its exchangeable cations. The ability of clays to exchange cations between interlayer spacing is a unique property and cationic exchanges with drugs are of special interest in pharmaceutical sciences, due to the interaction between drug-clay modifying the action of the drug in several ways, such as increasing stability, prolonged release, or increased dissolution [15].

Due to its high swelling power, which can reach up to twenty times its volume when immersed in water [16], bentonite is widely used as a pharmaceutical excipient, as a disintegrating agent in solid forms or to increase viscosity in liquid formulations [17]. As their layers form a kind of sandwich (phyllosilicates) can be seen in **Figure 2**, this characteristic allows them to absorb important amounts of water-soluble and fat-soluble substances, behaving in this way as cosmetic assets, the main differences being in the structure of the layers and metals (Fe, Zn, Cu, Mg etc.) that form each one [16].

In general, in Brazil, these segments use imported clays, because either there are no similar national products with the same degree of purity or the suppliers here are unable to maintain the pattern from one batch to the next. The aim of this work is to evaluate the potential use of four raw materials from different deposits of clays in the state of Sergipe, Brazil, after fractionation of the raw clay with the purpose of knowing its physical and chemical characteristics aiming at the possibility of use in products of high added value by the pharmaceutical and cosmetics industry. The

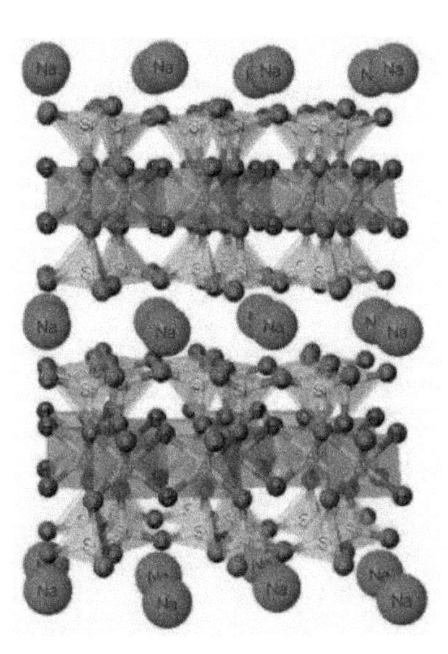

Figure 2.
Typical representation of the montmorillonite structure.

synthesis and study of clays and clay minerals are one of the widest fields of research in materials science and technology.

2. Materials and methods

The clays investigated in this work come from deposits known as Ventinha (VEN), Poço Verde (PV), Pau-de-leite (PDL) and Pinheiro (PIN), all located in the state of Sergipe, Brazil. Currently, these clay deposits are used in the production of ceramic tiles, as reported by [8–11], in addition to other traditional applications, such as bricks, blocks, tiles and handmade pieces. A sample of commercial bentonite clay from the Bentec brand (BEN) used in the pharmaceutical and cosmetics industry was used as a standard.

Initially, the raw materials from the clay deposits were placed in trays and air-dried for 72 h to be mechanically treated to break up the particles, being quartered, broken up and ground in a hammer mill with a 2 mm opening grid for homogenization, and dried at 60°C for 24 h. The fractionation of the raw clay was carried out by dispersion and centrifugation, according to [7], in which 30 g of dry clay were added to a metallic vessel containing 300 ml of distilled water, then the dispersion was stirred at 14000 rpm for 20 min, being then transferred to a 600 ml beaker and left to stand overnight at room temperature. After the resting time, the dispersion was again stirred, centrifuged at 1500 rpm for 15 min and the supernatant transferred to a container. At the end of the process, all samples were dried at 60°C for 24 h.

To determine the particle size distribution curves, the samples passed through a 297 μm aperture sieve. The technique used was Low Angle Laser Light Scattering (LALLS), according to the Fraunhofer diffraction method [18] in a Malvern equipment model Mastersizer MS2000E with dispersing agent, at 2000 rpm and ultrasound speed equal to 11. The light source is a He-Ne laser with a wavelength of 632.8 nm and the reliable particle size measurement range is 0.1 μm to 1000 μm.

To assess plasticity, liquidity, and plasticity limits (LL and PL) were measured according to the procedures of ASTM D4318:2010 [19], NBR 7180:1984 [20] and

NBR 6459:2016 [21]. The plasticity index (PI) is obtained from the arithmetic difference between the liquidity and plasticity limits.

X-ray fluorescence (XRF) analyzes determined the chemical compositions of the samples with a mass of 10.0 g pressed in a cylindrical shape with a diameter of 40.0 mm and a thickness of 4.0 mm kept in a vacuum of 10^{-6} bar. The equipment used was a Bruker model S8 Tiger, in which the percentages of constituent oxides were estimated using the semi-quantitative method. A mixture of 90% argon and 10% methane (P-10) was used in the proportional counter.

The crystalline phases present in the clays were determined by X-ray diffraction (XRD) in a Bruker D8 Advance equipment using $CuK_{\alpha 1}$ radiation (λ = 1.5418 Å) of the dry non-oriented powder in the continuous scanning mode in the range from 1° to 65° with increment of 0.02° and capture time of 0.4 s/step. To confirm the presence of montmorillonite, which is a clay mineral of the group of smectites with a potentially unstable laminar structure formed by stacking layers composed of an octahedral leaf interspersed with two tetrahedral leaves, the samples were saturated with ethylene glycol for 1 h, to induce increasing the interplanar distance. In this case, the scanning interval was between 1° and 15° [22]. The samples were calcined at 550°C for 2 h and the XRD analyzes were compared with the dry and glycolated samples. Analyzes were also carried out on samples oriented after fractionation of the raw clay, separated by centrifugation, and washed with H_2O_2 to eliminate organic matter and HCl to eliminate carbonates, according to [23]. The diffraction patterns were indexed using the Inorganic Crystal Structure Database (ICSD), according to the standard method based on the shape, position, and intensity of specific reflections.

The values of cation exchange capacity (CEC) of the clay fraction of the samples were determined according to ASTM-C837–09:2019 (Standard Test Method for Methylene Blue Index of Clay) [24].

The oil absorption of the clay fraction was determined according to ASTM D281–12:2016 [25], with 10 g of each sample placed on a glass plate and a drop of mineral oil was applied from a container previously weighed to the clay, being incorporated with the help of a spatula. The test is considered complete when, by sliding the spatula on the upper surface of the treated mass, a thin layer of oil is observed. The oil container was then weighed again to calculate the percentage of oil incorporated.

The rheological properties of the clay fraction were determined by a TA Instrument model DHR 10 rheometer, of the cone/geometric plate type with 50 mm spacing, with the stainless-steel cone having a diameter of 60 mm and an angle of 2°. The formulations were analyzed at (25.0 ± 1.0) °C. Each sample was applied to the lower plate, ensuring minimum shear, and allowing a rest time of 1 min before each removal. Each run lasted 4 min and was carried out with a shear speed from 0 to 200 s^{-1}. The data were adjusted using the Ostwald-de Waele model or Power Low model. For this, clay-water dispersions were prepared with a concentration of 4.86% by mass: 24.3 g of clay added to 500 ml of deionized water. The mixture was stirred for 20 min at 17000 rpm and left to stand for 24 h. After that time, the material was stirred for 5 min at 17000 rpm and the respective viscosities were determined.

3. Characterization of materials and results

The particle size distribution curves of the five clays studied after passing through a 297 μm sieve through laser light diffraction can be seen in **Figure 3**, in which an approximately Gaussian profile can be seen in all curves, the which confirms a multimodal distribution of the particles [26].

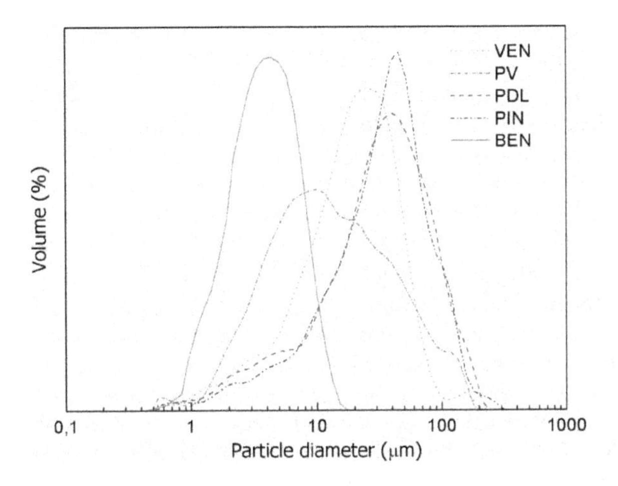

Figure 3.
Particle size distribution of samples by laser light diffraction.

According to ABNT NBR 6502:1995 [27], the particle size classification is: clay fraction (< 2 μm), silt fraction (2–20 μm) and sand fraction (> 20 μm), being that the proportion of particles with a diameter less than 2 μm is associated with the presence of clay minerals and is a determining factor for the plasticity and smoothness of the material. As expected, commercial bentonite clay (BEN) was the one with the highest proportion of particles with smaller dimensions, followed by PV and VEN.

Table 1 presents the results of the particle sizes and the Atterberg limits of the samples. Among the raw materials, PV was the one with the highest proportion of particles smaller than 2 μm, known as the clay fraction. It also showed the highest index of plasticity, which confirms the dependence between PI and the clay fraction, previously reported by [28]. Materials with PI between 1 and 7% are considered weakly plastic, from 7 to 15% are moderately plastic and above 15%, highly plastic [29]. According to this classification, the PI values determined for VEN, PV and PDL indicate that these clays are highly plastic, while PIN is moderately plastic (PI = 14%). The smoothness, linked to the small size of the particles, is important for therapeutic and cosmetic purposes of the skin, such as facial mask and body clay creams [30]. In this way, VEN, PV and PDL clays can be used for this purpose. Comparing the average diameter of the particles, PV (7.2 μm) stands out from the other clays and slightly approaches the value found in BEN (6.7 μm).

Table 2 shows the chemical compositions of the samples determined by XRF. The results show that they all contain considerable amounts of SiO_2 and Al_2O_3.

Samples	Particle size (%)				Atterberg limits (%)			
	< 2 (μm)	2–20 (μm)	20–200 (μm)	> 200 (μm)	d_m (μm)	LL	PL	PI
VEN	5.25	46.08	48.67	—	23.7	48	21	27
PV	14.23	61.44	24.33	—	7.2	56	24	32
PDL	6.67	44.38	48.95	—	21.1	51	27	24
PIN	4.81	44.69	50.50	—	28.3	37	23	14
BEN	48.17	51.83	—	—	6.7	69	25	44

Table 1.
Size distribution, average particle diameter and Atterberg limits of the samples.

These elements are associated with the tetrahedral sheet of silica and the octahedral sheet of alumina, the basic units that can form the structure of smectite and kaolinite, as well as Mg, K, Ca, Na and Fe, are associated with structures of clay minerals, quartz, and feldspars [31–33]. The high content of calcium oxide in PIN and VEN characterizes these clays as limestone [11, 34], but combined with Na_2O and K_2O it can be associated with the cations of the smectites interstitial space, usually Ca^{2+}, Na^{+}, K^{+} and Mg^{2+}, which balances the negative charge of the 2:1 layer of the isomorphic substitution in the crystalline structure [7]. The high amounts of Fe_2O_3 and MgO may be related to the isomorphic substitutions of Al^{3+} for Fe^{3+}, Fe^{2+} and Mg^{2+} in the octahedral leaves of smectite [16]. All samples have small amounts of TiO_2 (< 0.8%). The chemical composition of the commercial bentonite studied is in accordance with other works reported [35, 36].

The X-ray diffraction patterns of the dry non-oriented powder of the clays (bulk composition) are presented in **Figure 4** and correlate positively with the results observed by X-ray fluorescence. The crystalline phases were identified according to the Inorganic Crystal Structure Database (ICSD).

Oxides	VEN	PV	PDL	PIN	BEN
SiO_2	51.31	53.17	61.74	47.43	57.51
Al_2O_3	16.36	18.84	17.94	14.72	21.80
Fe_2O_3	6.07	6.81	4.22	7.04	6.11
CaO	6.81	2.08	0.88	11.93	3.23
K_2O	3.06	4.35	3.62	3.25	1.68
Na_2O	0.47	0.41	0.58	0.67	0.47
MgO	2.24	2.28	1.47	2.26	3.23
TiO_2	0.68	0.83	0.59	0.77	1.07
LOI	11.9	14.1	8.4	12.2	6.1

Table 2.
Chemical composition (main components, oxide form) of the samples from X-ray fluorescence analyses, indicated in mass %.

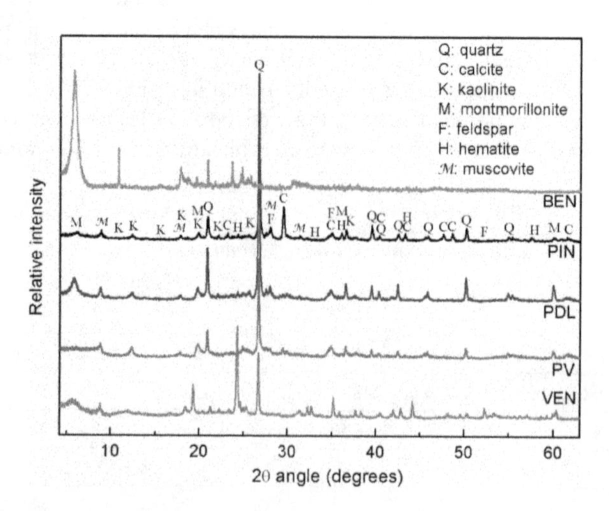

Figure 4.
X-ray diffraction patterns of the clays studied.

Regional clays are predominantly composed of quartz, followed by muscovite, kaolinite, montmorillonite, calcite, feldspar, and hematite (**Table 3**). The PDL sample presents the highest proportions of the clay minerals montmorillonite and kaolinite, followed by PV. These clay minerals are widely used in cosmetic products, such as creams, powders and emulsions, and pharmaceutical products, including gastrointestinal and dermatological protectors, anti-diarrheal and anti-inflammatory [36]. The calcite percentage varied considerably between the studied samples, with extremes of 1.31% (PDL) and 13.44% (PIN). This mineral has a high acid absorption capacity. The addition of HCl to calcite in a neutralization reaction gives rise to calcium chloride, releasing CO_2. Clay minerals can neutralize acidity by adsorbing H^+ ions from the external environment, properties that are useful in the pharmaceutical industry [13]. The BEN sample is composed mainly of montmorillonite and kaolinite and small amounts of quartz and hematite.

All samples from regional deposits are homogeneous in color, with PDL being the lightest, followed by PV, probably due to the greater amount of clay minerals and the small presence of hematite, while VEN has a reddish color. The color of clays is a very important parameter in cosmetic applications. Commercially, color is often associated with the purity and quality of clays, however, studies that attest to these properties are necessary [37].

To confirm the presence of montmorillonite by increasing the spacing between its structural layers due to the absorption of water or alcohol molecules, the diffraction pattern of the samples saturated with ethylene glycol was measured [38, 39]. In all samples, the typical expandable property of smectite was obvious, by increasing the interplanar distance related to the direction (001) and the consequent displacement of the diffraction peaks to smaller angles in relation to the dry sample tests [40]. Smectites are widely used in pharmaceutical products because they favor the release of the active ingredient because their particles can swell in water and decompose readily in the acidic environment of the stomach (pH $\sim$ 2) [14].

The X-ray diffraction patterns of the dried PDL sample and treated with ethylene glycol can be seen in **Figure 5**, in which we notice that the angle relative to the direction (001) of the glycolated sample has shifted to a smaller angle. According to Bragg's Law ($n\lambda = 2dsen\theta$), this reduction is caused by the increase in interplanar distance and these values can be calculated. The presence of montmorillonite in the PDL sample was confirmed by the displacement from 5.76° (d = 15.36 Å) to 5.31° (d = 16.66 Å) and in PV the interplanar distance that was 15.34 Å increased to 17.12 Å. In the VEN sample from 15.17 Å to 17.03 Å and from 13.95 Å to 15.88 Å in PIN.

Figure 6 shows the X-ray diffraction patterns of the samples in the region where there is a reflection close to 1.50 Å (61.72°), corresponding to the plane (060), indicating that they are dioctahedral smectites [41], probably a dioctahedral component

Minerals (%)	VEN	PV	PDL	PIN	BEN
Quartz	56.36	53.54	59.08	56.11	6.11
Kaolinite	6.86	13.08	9.21	5.95	17.69
Muscovite	9.11	10.74	11.48	12.03	1.12
Montmorillonite	6.21	4.49	9.84	4.96	69.12
Calcite	8.08	2.92	1.31	13.44	0.78
Feldspar	6.00	9.54	5.86	3.95	0.57
Hematite	5.61	5.02	2.79	1.97	3.12

Table 3.
Mineralogical compositions of samples determined by X-ray diffraction.

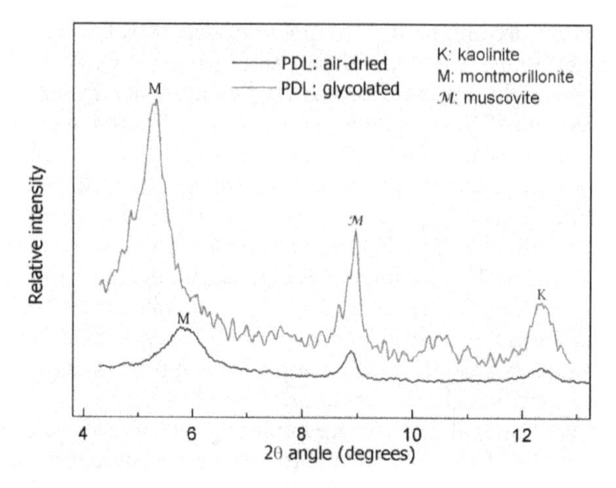

Figure 5.
X-ray diffraction patterns of the sample PDL after air-drying and glycolated.

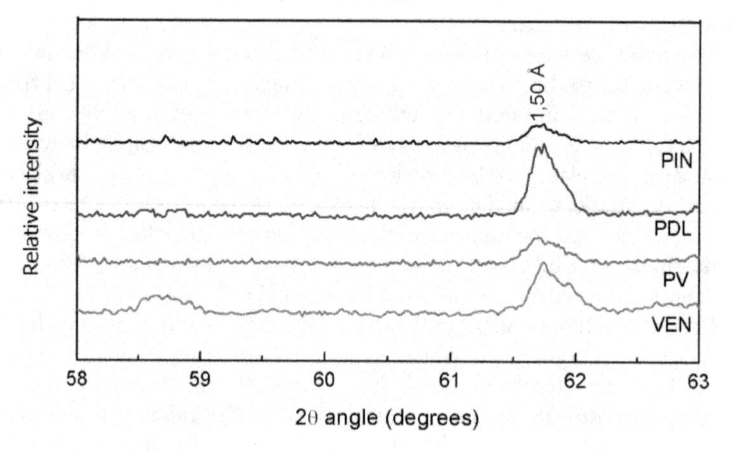

Figure 6.
X-ray diffraction patterns of non-oriented samples showing 060 peaks of the clays.

Fe-rich [42, 43], due to the chemical and mineralogical compositions observed in these samples. In addition, they have a very weak reflection at 1.54 Å, indicating small presence of trioctahedral smectite components, Fe-rich and Mg-rich [7, 23].

Figure 7 shows the X-ray diffraction curves of VEN, PV, PDL and PIN after heat treatment at 550°C. The air-dried samples show an intense reflection due to an interplanar spacing d_{001} of approximately 5.76° and 12.28° (**Figure 4**), corresponding to the reflections (001) of montmorillonite and kaolinite, respectively [44]. However, after heating, the characteristic collapse of these two clay minerals is observed. These changes are consistent with smectites and indicate that the samples do not reflect due to any other clay minerals, such as chlorites or vermiculites [7, 45]. The reflection in 8.83° (10.04 Å), which was not affected by chemical treatment or heating, indicated the presence of illite/muscovite [30].

The mineralogical compositions of the clay fractions were carried out after the fractionation of raw clay by dispersion and centrifugation. In terms of bulk composition, all samples are characterized by the presence of a significant non-clayey fraction represented by quartz, calcite, feldspar, and hematite, as well as considerable portions of clay minerals (**Table 3**). However, for use in pharmaceuticals and

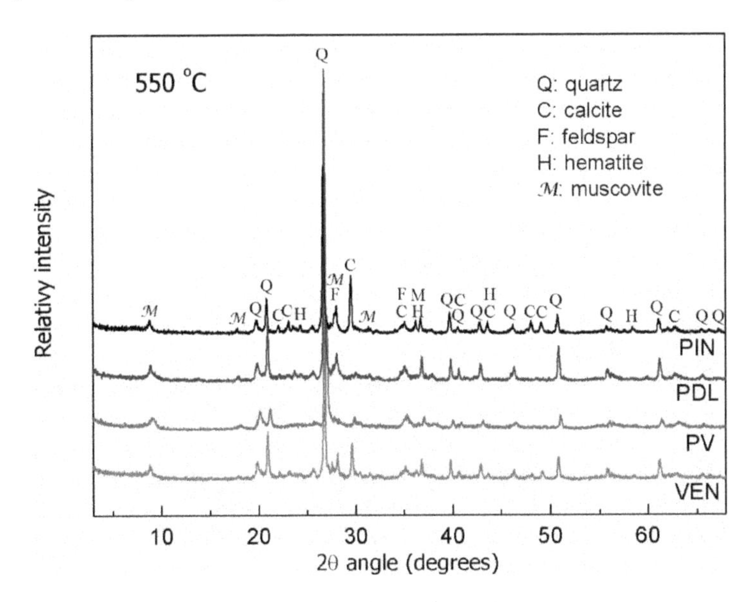

Figure 7.
Resulting phases after heat treatment at 550°C of the samples.

cosmetics, these impurities must be suppressed [3]. Montmorillonites with a high degree of purity have application in a wide variety of areas such as selective adsorbents, medicaments, membranes, production of organophilic clays, catalysts, among others [46], and should contain levels like the sample used as standard in this work (~70% montmorillonite, ~17% kaolinite).

The results of XRD after beneficiation (**Figure 8**) indicate that PDL is composed of 62% montmorillonite and 22% kaolinite, while PV has 55% montmorillonite and 28% kaolinite, both without the presence of Si-polymorphs (α-quartz or cristobalite). These results are consistent with the mineralogical compositions reported in the literature for commercial clays used in pharmaceuticals and cosmetics [30]. VEN (52% montmorillonite, 19% kaolinite) and PIN (47% montmorillonite, 16% kaolinite) are made up of smaller quantities of these clay minerals, with traces of hematite (VEN), calcite and muscovite (PIN).

The values of the cation exchange capacity (CEC) of the samples after centrifugation show significant differences, the highest being in PDL (92.5 meq/100 g) and PV (78.9 meq/100 g) due to the higher smectite content in these samples, because the CEC values of smectites (80–160 meq/100 g) are higher than those of kaolinite (4–20 meq/100 g) [13]. VEN showed a value of 70.7 meq/100 g and PIN 63.4 meq/100 g. The standard sample (BEN) presented the highest value among the five studied samples (118.2 meq/100 g).

The oil absorption capacity of the clays was expressive for the PDL (43%, w/v) and PV (41%, w/v) samples, approaching the BEN standard sample (48%, w/v). The oil absorption value obtained by this test method gives information about the vehicle demand of the fluid, evidencing possible use of these samples in applications that require high adsorption capacity, such as creams, powders, and emulsions [7]. VEN and PIN obtained the results of 30 and 23 (%, w/v), respectively.

The correlation between the strain gradient (shear stress) as directly proportional to the applied force (shear rate) defines the rheological behavior of a fluid [47]. Newtonian fluids follow Newton's law, showing a proportionality relationship between the rate and shear stress, resulting in constant viscosity$(\eta = \tan\alpha)$. The model used in this work was Ostwald-de Waele (or Power Law) [48], according to

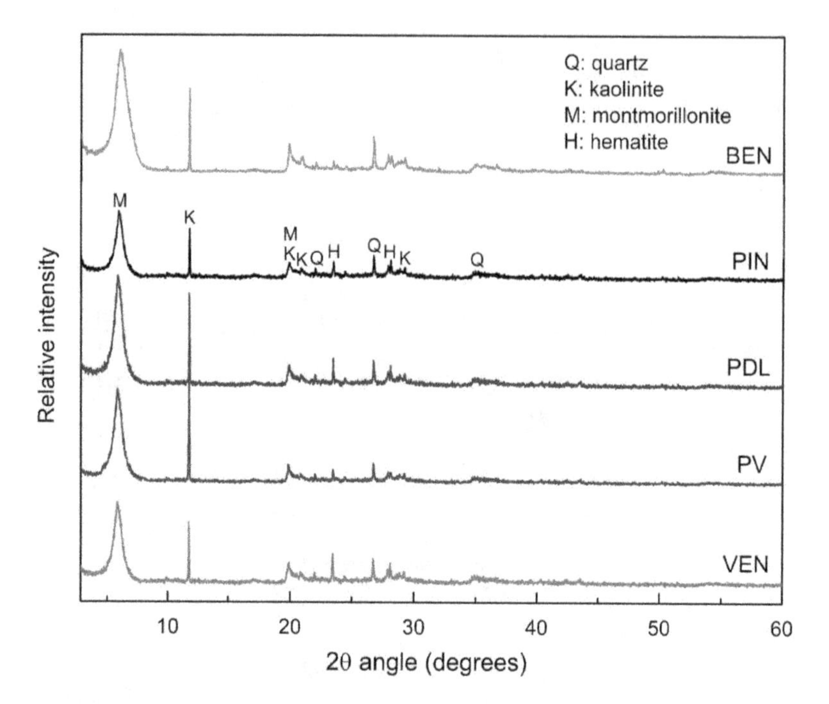

Figure 8.
X-ray diffraction patterns of the investigated samples (clay fraction).

Eq. (1), where η is the viscosity (Pa.s), $\dot{\gamma}$ corresponds to the shear stress (Pa) and $\dot{\gamma}$ is the shear rate (s^{-1}) [49]:

$$\sigma = n.\dot{\gamma} \tag{1}$$

In non-Newtonian fluids, this proportionality relationship does not exist and the viscosity is altered as a function of the shear rate. The evaluation of parameter η of Eq. (2) defines the behavior of the fluid in Newtonian or non-Newtonian. When $\eta = 1$ the system is considered Newtonian, $\eta < 1$ pseudoplastic and $\eta > 1$ dilating.

$$\sigma = K.\gamma^n \tag{2}$$

The reogram of the samples can be seen in **Figure 9** where the shear stress is a function of the shear rate. According to the rheological parameters presented in **Table 4** determined using the Ostwald-de Waele model, all samples have a linear correlation between the rate and shear stress, maintaining the constant viscosity typical of Newtonian behavior ($\eta = 1$) presenting values of $R^2 \geq 0.99991$, indicating an excellent correlation between experimental and theoretical data [49].

The viscosity of the material directly assists in the interpretation of the release tests, since the speed of diffusion of a drug with its consequent final release to the receiving middle, also depends on the barrier imposed by the viscosity of the system, which can facilitate or hinder the fraction of drug available per unit time [50]. By dispersing clay mineral particles in the water, the viscosity of the medium (water) is greatly increased. Thus, smectites can be used as a diluent in pharmaceutical and cosmetic preparations, as they are plastic when wet and particularly useful as stabilizers due to their thixotropic properties, and due to their large specific surface area and high adsorption capacity, they are suitable for act as carriers and releasers of drugs [13].

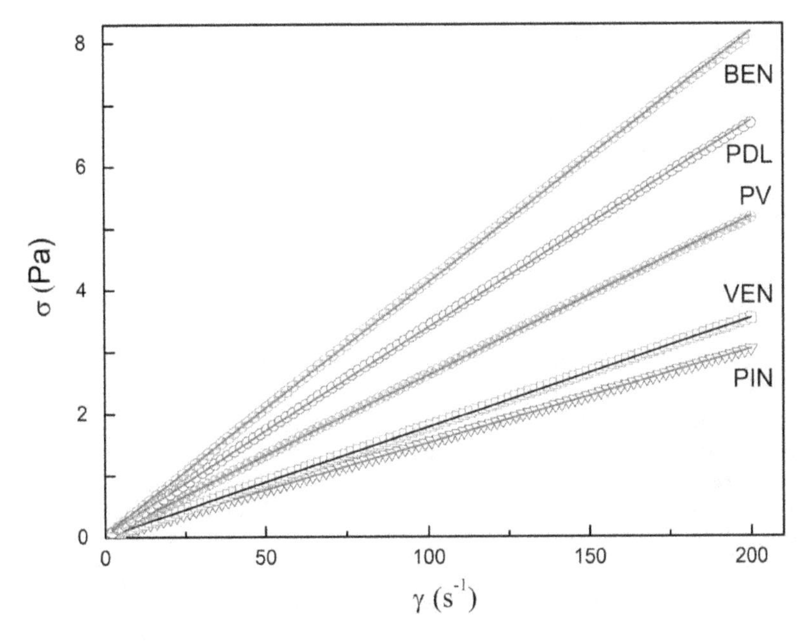

Figure 9.
Reogram of the investigated samples showing their Newtonian behavior.

Sample	Flow parameters	
	η (Pa.s)	R^2
VEN	0.01743	0.99998
PV	0.02552	0.99993
PDL	0.03307	0.99991
PIN	0.01515	0.99998
BEN	0.04068	0.99991

Table 4.
Viscosity values (η) and the correlation coefficient (R^2) of the samples.

The viscosity values of the PDL and PV clays, together with the size, particle distribution and quantity of clay minerals, make them suitable for the applications mentioned, as well as providing stability in emulsions and can be used in spas and esthetic centers for therapeutic purposes based on its smoothness, rheological properties, high water adsorption capacity and cation exchange, after mixing with natural water [51].

According to [52, 53], VEN and PIN can be used as drilling fluids for oil wells, as they have values above 15 cP (0.015 Pa.s), in accordance with the standard EP-1EP-00011-A [54]. For drugs and cosmetics, these samples have low values of η, probably due to the lower amount of clay minerals combined with impurities, such as quartz, calcite, and hematite.

4. Conclusions and outlook

We describe the chemical, mineralogical and rheological characterization of samples from four clay deposits before and after fractionation of the raw clays that are used in the production of ceramic tiles, bricks, blocks and artisanal pieces in the state of Sergipe, Brazil, for possible use in high value-added products, such as cosmetics and pharmaceuticals.

The PV sample showed the highest proportion of particles in the clay fraction, the smallest average particle diameter and the highest plasticity index among the raw samples. The chemical compositions show that they all contain considerable amounts of SiO_2 and Al_2O_3 and small amounts of TiO_2, with a high content of CaO in PIN and VEN.

PDL presents the highest proportions of montmorillonite and kaolinite, followed by PV. After heat treatment, the characteristic collapse of these clay minerals was observed, indicating that there is no reflection due to any other clay mineral, such as chlorites or vermiculites. The mineralogical compositions after fractionation showed the majority presence of clay minerals, with PDL composed of 62% montmorillonite and 22% kaolinite, while PV has 55% montmorillonite and 28% kaolinite, results consistent with reported in the literature for clays used in pharmaceutical products and cosmetics. However, VEN and PIN are made up of smaller quantities of these clay minerals, with traces of hematite (VEN), calcite and muscovite (PIN).

The values of cation exchange capacity after centrifugation show differences, being higher in PDL and PV due to the higher smectite content by them. The oil adsorption capacity was expressive in PDL and PV, approaching the standard sample used in this work, showing possible applications that require high adsorption capacity, such as creams, powders and emulsions.

The rheological parameters demonstrated an excellent linear correlation between the rate and shear stress, maintaining the constant viscosity typical of Newtonian behavior. These values in PDL and PV, combined with size, particle distribution, chemical composition, amount of clay minerals and high absorption capacity, show that they have the greatest potential for applications in cosmetics and drugs, as well as providing stability in emulsions and can be used in spas and esthetic centers for therapeutic purposes based on their softness and cation exchange capacity.

Acknowledgements

The authors would like to acknowledge the financial support by the Program Pesquisa Produtividade do Centro Universitário Estácio de Sergipe and Fundação de Apoio à Pesquisa e à Inovação Tecnológica do Estado de Sergipe (FAPITEC/SE).

Author details

Cochiran Pereira dos Santos[1]* and Adriana de Jesus Santos[2]

1 Centro Universitário Estácio de Sergipe, Aracaju, SE, Brazil

2 Universidade Federal de Sergipe, São Cristóvão, SE, Brazil

*Address all correspondence to: cochiran@hotmail.com

References

[1] R. Grim, Some applications of clay mineralogy, American Mineralogist: Journal of Earth and Planetary Materials, v. **45**, n. 3-4, p. 259-269 (1960). ISSN 0003-004X

[2] L.L.Y. Chang, Industrial Mineralogy: Materials, Processes, and Uses, Prentice Hall, Upper Saddle River, New Jersey (2002). ISBN 013917155X 9780139171550

[3] J.S. Nirwan, S. Farhaj, M.M. Chaudhary, Z. Khizer, S.S. Hasan, A. Angelis-Dimakis, A. Gill, H. Rasheed, N. Abbas, M.S. Arshad, T. Hussain, Y. Shahzad, A.M. Yousaf, T.A. Chohan, T. Hussain, H.A. Merchant, M.R. Akram, T.M. Khan, M. Ashraf, B.R. Conway, M. U. Ghori, Exploration of a New Source of Sustainable Nanomaterial from the Koh-e-Suleiman Mountain Range of Pakistan for Industrial Applications, Sci Rep **10** (2020) 577. https://doi.org/10.1038/s41598-020-57511-y

[4] J. Madejová, H. Pálkova, P. Kodamel, IR spectroscopy of clay minerals and clay nanocomposites, In: Spectroscopic Properties of Inorganic and Organometallic Compounds: Techniques, Materials and Applications, vol. **41** (2010) 22-71. **PDF eISBN** 978-1-84973-085-3

[5] H.H. Murray, Applied Clay Mineralogy: Occurrences, Processing and Applications of Kaolins, Bentonites, Palygorskite sepiolite, and Common Clays, Volume 2, 1st Edition, Elsevier Science, Amsterdam (2007). **eBook ISBN:** 9780080467870

[6] J.W. Stucki, Properties and behavior of ion in clay minerals, In: Bergaya, F., Theng, B.K.G., Lagaly, G. (Eds.), Handbook of Clay Science, 1st ed. Elsevier Science, Amsterdam (2006) 423-475. **eBook ISBN:** 9780080457635

[7] M.G.S. Valenzuela, M.M.C. Peralta, I. J. Sayeg, F.M.S. Carvalho, S.H. Wang, F. R.V. Díaz, Enrichment of clay from Vitoria da Conquista (Brazil) for applications in cosmetics, Applied Clay Science, v. **155** (2018) 111-119. https://doi.org/10.1016/j.clay.2018.01.011

[8] J.R. Goes, T.F. Azevedo, T.X.C. Dutra, V.B. Santos, J.B.S. Junior, L.S. Barreto, Avaliação da potencialidade de argilas da formação geológica Calumbi e Riachuelo em Sergipe para aplicação em revestimento cerâmico, Cerâmica **60** (2014) 211. https://doi.org/10.1590/S0366-69132014000200008

[9] C.P. Santos, H.A. Oliveira, R.M.P.B. Oliveira, Z.S. Macedo, Caracterização de argilas calcárias utilizadas na produção de revestimentos cerâmicos no Estado de Sergipe - Brasil, Cerâmica **62** (2016) 147-156. http://dx.doi.org/10.1590/0366-69132016623621983

[10] H.A. Oliveira, C.P. Santos, R.M.P.B. Oliveira, E. de Jesus, Z.S. Macedo, Avaliação do potencial de argilas de Sergipe e Alagoas na produção de agregados para uso em concreto, Cerâmica **63** (2017) 318-328. http://dx.doi.org/10.1590/0366-69132017633672106

[11] H.A. de Oliveira, C.P. dos Santos, Limestone Clays for Ceramic Industry [Online First], IntechOpen, London (2020). doi: 10.5772/intechopen.92506

[12] H. Bayram, M. Onal, H.; Yilmaz, Y. Sarikaya, Thermal analysis of a white calcium bentonite, Therm Anal Calorim, vol. **101**, p. 873-879 (2010). doi: https://doi.org/10.1007/s10973-009-0626-y

[13] M.I. Carretero, M. Pozo, Clay and non-clay minerals in the pharmaceutical industry Part I. Excipients and medical applications, Applied Clay Science **46** (2009) 73-80. https://doi.org/10.1016/j.clay.2009.07.017

[14] M.I. Carretero, M. Pozo, Clay and non-clay minerals in the pharmaceutical

and cosmetic industries Part II. Active ingredients, Applied Clay Science **47** (2010) 171-181. https://doi.org/10.1016/j.clay.2009.10.016

[15] C.B. Dornelas, L.A.M. Grillo, I.D.B. Junior, D.B. Nascimento, G.R. Ticiano, D.K. Resende, M.I.B. Tavares, A.S. Gomes, A.M. Junior, L.M. Cabral, Study of PVP-Bentonite Intercalation Process in Solution, Evaluation of the Influence from Time of Reaction, Polymer-Clay Proportion and Molar Mass, Polímeros: Ciências e Tecnologia, v. **20**, n. 4 (2010) 275-279. http://dx.doi.org/10.1590/S0104-14282010005000047

[16] P.S. Santos, Ciência e Tecnologia de Argilas, v.1, 2ª ed., Edgard Blucher, S. Paulo (1992).

[17] S.S. Ray, M. Okamoto, Polymer/Layered Silicate Nanocomposites: A Review from Preparation to Processing, Progress in Polymer Science, volume **28** (2003) 1539-1641.http://dx.doi.org/10.1016/j.progpolymsci.2003.08.002

[18] P. Kippax, Measuring particle size using modern laser diffraction techniques, Paint & Coatings Industry, (2005). http://www.malvern.com/malvern/kbase.nsf/allbyno/KB000930/$file/MRK696-01.pdf

[19] American Society for Testing and Materials, ASTM D4318:2010, Standard test method for Liquid Limit, Plastic limit, and plasticity index of soils (2010).

[20] Associação Brasileira de Normas Técnicas, NBR 7180:1984, Determinação do limite de liquidez de solos, Rio de Janeiro (1984).

[21] Associação Brasileira de Normas Técnicas, NBR 6459:2016, Determinação do limite de plasticidade de solos, Rio de Janeiro (2016).

[22] A.M. Bennour, S.E. Srasra et al., Composition, firing behavior and ceramic properties of the Sejnéne Clays (Northwest Tunisia), Applied Clay Science **115** (2015) 30-38. https://doi.org/10.1016/j.clay.2015.07.025

[23] D.M. Moore, R.C. Jr. Reynolds, X-ray Diffraction and the Identification and Analysis of Clay Minerals, 2nd edition. Oxford University Press, New York, 332 pp, (1997).

[24] ASTM C837-09:2019, Standard Test Method for Methylene Blue Index of Clay, ASTM International, West Conshohocken, PA (2019). www.astm.org.

[25] ASTM D281-12:2016, Standard Test Method for Oil Absorption of Pigments by Spatula Rub-out, ASTM International, West Conshohocken, PA (2016). www.astm.org

[26] F.H. Zaied, R. Abidi, N. Slim-Shimi, A.K. Somarin, Potentiality of clay raw materials from Gram area (Northern Tunisia) in the ceramic industry, Applied Clay Science **112-113** (2015) 1. doi:10.1016/j.clay.2015.03.027

[27] Associação Brasileira de Normas Técnicas, NBR 6502:1995, Terminologia - Rochas e Solos, Rio de Janeiro (1995).

[28] F.A. Andrade, H.A. Al-Qureshi, D. Hotza, Measuring the plasticity of clays: a review, Applied Clay Science **51**, 1-2 (2011) 1-7.

[29] S.C. Maestrelli, C.D. Roveri, A. Nunes, A.G.P. Nunes, L.M. Faustino, G. F. Aielo, L.P.A. Pinto, C. Manochio, T. M.L. Cal, F.F. Ribeiro, N.A. Mariano, Estudo da caracterização de argilas não plásticas da região de Poços de Caldas, Cerâmica **59** (2013) 242.

[30] M. Mattioli, L. Giardini, C. Roselli, D. Desideri, Mineralogical characterization of commercial clays used in cosmetics and possible risk for health, Applied Clay Science **119** (2016)

449-454. https://doi.org/10.1016/j.clay.2015.10.023

[31] A.C. Alcântara, M.S. Beltrão, H.A. Oliveira, I.F. Gimenez, L.S. Barreto, Characterization of ceramic tiles prepared from two clays from Sergipe-Brazil, Applied Clay Science **39** (2008) 160.

[32] M. Dondi, G. Guarini, P. Ligas, M. Palomba, M. Raimondo, I. Uras, Chemical, mineralogical and ceramic properties of kaolinitic materials from the Tresnuraghes mining district (Western Sardinia, Italy), Applied Clay Science **18** (2001) 145.

[33] P.S.C. Silva, S.M.B. Oliveira, L. Farias, D.I.T. Fávaro, B.P. Mazzilli, Chemical and radiological characterization of clay minerals used in pharmaceutics and cosmetics, Applied Clay Science, Volume **52**, Issues 1-2 (2011) 145-149. https://doi.org/10.1016/j.clay.2011.02.013

[34] F. Gonzalez, V. Romero, G. Garcia, M. Gonzalez, Firing transformations of mixtures of clays containing illite, kaolinite and calcium carbonate used by ornamental tile industries, Applied Clay Science **5** (1990) 361.

[35] C. Zanelli, C. Iglesias, E. Domínguez, D. Gardini, M. Raimondo, G. Guarini, M. Dondi, Mineralogical composition and particle size distribution as a key to understand the technological properties of Ukrainian ball clays, Applied Clay Science, Volume **108** (2015) 102-110. https://doi.org/10.1016/j.clay.2015.02.005

[36] M.I. Carretero, C.S.F. Gomes, F. Tateo, Clays, drugs, and human health, In: Bergaya, F., Lagaly, G. (Eds.), Handbook of Clay Science. Elsevier, Amsterdam (2013) 711-764.

[37] M. Rautureau, C. Gomes, N. Liewig, M. Katouzian-Safadi, Clays and health: Properties and therapeutic uses, Springer (2017). https://doi.org/10.1007/978-3-319-42884-0

[38] R.E. Grim, Applied Clay Mineralogy, New York, Ed. Mc-Graw Hill Publ, Company Ltd (1962).

[39] H. Kodama, R.E. Grim, Clay mineral - rock, [online] Encyclopedia Britannica, Available at: https://www.britannica.com/science/clay-mineral (2019).

[40] A.P.F. Albers, F.G. Melchiades, R. Machado, J.B. Baldo, A.O. Boschi, Um método simples de caracterização de argilominerais por difração de raios X, Cerâmica **48** (2002) pp. 32-36. http://dx.doi.org/10.1590/S0366-69132002000100008

[41] G.W. Brindley, Order-disorder in clay mineral structures: in: Crystal Structures of Clay Minerals and their X-ray Identification (GW Brindley and G Brown, editors), Mineralogical Society, London (1980) pp. 125-195. https://doi.org/10.1180/mono-5.2

[42] S.M. Chemtob, R.D. Nickerson, R.V. Morris, D.G. Agresti, J.G. Catalano, Synthesis and structural characterization of ferrous trioctahedral smectites: implications for clay mineral genesis and detectability on Mars. J. Geophys. Res. Planets **120** (2015) 1119-1140. https://doi.org/10.1002/2014JE004763

[43] C.E. Weaver, Clays, Muds, and Shales (Developments in Sedimentology), Volume **44**, 1st Edition, Elsevier, Amsterdam (1989). **ISBN: 9780080869582**

[44] S. Mukherjee, The Science of Clays: Applications in Industry, Engineering, and Environment, Springer Netherlands (2013). ISBN 978-94-007-6683-9

[45] A. Meunier, Clays, Springer-Verlag Berlin Heidelberg, Original French edition published by Gordon & Breach (2005). ISBN 978-3-540-27141-3

[46] F. Uddin, Montmorillonite: An introduction to properties and utilization. Current Topics in the Utilization of Clay in Industrial and Medical Applications **1** (2018). https://doi.org/10.5772/intechopen.77987

[47] M.A. Sheraz, M.F. Khan, S. Ahmed, S.H. Kazi, S.R. Khattak, I. Ahmad, Factors affecting formulation characteristics and stability of ascorbic acid in water-in-oil creams. International Journal of Cosmetic Science **36** (5) (2014) 494-504. doi: 10.1111/ics.12152

[48] V.M. Shapovalov, On the Applicability of the Ostwald-De Waele Model in Solving Applied Problems, J Eng Phys Thermophy **90** (2017) 1213-1218. https://doi.org/10.1007/s10891-017-1676-9

[49] G. Schramm, Reologia e reometria: fundamentos teóricos e práticos, 2ª ed, Artliber Ed., São Paulo (2006). ISBN 9788588098343

[50] M.A. Correa, M.V. Scarpa, M.C. Franzini, A.G. Oliveira, On the incorporation of the non-steroidal anti-inflammatory naproxen into cationic O/W microemulsions, Colloids and Surfaces B: Biointerfaces, v. **43**, n. 2, (2005) 108-114.

[51] F. Veniale, A. Bettero, P. Jobstraibizer, M. Setti, Thermal muds: perspectives of innovations, Applied Clay Science **36** (2007) 141-147. doi: 10.1016/j.clay.2006.04.013

[52] P.M. Bastos, B.M.A. Brito, A.J.A. Gama, J.M. Cartaxo, G.A. Neves, L.F.A. Campos, Modeling rheological properties of smectite clays from Paraíba State for use in oil wells drilling fluids, Cerâmica **63** (2017) 187-196. https://doi.org/10.1590/0366-69132017633662100

[53] Z. Wang, H. Zhang, H. Mao, W. Qin, Effects of Fine Minerals on Pulp Rheology and the Flotation of Diaspore and Pyrite Mixed Ores, Minerals **10** (1): 60 (2020) doi: 10.60.10.3390/min10010060

[54] Petrobras, Ensaio de viscosificante para fluidos base água na exploração e produção de petróleo, código EP-1EP-00011-A (2011).

Chapter 5

Magnetic Assembly and Functionalization of One-Dimensional Nanominerals in Optical Field

Meng Fu, Zepeng Zhang, Rui Jiang and Hongbao Liu

Abstract

Magnetic particles can be oriented along the magnetic field direction to achieve orderly arrangement under the magnetic field. Optical functional materials such as photonic crystal and liquid crystal can be obtained according to magnetic induced ordered nanostructure assembly. One-dimensional natural clay minerals with unique structure, composition and properties can be used as structural base to prepare anisotropic magnetic nanoparticles by decorated with magnetic particles, achieving unique optical functional properties. In this chapter, one-dimensional clay minerals@Fe_3O_4 nanocomposites were prepared by co-precipitation. The resulting one-dimensional clay minerals@Fe_3O_4 nanocomposites are superparamagnetic. They can be oriented along the direction of the magnetic field and produce an instantaneously reversible response. These magnetic mineral materials can be dispersed in a dilute acid solution to form stable colloid solutions. These stable colloid solutions produce a similar magnetically controlled liquid crystal with Bragg diffraction under an external magnetic field. Their optical properties are affected by magnetic field intensity, magnetic field direction and solid content. The results show that the functionalization of one-dimensional clay minerals has potential applications in display devices, photonic switches and other fields.

Keywords: One-dimensional clay minerals, magnetic assembly, magnetically controlled liquid crystal, photonic crystal

1. Introduction

The pursuit of nanomineral functional materials with novel properties and improved performance is a continually expanding research area that covers chemistry, physics, biology and materials science. It is an important research direction in the field of mineral functional materials to explore, develop and apply the electrical, optical, magnetic, acoustic and thermal properties of natural minerals and rocks, especially to study and prepare mineral functional materials with electrical, optical, magnetic, acoustic and thermal properties by using the unique structure, composition and morphology of natural minerals. Among the various explored nanostructures, the study of one-dimensional (1D) nanominerals such as wires, rods, and tubes has entered a period of fast development within the past several years, and is presently the focus of many research groups [1–3]. Considering that magnetic nanoparticles can be controlled reversibly by the magnetic field, superparamagnetic Fe_3O_4 nanoparticles can be coated on the surface of the anisotropic 1D clay minerals to realize the magnetic field induced anisotropic ordered orientation and form liquid crystal phase. In recent years, research efforts have been directed on the one-dimensional nanominerals coated or assembled with magnetic nanoparticles [4–7]. The research on the magnetic response and optical properties of magnetic mineral composites is helpful to improve the added value of natural mineral materials, develop mineral functional materials with special optical and magnetic properties, and accelerate the development of mineral industry.

In this chapter, one-dimensional natural nano-clay-minerals with unique structures, compositions and properties have been used as structural base to prepare anisotropic magnetic one-dimensional nanomaterials by decorated one-dimensional natural nano-clay-minerals with magnetic particles. Magnetic particles can be oriented along the magnetic field direction to achieve orderly arrangement under the magnetic field. Optical functional materials with unique optical functional properties such as photonic crystal and liquid crystal have been obtained according to magnetic induced ordered nanostructure assembly. All the related research progress our research group made are summarized as well as existing problems and prospects of the future application and development direction.

2. Raw material

Clay mineral is the main component of clay rock and soil, which is a kind of rich non-metallic mineral resources on the earth. In recent years, people have been constantly studying the structure and properties of clay minerals, and exploring the composite of clay minerals and other materials, in order to expect that the composite materials will make a breakthrough in the field of deep processing and application of non-metallic minerals, and also obtain a series of research results. In these studies, the research objects mainly include layered silicate minerals represented by montmorillonite group, kaolinite group, illite group, vermiculite group, and fibrous silicate minerals represented by sepiolite group [8]. Attapulgite and sepiolite are typical one-dimensional nanominerals. Their research direction and content are also very representative. In recent years, researchers at home and abroad mainly focus on the following aspects: ① as adsorbents [9], they can adsorb heavy metal ions or pollutants; ② As a carrier, it catalyzes other chemical reactions or provides a place for other reactions [10]; ③ When clay minerals are compounded with other polymers or organic materials, the mechanical properties, thermal stability, flame retardancy and barrier properties of the materials can be significantly improved [11]; ④ As catalyst of reaction [12]; ⑤ As a rheological control agent, it is used in oil-based drilling fluid [13]; In addition, the two minerals also have a lot of research and application in animal husbandry, medicine and so on. Here, attapulgite and sepiolite will be taken as examples to introduce the structure and properties of one-dimensional clay minerals.

2.1 Attapulgite

In this chapter, we use attapulgite (short crystal rod) as the research object. Wang Aiqin et al. [14] pointed out in "*Attapulgite rod bundle dissociation and its nano functional composites*" that the products of hydrothermal alteration have soft appearance, good crystallinity and long fiber, which are usually called palygorskite; However, the sedimentary products are characterized by dense appearance, poor crystallization performance, short crystal rod and high iron content, which are called attapulgite. In the following content, we will use the naming principle mentioned in "*Attapulgite rod bundle dissociation and its nano functional composites*" to unify these short rod minerals as attapulgite.

2.1.1 Crystal structure

The molecular formula of attapulgite is $Mg_5[Si_4O_{10}]_2(OH)_2{\cdot}8H_2O$, which belongs to monoclinic system with space group C2/m (no.12); a = 13.24 Å, b = 17.89 Å, c = 5.21 Å, $\alpha = \gamma = 90$ Å, $\beta = 8$, Z = 2 [15]. The crystal structure is shown in **Figure 1(a)**. A $[Mg\ (O, OH)_6]$ octahedron is sandwiched by two $[SiO_4]$ tetrahedrons, forming a TOT type "I beam" with one-dimensional infinite extension along the c-axis, and its width is about 18 Å. The adjacent TOT type "I beam" is staggered up and down, forming a wide channel along the c-axis at the position of inert oxygen, which is about 3.7 Å × 6.4 Å. The channel is filled with water molecules. There are three forms of water in attapulgite, one is structural water hydroxyl, the second is crystal water coordinated with octahedral cation, the third is zeolite water connected by hydrogen bond in the channel. The $[SiO_4]$ tetrahedron by a common edge forms a six membered ring at the same height, and the $[Mg\ (O, OH)_6]$ octahedron is also joined into a layer by a common edge, so attapulgite has both chain and layered structure.

2.1.2 Microstructure and physicochemical properties

Figure 1(e) and **(f)** show the size distribution histograms of these monodisperse attapulgite nanocrystals counted from **Figure 1(b)** [16]. The average length and width of attapulgite rods are 0.85 μm and 63 nm, respectively.

The color of attapulgite is white, gray or light brown with glass luster, hardness of 2–3, specific gravity of 2.05–2.32, a sense of smoothness [15]. It has viscosity and plasticity, strong water absorption, no expansion in water. Because of isomorphism, the surface of attapulgite is negatively charged, and it has cation exchange performance, but lower than that of montmorillonite. It has a strong adsorption function, because the wide channels in the crystal structure greatly increase the specific surface area of attapulgite.

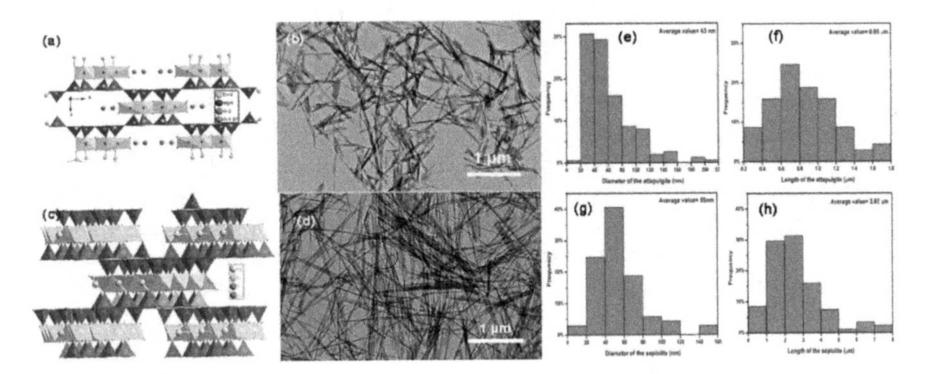

Figure 1.
Raw materials: (a) the crystal structure of attapulgite; (b) the microstructure of attapulgite in TEM; (c) the crystal structure of Sepiolite; (d) the microstructure of sepiolite in TEM; distribution histograms: (e) diameter of attapulgite; (f) length of attapulgite; (g) diameter of sepiolite; (h) length of sepiolite.

2.2 Sepiolite

2.2.1 Crystal structure

The molecular formula of sepiolite is $Mg_8[Si_6O_{15}]_2(OH)_4 \cdot 12H_2O$, which belongs to orthorhombic system with space group Pncn (no.52); a = 13.40 Å, b = 36.80 Å, c = 5.28 Å, $\alpha = \gamma = \beta = 90$ Å, Z = 2 [15]. The crystal structure is shown in **Figure 1(c)**, which is basically similar to that of attapulgite. The difference is that the Mg and H_2O content of sepiolite is higher than that of attapulgite; Structurally, the TOT type "I-beam" width of sepiolite is larger, about 27 Å; The cross-sectional area of through passage is also larger than that of attapulgite, about 3.7 Å × 10.6 Å.

2.2.2 Microstructure and physicochemical properties

Figure 1(g) and **(h)** shows the size distribution histograms of these monodisperse sepiolite nanocrystals counted from **Figure 1(d)**. The average length and width of sepiolite fibers are 2.6 μm and 55 nm, respectively [16]. Compared with the size of attapulgite, sepiolite has higher aspect ratio.

Sepiolite is usually white, light gray or maroon, also has glass luster, hardness of 2–3, specific gravity of 2–2.5, with a sense of smoothness, soft texture [15]. Since the similar crystal structure with attapulgite, sepiolite has negative charge on its surface, and its cation exchange properties, large specific surface area, good adsorption property are similar to those of attapulgite.

3. Magnetic assembly of one-dimensional nanominerals

3.1 Construction of one-dimensional clay mineral magnetic materials

The magnetic particles coated on the surface of one-dimensional clay minerals can bring magnetism to non-magnetic one-dimensional clay minerals. The most common method to load magnetic particles on clay mineral surface is to synthesize Fe_3O_4 nanoparticles in solution with clay minerals as dispersed phase. The Fe_3O_4 nanoparticles cannot be coated uniformly on the one-dimensional clay surface minerals is the main problem. There are many methods for the synthesis of Fe_3O_4, including co-precipitation, thermal solvent and so on. A lot of literature shows that the synthesis method of Fe_3O_4 has no obvious influence on the uniform coating on the carrier. The surface morphology and crystal defects of the carrier, the active functional groups on the carrier surface, the affinity between the carrier and Fe_3O_4, suitable heterogeneous nucleation environment have a decisive influence on the uniform coating of the carrier. In this section, the magnetic assembly process of one-dimensional clay minerals (as shown in **Figure 2**) will be described by co-precipitation method. The first is to modify one-dimensional clay minerals by modifier, which helps clay minerals evenly disperse in the solution, and at the same time, it can also bring more active functional groups to clay minerals surface and help deposit Fe_3O_4 uniformly on the surface of clay minerals. The second is the uniform coating of Fe_3O_4 on the surface of one-dimensional clay minerals. When Fe_3O_4 nanoparticles are deposited on the surface of one-dimensional clay minerals, the control of heterogeneous nucleation conditions is very important. Influence factors, including suitable surface adhering surfactants, modifier concentration, Fe^{2+}/Fe^{3+} concentration, temperature etc. affect the uniform deposition and particle diameter of Fe_3O_4 on the surface of clay minerals by influencing the homogeneous nucleation rates, heterogeneous nucleation rates and particle growth rate.

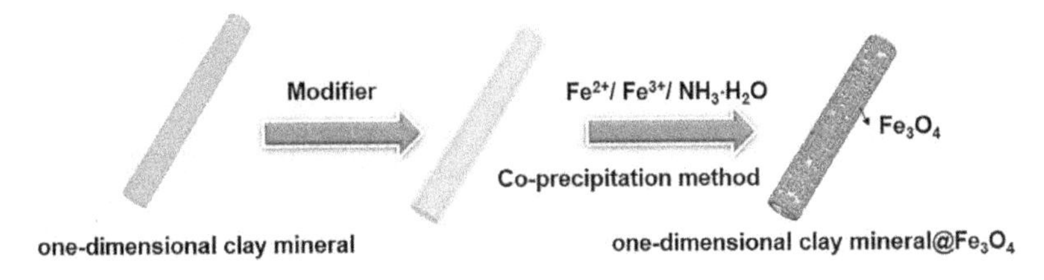

Figure 2.
Magnetic coating of one dimensional nano clay minerals.

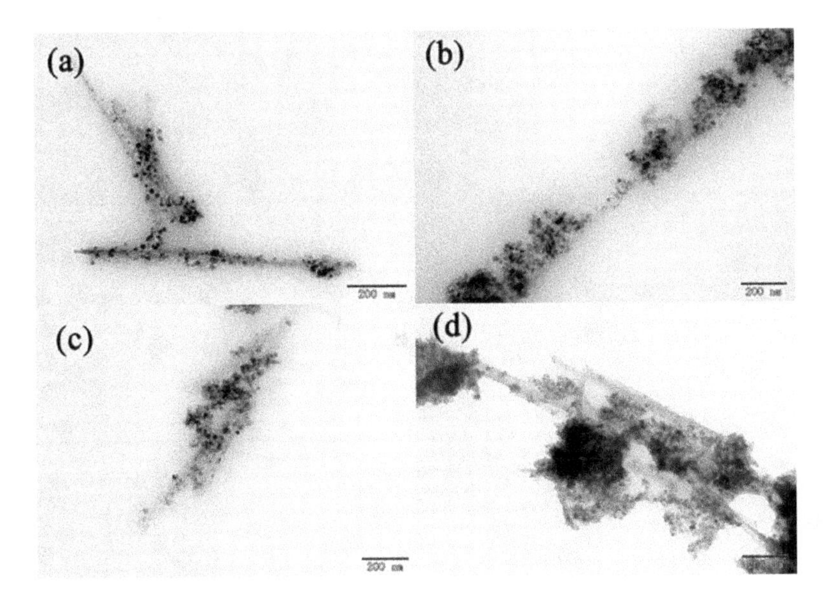

Figure 3.
TEM images of attapulgites-Fe_3O_4 one-dimensional nanocomposites synthesized (no surfactant) with different concentrations of $FeCl_3 \cdot 6H_2O$: (a) 0.01 mmol/L; (b) 0.02 mmol/L; (c) 0.03 mmol/L; (d) 0.04 mmol/L.

3.2 Influence factor of one-dimensional clay mineral magnetic assembly

3.2.1 Surface modification of one-dimensional nanominerals

Uniform Fe_3O_4 shell decorated on the surface is not available while no surface pretreatments were carried out to introduce new surface functional groups. Fe_3O_4 microspheres or irregular islands will grow onto the surface of 1D nanominerals (**Figure 3**) [17], which may be attributed to a significantly different crystalline structure in lattice symmetry and lattice constant between Fe_3O_4 and 1D nanominerals as well as the amorphization of natural mineral. Only by modifying the surface of non-magnetic 1D nanomineral and improving the surface affinity between 1D nanomineral and Fe_3O_4, can the uniform growth or uniform assembly of magnetic particles on the 1D nanomineral surface be promoted. Modification methods include inorganic modification and organic modification.

3.2.1.1 Inorganic modification

Inorganic modifiers HCl and H_2O_2 are often used to modify nanominerals.

The TEM images of acid treated attapulgite@Fe_3O_4 were illustrated in **Figure 4**. Compared to the growth of Fe_3O_4 nanoparticles on the raw attapulgite (**Figure 3**),

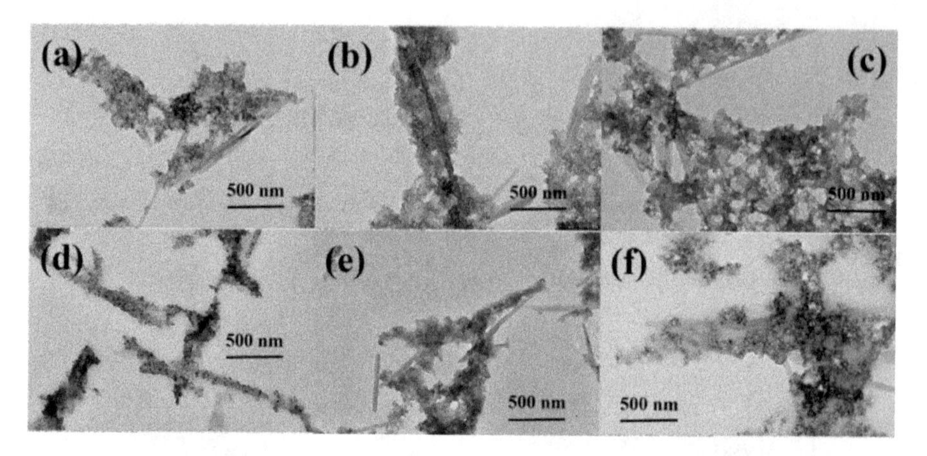

Figure 4.
The TEM images of acid treated attapulgite@Fe_3O_4 with different acid concentrations (a) 0.5 Mol·L^{-1}; (b) 1.0 Mol·L^{-1}; (c) 1.5 Mol·L^{-1}; (d) 2.0 Mol·L^{-1}; (e) 2.5 Mol·L^{-1}; (f) 3.0 Mol·L^{-1}.

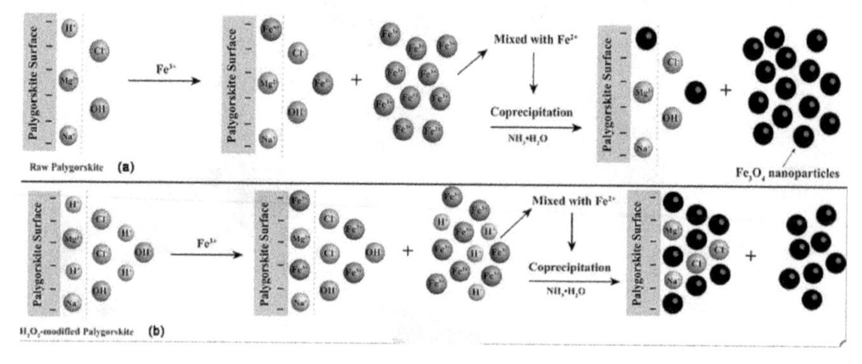

Figure 5.
Proposed growth mechanism of Fe_3O_4 nanoparticles on (a) acid-modified attapulgite/palygorskite; (b) H_2O_2-modified attapulgite/palygorskite.

the acid modification was found to help Fe_3O_4 nanoparticles adhere on the surface of attapulgite [18]. It could be observed from **Figure 4** that when the HCl concentration was 2.0 mol·L^{-1}, the Fe_3O_4 nanoparticles on modified attapulgite surface were the most uniform.

It is well known that one-dimensional clay mineral has zeolite-like channels and exchangeable cations such as Na^+, K^+, and Mg^{2+}, which allows H^+ to interact with the mineral. While H^+ cations attached on the surface of one-dimensional clay mineral, the Si-O bonds were corroded and Al^{3+} or Mg^{2+} cations in octahedron were displaced by H^+ cations to expose more negative active sites, so that more H^+ cations could absorb on attapulgite surface and the Cl^- ions continuously gravitated to H^+ via electrostatic attraction. The new electric double layer was formed on the modified one-dimensional clay mineral surface (as shown in the **Figure 5(a)**), resulting in the increase of zeta potential absolute values. Besides, the impurities in the one-dimensional clay mineral channels such as carbonate, amorphous silica etc. were dissolved so that the channels were cleared, leading to the increase of specific surface area. With the absolute values of Zeta Potential and specific surface area enlargement, the acid modified one-dimensional clay mineral could absorb more Fe^{3+}/Fe^{2+} cations. When $FeCl_3$ was added into the modified one-dimensional clay mineral suspension, Fe^{3+} cations would replace H^+ ions absorbed on one-dimensional clay mineral surface, then H^+ ions were released into solution. Once $NH_3{\cdot}H_2O$ was added into the system, many Fe_3O_4 nuclei were generated on the surface of attapulgite simultaneously in a short time, resulting in a dense Fe_3O_4 shell composed of small Fe_3O_4 nanoparticles with a mean size of about 10–30 nm.

The TEM images of H_2O_2 treated attapulgite@Fe_3O_4 were illustrated in **Figure 6** [18]. Compared to the growth of Fe_3O_4 nanoparticles on the raw attapulgite (**Figure 3**), the attapulgite nanorods were covered more uniformly by Fe_3O_4 nanoparticles. It could be observed from **Figure 6(d)** that when the H_2O_2 concentration was 25%, the Fe_3O_4 nanoparticles on modified attapulgite surface were the most uniform. H_2O_2 can help one-dimensional clay mineral absorb more Fe^{3+} cations as shown in **Figure 5(b)**, thus depositing more evenly Fe_3O_4 nanoparticles on the surface.

3.2.1.2 Organic modification

When modifying one-dimensional clay minerals with organic compound, the modifier is often selected according to the structural characteristics of one-dimensional clay minerals. For one-dimensional clay minerals with negative surface, cationic or poly-cationic modifiers are often used.

The effects of polyethylenimine (PEI) concentration on the morphology of the one-dimensional nanocomposites were examined by TEM and SEM and displayed in **Figure 7**. The left is TEM result and the right is SEM result [17]. The figure shows that when PEI is not added to the solution, Fe_3O_4 adheres to the surface of attapulgite in the form of microsphere or island structure. The microsphere or island structure does not form close packing, and there are a lot of gaps between the microspheres. Therefore, Fe_3O_4 cannot grow on the outer surface of attapulgite forming a uniform core-shell structure. It may be due to the lattice mismatch between Fe_3O_4 and attapulgite. At the same time, the existence of a large number of amorphous regions on the surface of attapulgite brings the unreachable interface energy to the growth of Fe_3O_4. On the other hand, the surface inhomogeneity of natural attapulgite determines that different positions on the surface of attapulgite have different reactivity and position dependent interfacial tension. These factors make it difficult for Fe_3O_4 to grow directly on the surface of attapulgite. When the PEI content is 0.1 mg/mL, there are still a lot of uncoated attapulgite. When the

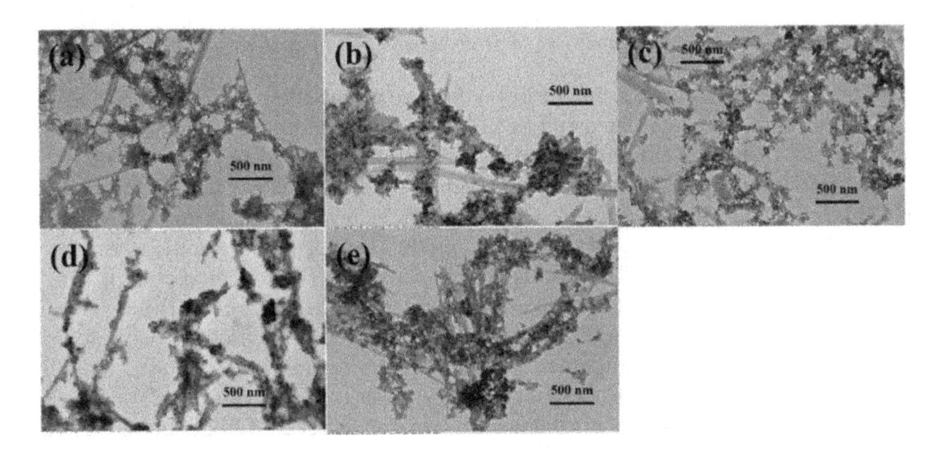

Figure 6.
The TEM images of H_2O_2 treated attapulgite@Fe_3O_4 with different H_2O_2 concentrations: (a) 10%; (b) 15%; (c) 20%; (d) 25%; (e) 30%.

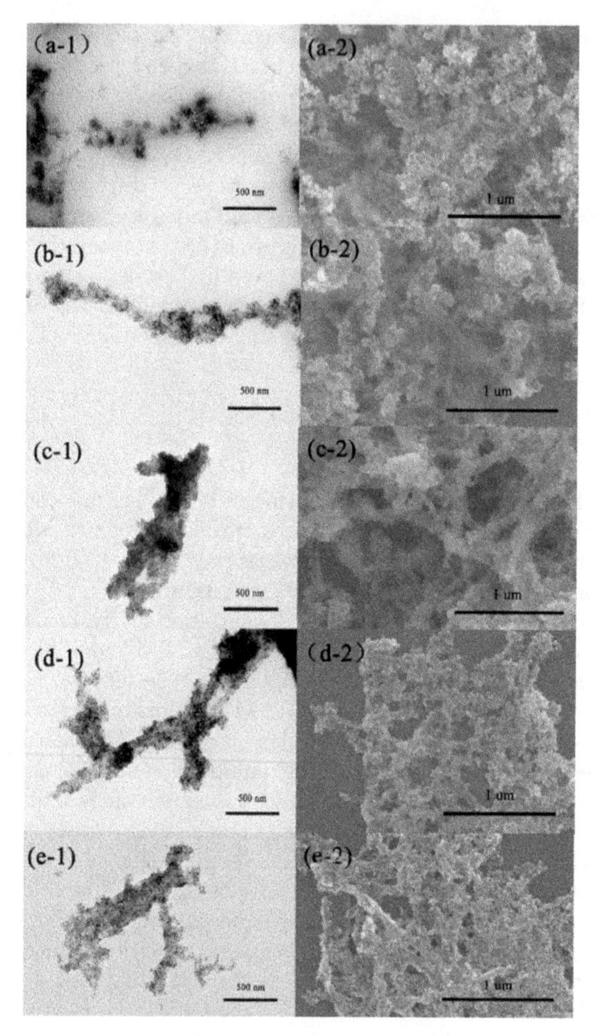

Figure 7.
Images of attapulgites-Fe_3O_4 one-dimensional nanocomposites synthesized with different concentrations of PEI: TEM: (a-1) 0 mg/mL; (b-1) 0.1 mg/mL; (c-1) 0.2 mg/mL; (d-1) 0.5 mg/mL; (e-1) 1 mg/mL; SEM: (a-2) 0 mg/mL; (b-2) 0.1 mg/mL; (c-2) 0.2 mg/mL; (d-2) 0.5 mg/mL; (e-2) 1 mg/mL.

amount of PEI is 0.2 mg/mL, more PEI is adsorbed on the surface of attapulgite, and PEI acts as a link to adsorb Fe^{3+} and Fe^{2+}. When alkali solution is added, Fe_3O_4 particles are formed in situ on the surface of attapulgite, realizing 100% close packed coating of Fe_3O_4 nanoparticles. When the PEI content was further increased (0.5 mg/mL or 1.0 mg/mL), the Fe_3O_4 nanoparticles became smaller and no longer accumulated tightly on the surface of attapulgite. They dispersed evenly, even scattered into the solution. The results may be caused by the diffusion of high concentration PEI into the solution and the increase of the viscosity of the solution, which makes it difficult for Fe_3O_4 particles to diffuse, move and form close packing. The growth of Fe_3O_4 is accompanied by the adsorption of PEI in the solution, which prevents the growth of Fe_3O_4 nanoparticles and leads to the formation of nanoparticles with small size. In conclusion, with the increase of PEI content, Fe_3O_4 gradually dispersed and coated on the surface of attapulgite from island aggregation state, achieving uniform and compact coating. 0.2 mg/mL was the best PEI content for the formation of attapulgites@Fe_3O_4 one-dimensional nanocomposites.

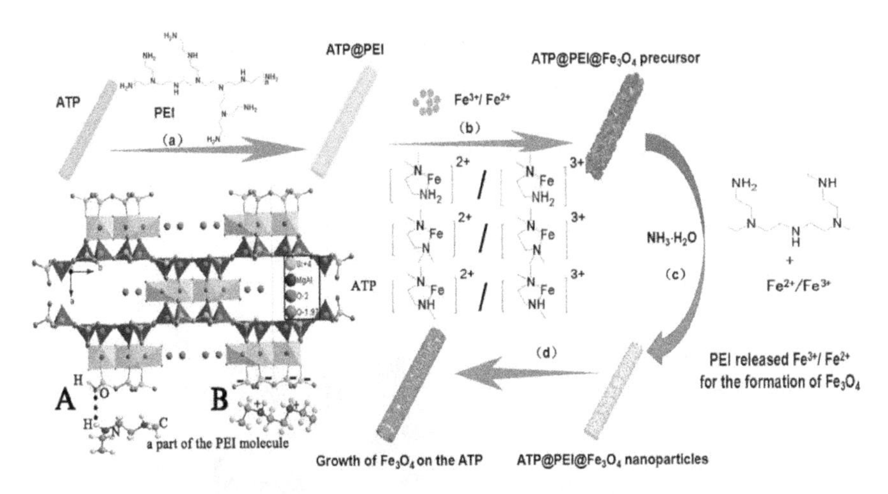

Figure 8.
Proposed scheme for the growth of uniform Fe_3O_4 nanostructures on the surface of the one-dimensional clay minerals with PEI by co-precipitation method.

The growth mechanism of uniform coating of Fe_3O_4 on the surface of one-dimensional clay minerals is shown in **Figure 8**. Firstly, PEI is adsorbed on the surface of attapulgite by hydrogen bonding and electrostatic interaction. Then Fe^{3+}/Fe^{2+} was added to the system, and the PEI on the surface of attapulgite adsorbed Fe^{3+}/Fe^{2+} onto the surface of attapulgite through complexation by PEI. Stable five membered cyclic complexes can be formed between PEI and Fe^{3+}/Fe^{2+}, and iron salts are continuously accumulated to form the precursor of Fe_3O_4. With the addition of ammonia, a large number of Fe_3O_4 nuclei are formed at the same time. At this time, PEI releases Fe3+/Fe^{2+} for the in-situ formation and growth of Fe_3O_4. On the other hand, suitable temperature and iron salt concentration can promote the heterogeneous nucleation of Fe_3O_4 on the surface of attapulgite. With the increase of time, Fe_3O_4 nanoparticles move and diffuse on the surface of attapulgite to minimize the surface energy of the system, thus forming a one-dimensional composite. With the smallest particles dissolving and the larger ones growing up by Ostwald ripening, the attapulgites-Fe_3O_4 core-shell nanocomposites are obtained finally [17].

3.2.2 Effects of ferric salt concentration

The TEM and SEM results of attapulgites-Fe_3O_4 one-dimensional nanocomposites with different $FeCl_3 \cdot 6H_2O$ content are shown in **Figure 9** [17]. The left side is TEM and the right side is SEM of corresponding samples. a/b/c/d is the sample with 0.01/ 0.02 / 0.03/ 0.04 mmol/L of Fe^{3+}. It can be seen from the figure that with the increase of iron salt content, Fe_3O_4 on the surface of attapulgite changes from sparse dispersion to close packing (thickness: 10–20 nm), and finally becomes thicker (outer layer thickness: 30–40 nm). However, when the addition amount of Fe^{3+} reached 0.04 mmol/L, the inhomogeneous coating appeared again. Low supersaturation promotes heterogeneous nucleation of Fe_3O_4 on the surface of attapulgite to obtain large nanoparticles; High supersaturation leads to similar homogeneous and heterogeneous nucleation rates and small nanoparticles. Therefore, when the concentration of Fe^{3+} exceeds the critical value, the relative supersaturation of Fe_3O_4 is too large, resulting in the same rate of homogeneous nucleation and heterogeneous nucleation, small Fe_3O_4 nanoparticles appear, and form a large number of nanoparticle aggregates, and finally incomplete coating

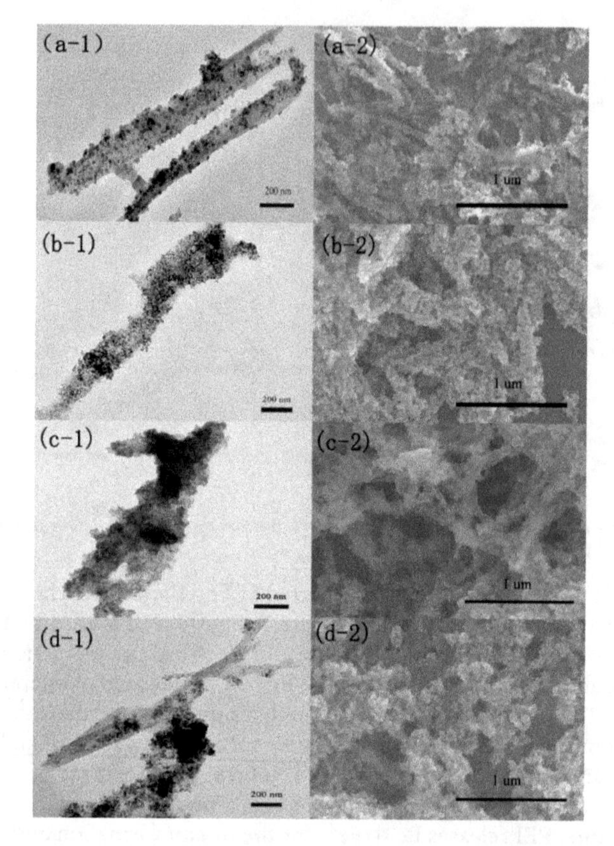

Figure 9.
Images of attapulgites-Fe_3O_4 one-dimensional nanocomposites synthesized with different concentrations of $FeCl_3{\cdot}6H_2O$: TEM: (a-1) 0.01 mmol/L; (b-1) 0.02 mmol/L; (c-1) 0.03 mmol/L; (d-1) 0.04 mmol/L; SEM: (a-2) 0.01 mmol/L; (b-2) 0.02 mmol/L; (c-2) 0.03 mmol/L; (d-2) 0.04 mmol/L.

results. It can be seen that the uniform coating of Fe_3O_4 on the surface of attapulgite can be achieved when the concentration of Fe^{3+} does not exceed the critical concentration (< 0.04 mmol/L), and the thickness of Fe_3O_4 layer can be changed by changing amount of Fe_3O_4.

3.2.3 Effects of temperature

Figure 10 shows the TEM and SEM of attapulgite@Fe_3O_4 synthesized at different temperatures. a, b, c and d were 40°C, 60°C, 80°C and 100°C respectively. The figure shows that too high and too low temperature are not conducive to the uniform coating of Fe_3O_4 on the surface of attapulgite. This is because the supersaturation of the solution is too high at low temperature, which leads to the same homogeneous nucleation rate with heterogeneous nucleation rate of Fe_3O_4. It makes Fe_3O_4 aggregates instead of nucleating on the surface of attapulgite. Too high temperature will lead to too low relative supersaturation. Although it is conducive to heterogeneous nucleation, the nucleation rate of Fe_3O_4 is low. The high temperature will also make Fe_3O_4 particles move rapidly, forming some very thick Fe_3O_4 coating and some completely uncoated attapulgite, which is not a very good coating effect. Therefore, 60–80°C is the most favorable temperature for the formation of attapulgite@Fe_3O_4.

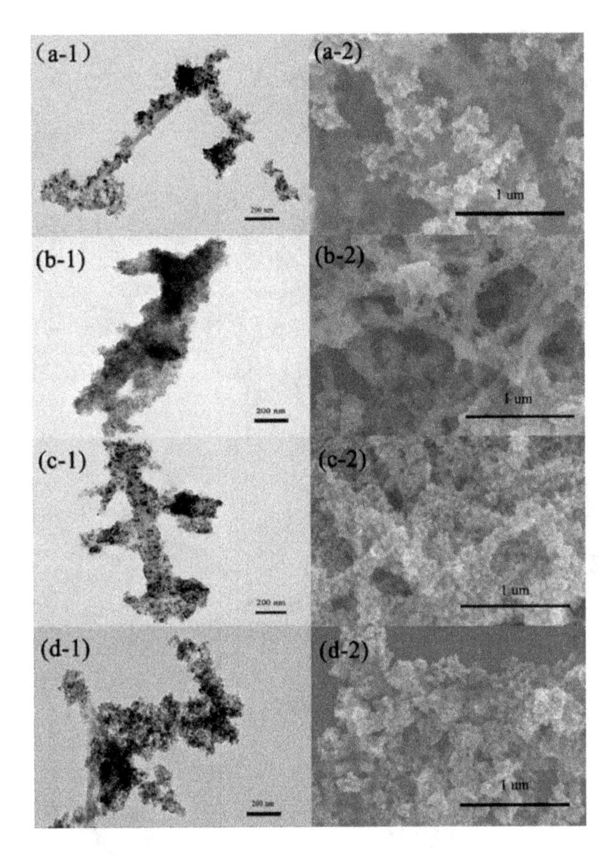

Figure 10.
Images of attapulgites-Fe_3O_4 one-dimensional nanocomposites synthesized in different temperature: TEM: (a-1) 40°C; (b-1) 60°C; (c-1) 80°C; (d-1) 100°C; SEM: (a-2) 40°C; (b-2) 60°C; (c-2) 80°C; (d-2) 100°C.

3.2.4 Effect of mixing method

In the process of synthesizing mineral-Fe_3O_4 one-dimensional nanocomposites, the stirring mode also has an effect on the uniform deposition of magnetic particles on the surface of one-dimensional nanominerals. **Figure 11** shows the effect of magnetic stirring and electric stirring on the uniform deposition of magnetic particles on the surface of mineral materials. From the TEM in **Figure 11**, it can be seen that a few Fe_3O_4 nanoparticles are coated on the surface of the sample prepared by magnetic stirring and most of the sepiolite frameworks are naked (**Figure 11C** and **D**). The Fe_3O_4 coated on the surface of sepiolite prepared by electric stirring are more uniform. This is due to the existence of magnetons in the magnetic stirring system, which leads to the aggregation of Fe_3O_4 particles on the surface of magnetons and inhibits the deposition of Fe_3O_4 particles on the surface of sepiolite nanorods. In addition, the force of magnetic stirring on the sample is relatively weak and the dispersion effect is poor, resulting in less Fe_3O_4 nanoparticles on the surface of sepiolite. In the electric stirring system of high stirring speed, the Fe_3O_4 particles are uniformly dispersed and the particle size is smaller.

3.2.5 Effect of dispersant

In the process of magnetic 1D nanominerals synthesis, there is a problem of agglomeration, so it is necessary to add dispersant. **Figure 12** shows the TEM images

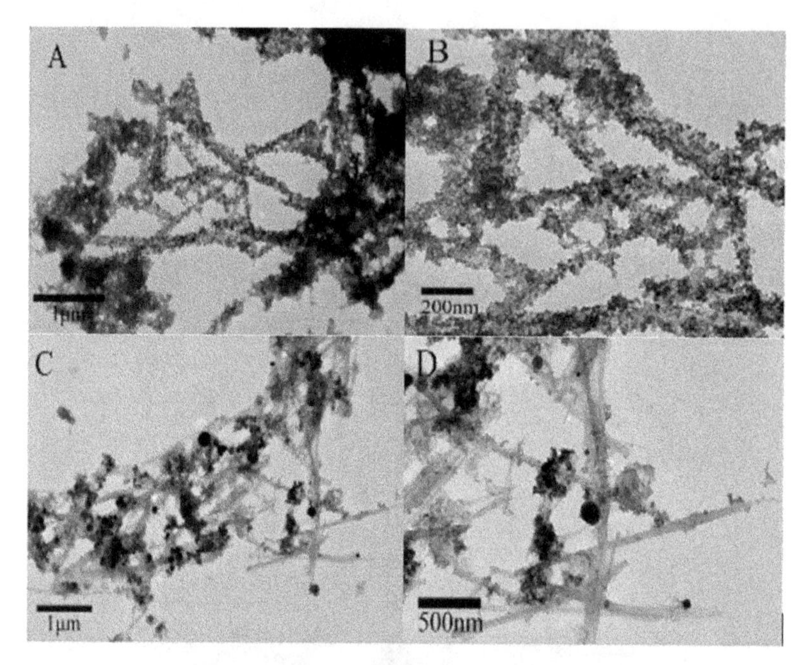

Figure 11.
Magnetic sepiolite rods prepared by electric stirring (A and B) and magnetic stirring (C and D).

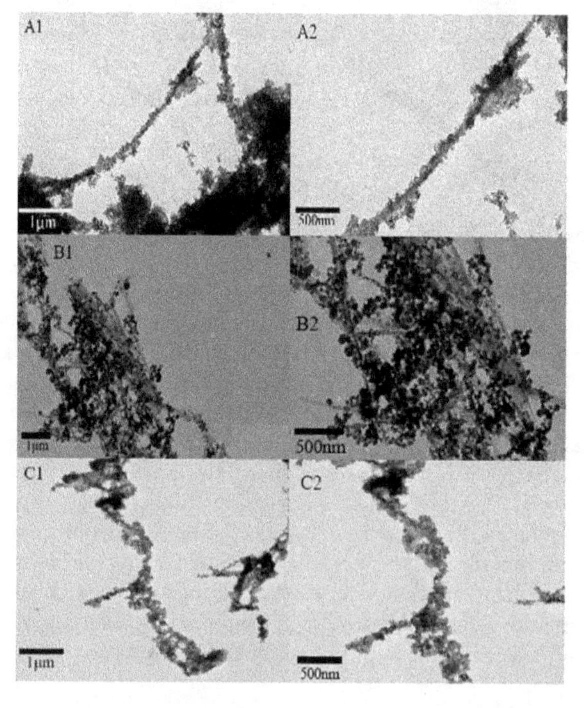

Figure 12.
TEM of magnetic 1D nanominerals prepared by adding dispersant. A1 and A2: Sepiolite@Fe_3O_4 without adding dispersant; B1 and B2: Sepiolite@Fe_3O_4 with organic dispersant; C1 and C2: Sepiolite@Fe_3O_4 with inorganic dispersant.

of magnetic 1D nanominerals prepared by adding inorganic/organic dispersant. The results show that the Fe_3O_4 nanoparticles decorated on the surface of the sample with ammonium cationic organic dispersant are less and non-uniform, the particle size of Fe_3O_4 is large and there is an aggregation between sepiolite nanorods (**Figure 12** A1 and A2). However, the Fe_3O_4 nanoparticles decorated on the surface of the sample with inorganic dispersant is more uniform, the size of Fe_3O_4 nanoparticles is smaller and the dispersion between nanorods is more uniform (**Figure 12** C1 and C2). The inorganic dispersant can be adsorbed on the surface of the 1D magnetic composite and make the composite negatively charged. Through electrostatic repulsion, Fe_3O_4 can be coated uniformly and agglomeration can be reduced at the same time. However, ammonium cationic organic dispersants have weak interaction with the composites, resulting in poor dispersion effect.

3.3 Preparation of one-dimensional clay mineral magnetic composites

Here, attapulgite and sepiolite are taken as examples to illustrate the method of synthesizing one dimensional clay mineral magnetic composites is feasible.

3.3.1 Preparation of attapulgite@Fe_3O_4 one dimensional magnetic composite

The attapulgites, Fe_3O_4 nanoparticles and prepared attapulgites@Fe_3O_4 one-dimensional nanocomposites were characterized by XRD, SEM, TEM and infrared spectroscopy to evaluate the morphology and structural characteristics [17]. The results are listed in **Figure 13. Figure 13(d)** shows the XRD patterns of pure Fe_3O_4 nanoparticles, attapulgite samples and attapulgite@Fe_3O_4 nanocomposites. Compared with the standard card of Fe_3O_4, the synthesized Fe_3O_4 nanoparticles are

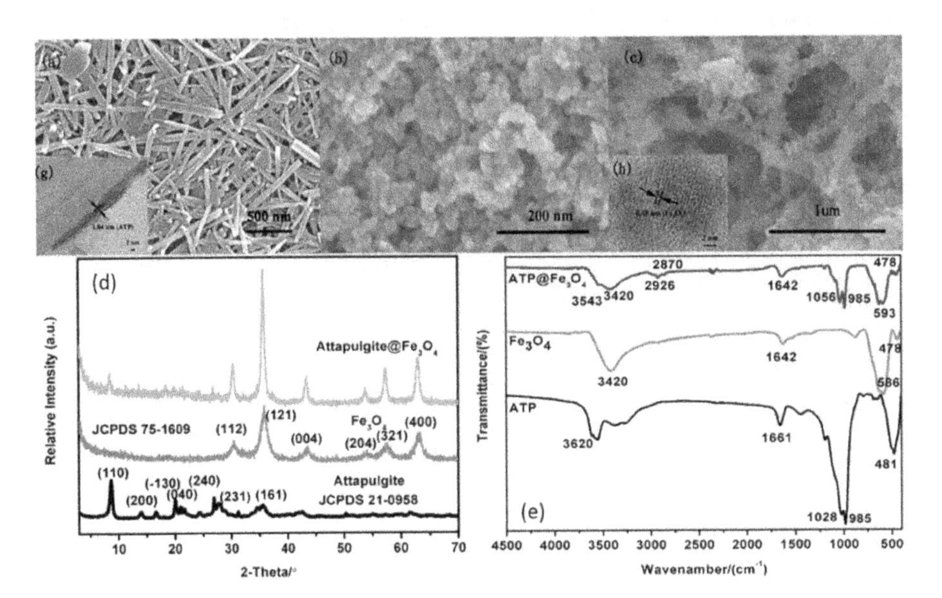

Figure 13.
Structural characterization of attapulgite, Fe_3O_4 and attapulgite@Fe_3O_4 nanorods: (a) SEM images of attapulgite; (b) SEM images of Fe_3O_4; (c) SEM images of attapulgite@Fe_3O_4; (d) XRD patterns of attapulgite, Fe_3O_4 and attapulgite@Fe_3O_4; (e) FTIR spectra of attapulgite, Fe_3O_4 and attapulgite@Fe_3O_4 (g) HRTEM image of attapulgite; (h) HRTEM image of attapulgite@Fe_3O_4.

relatively pure with almost no impurity peak. The XRD patterns of attapulgite-Fe_3O_4 composites correspond well with the standard cards of Fe_3O_4 and attapulgite, indicating that attapulgite-Fe_3O_4 composites can be synthesized by coprecipitation method. **Figure 13(a)–(c)** showed the typical scanning electron microscopy (SEM) images of the pristine attapulgites, Fe_3O_4 nanoparticles and attapulgites@Fe_3O_4 nanocomposites. **Figure 13(a)** show that the surface of attapulgite is smooth without special impurities. **Figure 13(b)** shows the synthesized pure Fe_3O_4 nanoparticles are spherical with a diameter of 10–30 nm. **Figure 13(c)** indicates that the surface of attapulgite is evenly coated with a layer of spherical particles. **Figure 13(g)** shows lattice image of attapulgite by high resolution transmission electron microscope, in which the (110) crystal plane of attapulgite can be found with a spacing of 1.04 nm. Because of the natural production of attapulgite, the crystallinity is low, and the surrounding of attapulgite is wrapped by spherical particles, it is difficult to find the crystal lattice of attapulgite in **Figure 13(h)**. However, there are a lot of new lattice fringes, which are 0.48 nm, and the lattice spacing just corresponds to the (111) plane of Fe_3O_4. The above electronic imaging characterization method show that the nanoparticles coated on the surface of attapulgite are Fe_3O_4. The infrared spectra of attapulgite, Fe_3O_4 and attapulgite-Fe_3O_4 composites are shown in **Figure 13(e)**. The 1028 cm^{-1} of attapulgite belongs to the stretching vibration of Si-O structure skeleton, and the 3620 cm^{-1} belongs to the stretching vibration of Al/Mg structure hydroxyl group; 586 cm^{-1} of Fe_3O_4 belongs to the stretching vibration of Fe-O. After the synthesis of attapulgite-Fe_3O_4 composite, it is found that the wave numbers of Si-O, Al/Mg hydroxyl and Fe-O shifted to 1056 cm^{-1}, 3543 cm^{-1} and 593 cm^{-1}, respectively, indicating the change of chemical environment of each group. This change directly proved that Fe_3O_4 coated on the surface of attapulgite. All results and phenomena above provided the useful information that the Fe_3O_4 are successfully bound to the attapulgite uniformly.

3.3.2 Preparation of sepiolite@Fe_3O_4 one dimensional magnetic composite

In accordance with the method of attapulgite@Fe_3O_4 one dimensional magnetic composite, we try to coat the surface of sepiolite with a layer of Fe_3O_4

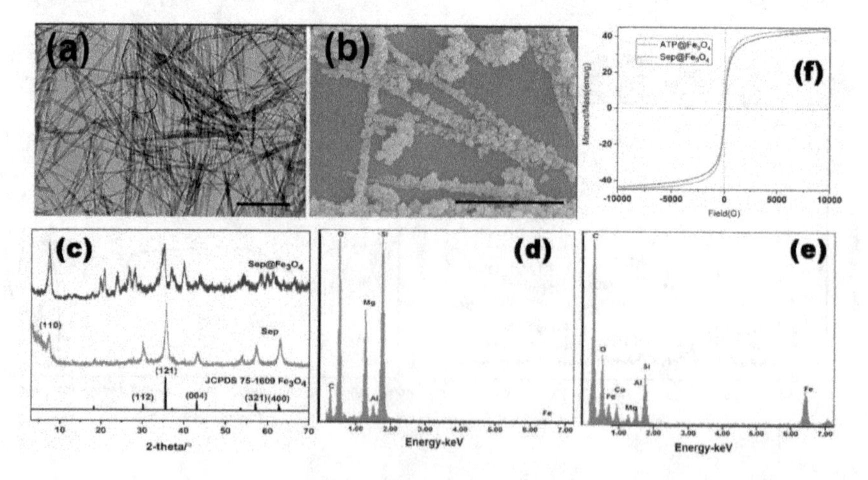

Figure 14.
Structural characterization of sepiolite, Fe_3O_4 and sepiolite@Fe_3O_4 nanorods: (a) SEM images of sepiolite; (b) SEM images of sepiolite@Fe_3O_4; (c) XRD patterns of sepiolite, Fe_3O_4 and sepiolite@Fe_3O_4; (d) EDS analysis of sepiolite; (e) EDS analysis of sepiolite@Fe_3O_4; (f) magnetization curves measured at 300 K of one dimensional clay minerals@Fe_3O_4: ATP: Attapulgite; Sep: Sepiolite.

nanoparticles. The XRD of sepiolite@Fe_3O_4 composites is shown in **Figure 14(c)**. It can be seen that sepiolite@Fe_3O_4 samples contain (110) crystal surface of sepiolite and (112), (121), (004), (321) and (400) of Fe_3O_4. Thus, sepiolite@Fe_3O_4 composite can be prepared by the same co-precipitation method with the SEM shown in **Figure 14(b)**. The fiber in **Figure 14(a)** and **(b)** are analyzed by energy spectrum. As shown in **Figure 14(d)**, sepiolite mainly contains Si, Mg and Al elements, and there are a few Fe elements due to the existence of isomorphism. By co-precipitation, spherical particles adhere uniformly and intensively to the surface of sepiolite (**Figure 14(b)**). The energy spectrum analysis of the composite (**Figure 14(e)**) shows that the content of Fe is greatly increased. According to the XRD, the Fe_3O_4 nanoparticles are wrapped on the outer surface of sepiolite. In conclusion, the co-precipitation method can also be used to uniformly cover the surface of fibrous sepiolite.

3.3.3 Magnetic properties of one-dimensional clay mineral magnetic composites

Figure 14(f) shows hysteresis loops of attapulgite@Fe_3O_4 and sepiolite@Fe_3O_4 at 300 K, respectively. Both of them are prepared under the same initial ferric salt concentration. Both saturation magnetizations of the obtained samples are about 40 emu/g [16], indicating the magnetic properties of the magnetic composites depend on the content of Fe_3O_4. They maintain good superparamagnetism and can timely response to the external magnetic field. It also proves that superparamagnetism can be given to non-magnetic 1D clay minerals by the combination of similar modification and co-precipitation method.

4. Construction of sol system with one dimensional magnetic mineral composite

Due to the large specific surface area and high surface energy, nano materials are easy to agglomerate, which affects the dispersion of nano particles in the substrate material, and further weakens the interaction between particles. Therefore, the dispersion of nanoparticles is the key problem to be solved in the preparation of nano functional materials with excellent performance. The dispersion method of nanoparticles has physical and chemical methods. Physical methods are mainly through mechanical stirring, high-energy acoustic dispersion, high-pressure homogenization and other physical dispersion methods. Chemical methods mainly achieve the stability of the whole dispersion system by adding dispersant, including electrostatic repulsion stabilization mechanism, steric hindrance stabilization mechanism, electrostatic hindrance stabilization mechanism, etc. The selection of solvent is also one of the important factors for the stable dispersion of nano materials. Chemical methods often need the assistance of physical methods to achieve the uniform dispersion of nano materials in the solution. Similarly, for inorganic liquid crystals, the formation of stable colloidal dispersion is the premise of the formation of inorganic liquid crystals.

In this part of the research work, chemical method was used by adding a certain concentration of hydrochloric acid to adjust the ionic strength of the 1D clay mineral@Fe_3O_4 system. A certain amount of surface charge on the surface of the 1D clay mineral@Fe_3O_4 form an electric double layer, and preventing the agglomeration of the 1D clay mineral@Fe_3O_4 nanoparticles through the repulsive force between the electric double layers. With the help of high intensity ultrasound, the whole system is stable.

4.1 Preparation of attapulgite@Fe_3O_4 colloidal dispersion

4.1.1 Effects of pH

The effect of pH on the dispersion of attapulgite@Fe_3O_4 in aqueous phase is shown in **Figure 15**. With the decrease of pH, the concentration of hydrochloric acid is increased from 0.0001 mol/L, 0.001 mol/L, 0.005 mol/L, 0.01 mol/L to 0.05 mol/L), the zeta potential of attapulgite@Fe_3O_4 first increases and then decreases. When the zeta potential of the solution is greater than +30 mV, the nanoparticles reach a stable state. The zeta potential of attapulgite@Fe_3O_4 is the highest at pH = 3 (+35 mV), which is enough to provide colloidal stability for particles. The zeta potential of attapulgite@Fe_3O_4 decreases from +35 mV to +27 mV when the pH of the solution decreases from 3 to 2. When the pH of the solution is greater than 3, the zeta potential also decreases sharply. It can be seen that when the pH of the solution is adjusted to 3, the surface charge of attapulgite@Fe_3O_4 nanoparticles is high enough to provide mutual repulsion force for particle stability, so that the whole system is uniformly dispersed and stable.

4.1.2 The dispersion of attapulgite@Fe_3O_4 in aqueous phase

Using the method in 4.1.1, the attapulgite@Fe_3O_4 was dispersed in dilute acid solution with pH = 3. After ultrasonic dispersion for 10 minutes, they could be stored for half a month without obvious sedimentation. Under the optical microscope, the sample is a non-transparent homogeneous liquid, and no particulate matter can be seen by naked eye as shown in **Figure 16(a)**. When attapulgite@Fe_3O_4 is directly dispersed in water, stable colloidal dispersion cannot be obtained even with long-term ultrasound. Under the optical microscope, a large number of agglomerated composite particles can be seen in the dispersion as shown in **Figure 16(b)**.

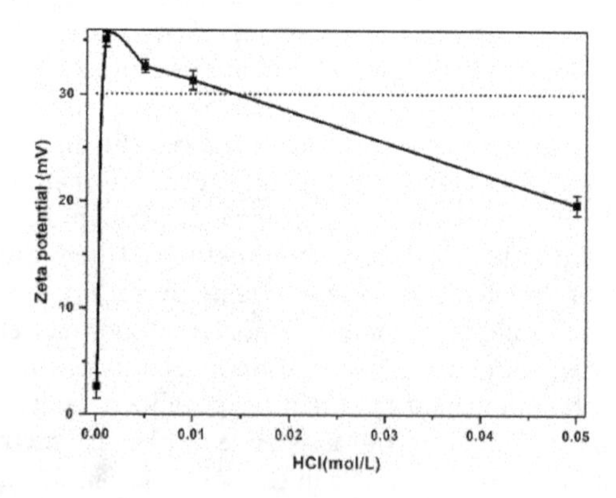

Figure 15.
The relationship between hydrochloric acid concentration and stability of attapulgite@Fe_3O_4 in water.

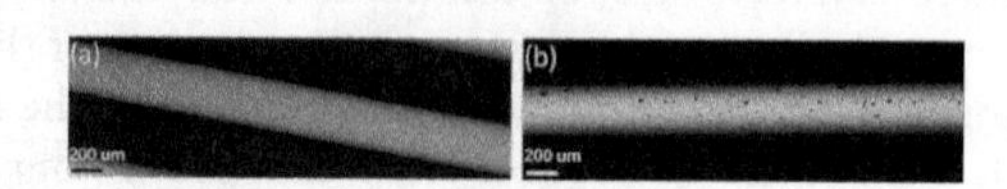

Figure 16.
Optical microscope of attapulgite@Fe_3O_4 dispersion: (a) the solvent was hydrochloric acid with pH = 3; (b) the solvent was water.

4.2 Preparation of sepiolite@Fe_3O_4 colloidal dispersion

Sepiolite@Fe_3O_4 was dispersed into dilute acid solution with pH = 3 by the same method as attapulgite@Fe_3O_4. The zeta potential of sepiolite@Fe_3O_4 dispersion was +32 mV. It can exist in the acid solution and form stable colloid.

5. Functional properties of one-dimensional magnetic clay mineral sol

5.1 Orientation structure comparison of one-dimensional clay mineral@Fe_3O_4 under magnetic field

When the colloids of one-dimensional clay mineral@Fe_3O_4 are dripped on the copper mesh and dried naturally under the condition of an external magnetic field, the structure oriented along the magnetic field can be obtained as shown in **Figure 17**. **Figure 17(a)** shows the TEM image of sepiolite@Fe_3O_4 orientation structure. Sepiolite fiber is a long fiber with an average diameter of 55 nm and an average length of 2.62 um (**Figure 6**). The diameter of Fe_3O_4 nanoparticles coated outside is about 20 nm (**Figure 13(b)**). The width of single rod magnetic composite material should be about 100 nm, but the orderly oriented fiber seen from **Figure 17(a)** is 200–600 nm, which indicates that sepiolite@Fe_3O_4 long fibers tend to aggregate into larger bundles first, and then end-to-end to form longer fiber chains under the magnetic field. The distance between the ordered structures is about 3–4 um. Attapulgite@Fe_3O_4 (**Figure 17(b)**) tends to connect single rod with each other. Along the magnetic field orientation, the distance between ordered rods is much closer than sepiolite@Fe_3O_4, most of which are below 500 nm. Although sepiolite@Fe_3O_4 and attapulgite@Fe_3O_4 have a large number of short-range disordered positions, they are all one-dimensional ordered in the long-range. The different orientation structures of the two 1D clay minerals@Fe_3O_4 based colloidal dispersions on the copper mesh fully explain the influence of the particle size and morphology of the structural elements on the ordered structure.

5.2 Liquid crystal properties of one dimensional magnetic functional mineral

Liquid crystal (LC) has attracted much attention due to its fluidity and birefringence. Its unique anisotropy makes it widely used in TV, notebook computer, mobile phone and other display technologies. Anisotropic nanostructures can be used as structural units to prepare inorganic liquid crystals. Magnetic induced assembly is an effective method to prepare ordered structures. In this part, we will use the magnetic field to induce the orientation of one-dimensional clay mineral@Fe_3O_4 composites in solution system to prepare ordered materials, and

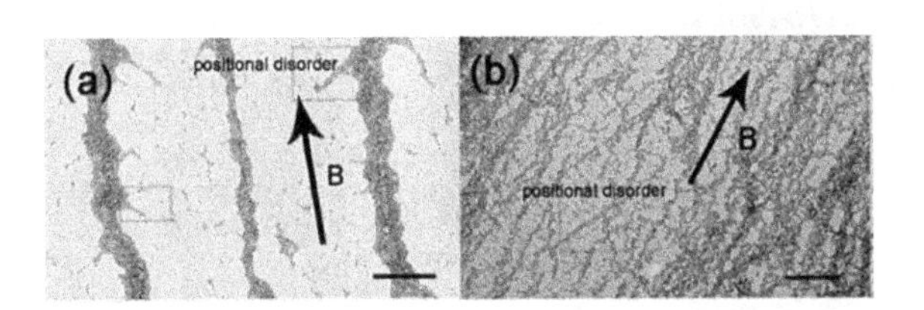

Figure 17.
TEM images of aligned (a) sepiolite@Fe_3O_4; (b) attapulgite@Fe_3O_4. Scare bars: 1 μm.

discuss the influence of solid content, magnetic field, magnetic field strength, and elemental geometry on their liquid crystal properties.

Attapulgite@Fe_3O_4 was dispersed in dilute acid solution with pH = 3. After ultrasonic dispersion for 10 minutes, attapulgite@Fe_3O_4 in dilute acid solution was observed under polarizing microscope. As shown in **Figure 18(a)**, the field of vision is completely dark. Attapulgite@Fe_3O_4 colloidal dispersion is in isotropic state. Three NdFeB magnets are placed 1 cm away from the sample, and a bright path can be seen in the field of vision (**Figure 18(b)**). When the external magnetic field is removed, the field of vision immediately becomes dark (**Figure 18(c)**). The reversible magnetic response shows that the liquid crystal with birefringent phase controlled by magnetic field can be obtained by coating attapulgite with magnetic particles. Meanwhile, the relaxation time of the liquid crystal is very short within 1 s.

When the particle solid content increased, the colloidal dispersion of attapulgite@Fe_3O_4 changed from isotropic phase to homogeneous birefringent phase (**Figure 18(d)**) [19]. The light intensity in the polarizing microscope increases gradually, which may be due to the increase of the ordered structure with the increase of the concentration. With the increase of solid content, the color of transmission light in polarizing microscope also changes, which is caused by the color of Fe_3O_4 nanoparticles.

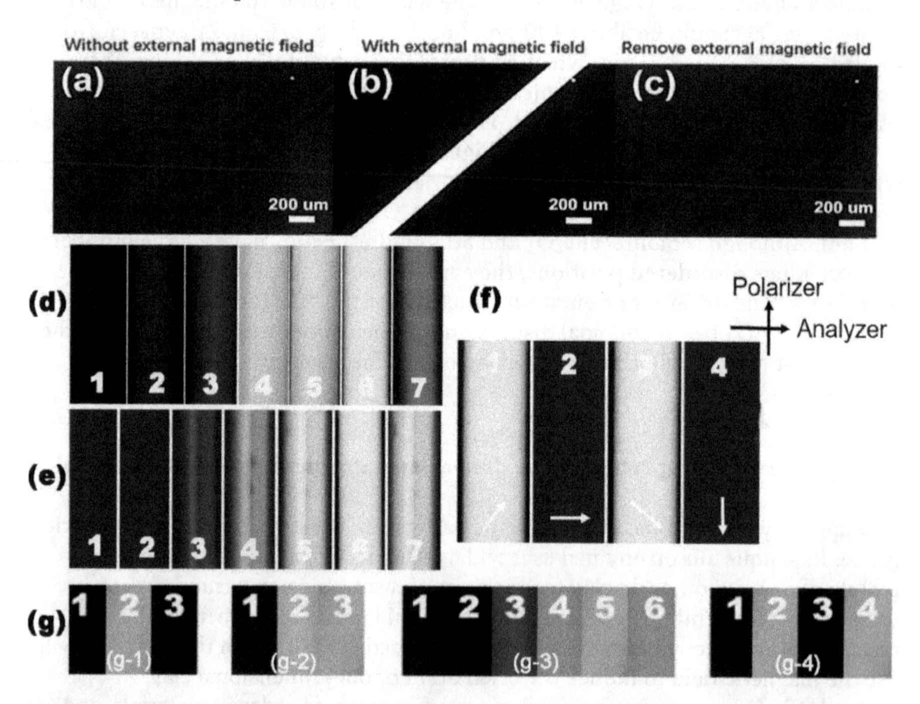

Figure 18.
Polarizing microscope of attapulgite@Fe_3O_4 colloidal dispersion: (a) without magnetic field; (b) adding magnetic field; (c) remove the external magnetic field; (d) different solid content of attapulgite@Fe_3O_4: (1) 0.0625 mg/mL; (2) 0.125 mg/mL; (3) 0.25 mg/mL; (4) 0.5 mg/mL; (5) 0.75 mg/mL; (6) 2 mg/mL; (7) 10 mg/mL; (e) polarizing microscope images of attapulgite@Fe_3O_4 dispersion (2 mg/mL) under different magnetic field intensities: Distance between magnet and sample from left to right: (1) 15 cm; (2) 11 cm; (3) 7 cm; (4) 5 cm; (5)3 cm; (6) 2 cm; (7) 1 cm; polarizing microscope of attapulgite@Fe_3O_4 dispersion in different magnetic field directions. The white arrow indicates that the angle between the magnetic field direction and the polarizer direction is: (1) 45°; (2) 90°; (3) 135°; (4) 180°; (g) polarizing microscope of sepiolite@Fe_3O_4 colloidal dispersion: (g-1): (1) No magnetic field; (2) the distance between the three magnets and the sample is 2 cm; (3) remove the magnetic field; (g-2) samples with different solid contents: (1) 0.0625 mg/mL; (2) 0.5 mg/mL; (3) 2.5 mg/mL (g-3) the distance between the magnet and the sample: (1) 15 cm; (2) 11 cm; (3) 5 cm; (4) 3 cm; (5) 2 cm; (6) 1 cm; (g-4) the angle between the magnetic field direction and polarizer is (1) 0°; (2) 45°; (3) 90°; (4) 135°.

By changing the distance between the NdFeB magnet and the sample, the magnetic field intensity changes, and the liquid crystal transmittance of attapulgite@Fe_3O_4 shows a high dependence on the magnetic field intensity (**Figure 18(e)**) [19]. With the increase of magnetic field intensity, the transmittance of liquid crystal first increases and then decreases. There is an optimal magnetic field intensity, which makes the order and stability of the whole system reach the best and the optical properties also reach the best.

Figure 18(f) shows the effect of the magnetic field direction on the optical properties of the liquid crystal phase [19]. The orientation of attapulgite@Fe_3O_4 is directly affected by the direction of magnetic field. When the magnetic field is perpendicular or parallel to the polarizer, the whole field of vision is dark. When the angle between the magnetic field and the polarizer is 45°, we can see the strongest transmission light. Changing the direction of magnetic field is equivalent to changing the direction of light. It can be seen that we can control the transmittance of the magnetic controlled liquid crystal by adjusting the direction of the magnetic field.

Using the same method, sepiolite@Fe_3O_4 was dispersed in dilute acid solution with pH = 3, and the liquid crystal controlled by magnetic field was obtained by ultrasonic dispersion for 10 minutes [16]. As shown in **Figure 18** (g-1), it can change from isotropic phase to homogeneous birefringent phase under the magnetic field, and return to isotropic phase after removing the magnetic field. Sepiolite@Fe_3O_4 based liquid crystal with long fiber structure is similar to attapulgite@Fe_3O_4 based liquid crystal with short rod structure, and is affected by solid content (**Figure 18** (g-2)), magnetic field intensity (**Figure 18** (g-3)) and magnetic field direction (**Figure 18** (g-4)).

The varied light transmittance of one-dimensional clay minerals@Fe_3O_4 suspensions are explored between a pair of orthogonal polarizers under external magnetic field. Since the color of the Fe_3O_4 is reddish brown, the colloidal dispersions absorb the natural white light to a certain extent. It can be seen from **Figure 19** that the colloidal dispersions mainly transmit the visible light with wavelength from 550 to 750 nm [16]. **Figure 19(a)** shows the effect of magnetic field intensity on the transmittance. It can be seen from the figure that at the same concentration, the transmittance of attapulgite@Fe_3O_4 colloid first increases and then decreases with the increase of magnetic field intensity; The transmittance of sepiolite@Fe_3O_4 decreases with the increase of magnetic field intensity. The transmittance of attapulgite@Fe_3O_4 is better than that of sepiolite@Fe_3O_4. In order to get the highest transmittance, it is necessary to form a stable ordered structure, and the magnetic

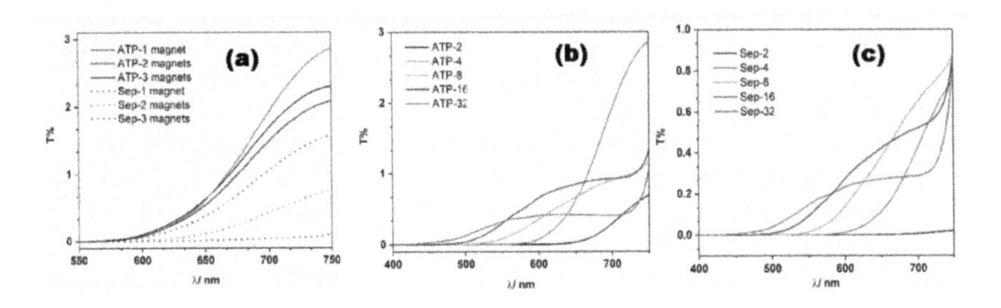

Figure 19.
The transmittance of one dimensional clay minerals@Fe_3O_4 suspension through two crossed polarizers: (a) at 1.0 mg/mL under different magnetic field strength. "Clay-n magnets": n magnets are placed 1 cm away from the sample. (b) by different attapulgite@Fe_3O_4 solid content with 2 magnets placed 1 cm away from the sample. ATP-2: 2.0 mg/mL; ATP-4: 1.0 mg/mL; ATP-8: 0.5 mg/mL; ATP-16: 0.25 mg/mL; ATP-32: 0.125 mg/mL; (c) with different sepiolite@Fe_3O_4 solid content by 2 magnets placed 1 cm away from the sample; Sep—Sepiolite. Sep-2: 2.0 mg/mL; Sep-4: 1.0 mg/mL; Sep-8: 0.5 mg/mL; Sep-16: 0.25 mg/mL; Sep-32: 0.125 mg/mL. ATP—Attapulgite; Sep—Sepiolite.

attraction and intermolecular repulsion must reach a balance. There must be a fixed magnetic field for them to get the best optical properties of liquid crystal. **Figure 19(b)** and **(c)** show the liquid crystal transmittance of attapulgite@Fe_3O_4 and sepiolite@Fe_3O_4 under constant magnetic field, respectively. With the increase of concentration, the transmittance first increases and then decreases. The larger the concentration is, the smaller the distance between particles is, and the greater the repulsion is; On the contrary, the smaller the repulsion is. Thus, it will show the law of changing with the concentration in a fixed magnetic field. In the previous discussion, the field of vision is dark under the polarized light microscope when the concentration of one-dimensional clay mineral@Fe_3O_4 composite is low enough. That is to say, there is no liquid crystal phase even in the presence of magnetic field. It can be inferred that the magnetic controlled liquid crystal prepared by 1D clay minerals is lyotropic liquid crystal, and the liquid crystal phase can be formed only when the concentration requirement is met. The difference of light transmittance between attapulgite@Fe_3O_4 and sepiolite@Fe_3O_4 at the same concentration may be caused by the different concentration requirement for the formation of lyotropic liquid crystal, and the result may be related to the structure or properties of the 1D clay mineral itself. In addition, the shorter structure may be easier controlled by magnetic field, forming a more regular ordered structure, showing differences in optical properties. It may be the reason why the transmittance of attapulgite@Fe_3O_4 based magnetically controlled liquid crystal is slightly better than that of sepiolite@Fe_3O_4 based magnetically controlled liquid crystal. The influence of Fe_3O_4 on the transmittance of the system is significant. When the solid content of the system increases, the amount of Fe_3O_4 particles increases, the absorption of the colloidal system to the light in the low wavelength range increases, resulting in the low transmittance in the low wavelength range; When the solid content decreases, Fe_3O_4 particles decrease. Although the light transmittance in the high wavelength range decreases, the light transmittance in the low wavelength range increases.

5.3 Photonic crystal properties of one dimensional magnetic functional mineral

Colloidal periodic structure formed by self-assembly of monodisperse colloidal structural units is a kind of photonic band gap materials. A new type of photonic band gap material——colloidal magnetic photonic crystal can be formed by adding magnetic components into colloidal structural units. This kind of colloidal magnetic photonic crystal can produce instantaneous response to the magnetic field. Under the magnetic field, the light with a certain frequency in the visible light region can be reflected by the photonic crystal, which makes the photonic crystal show color. This kind of light effect is called Bragg diffraction. By controlling the intensity of external magnetic field, the optical properties of photonic crystal can be easily controlled. In this part, after giving a strong light to the prepared one dimensional magnetic functional minerals colloidal dispersion, the obvious Bragg diffraction can be seen under the external magnetic field, and the influence of magnetic field direction, magnetic field intensity and solid content on the Bragg diffraction effect is discussed.

Attapulgite@Fe_3O_4 colloidal dispersion is irradiated by a strong light (**Figure 20(a)**). A magnet is used to apply a magnetic field to the colloidal dispersion. As shown in **Figure 20(b)**, bright strong light is reflected by the colloidal dispersion. According to the ordered orientation of the magnetic particles in the magnetic field, it can be inferred that the spacing between the ordered structural units is just comparable to the wavelength of the visible light, so the light in a certain wavelength range is diffracted, and a strong yellow Bragg diffraction light is obtained [19].

The Bragg diffraction light effect of attapulgite@Fe_3O_4 colloidal dispersion is affected by the magnetic field intensity. As shown in **Figure 21(a)**, with the increase

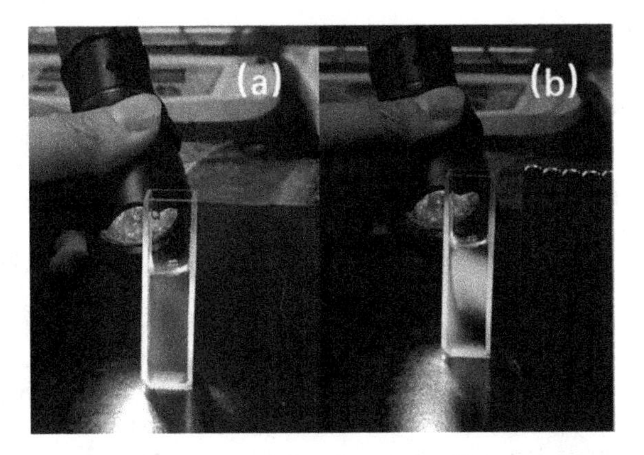

Figure 20.
The optical effects of attapulgite@Fe_3O_4 colloidal dispersion under strong light: (a) no external magnetic field (b) there is an external magnetic field.

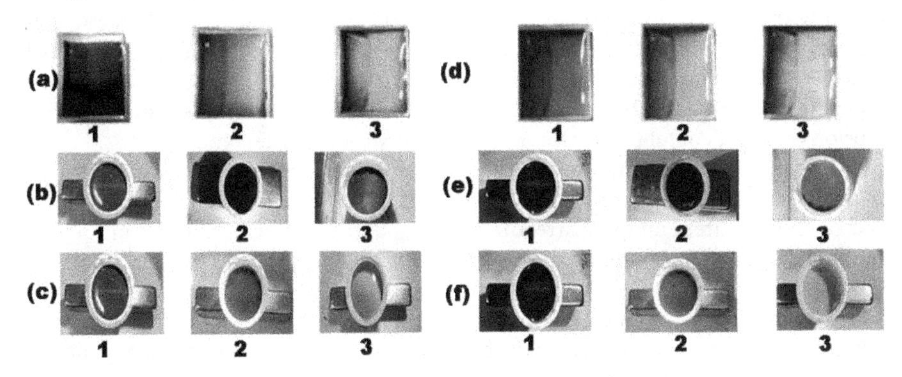

Figure 21.
The light effect of attapulgite@Fe_3O_4 colloidal dispersion under strong light (a) with the increase of magnetic field intensity: (1) no magnetic field; (2) the distance between the three magnets and the sample is 1 cm; (3) the distance between the three magnets and the sample is 0.2 cm; (b) different directions of magnetic field; (c) different solid contents: (1) 2 mg/mL; (2) 0.5 mg/mL; (3) 0.0625 mg/mL; the optical effects of sepiolite@Fe_3O_4 colloidal dispersion under strong light (d) with the increase of magnetic field intensity: (1) no magnetic field; (2) the distance between the magnets and sample is 1 cm; (3) the distance between the magnets and sample is 0.2 cm; (e) by the direction of magnetic field; (f) different solid contents: (a) 2 mg/mL; (b) 0.5 mg/mL; (c) 0.0625 mg/mL.

of magnetic field intensity, the intensity of diffraction light gradually increases from (a) to (c). This is related to the regularity of the ordered structure. In a certain range of magnetic field, the larger the magnetic field intensity is, the more regular the ordered structure is formed, and the stronger the Bragg diffraction intensity is.

The optical effect of attapulgite@Fe_3O_4 colloidal dispersion is affected by the direction of magnetic field under strong light. We adjust the magnetic field direction of the sample by changing the position between the rectangular magnets and the sample as shown in **Figure 21(b)** [16]. When the largest surface of the magnet is perpendicular to the sample (**Figure 21** (b-1)), only a bright yellow line appears in the middle of the whole circular sample surface. When the largest surface of the magnet is parallel to the sample (**Figure 21** (b-2)), there is no Bragg diffraction in the whole sample. When the magnet is placed parallel to the sample, a bright yellow band appears in the middle of the sample(**Figure 21** (b-3)). It can be seen that the orientation of the one dimensional nano magnetic functional minerals is determined by the direction of the magnetic field, which determines if the Bragg diffraction can be formed.

The light effect of attapulgite@Fe_3O_4 colloidal dispersion under strong light is affected by solid content. As shown in **Figure 21(c)** [16], with the decrease of solid content, the bright Bragg diffraction line in the middle becomes shallower and shallower until it is invisible. Different solid content determines the intermolecular force. Under the same magnetic field, the magnetic field counteracts the intermolecular force, forming different ordered structure spacing, which leads to different Bragg diffraction effect.

The light effect of sepiolite@Fe_3O_4 colloidal dispersion controlled by magnetic field and solid content under strong light is similar to that of attapulgite@Fe_3O_4 colloidal dispersion as shown in **Figure 21(d)–(f)** [16].

We drop attapulgite@Fe_3O_4 colloids and sepiolite@Fe_3O_4 colloids with different concentrations from 0.00625 mg/mL to 2.0 mg/mL onto the solid substrate, orienting them under the magnetic field, drying them naturally, and observing them under the optical microscope (reflection state) (**Figure 22**). It is found that when the concentration of attapulgite@Fe_3O_4 is 0.0125 mg/mL, a brilliant rainbow film can be formed on a solid substrate (**Figure 22(a)**). In a certain region, uniform yellow/purple/blue light can be seen and the boundaries of various colors are consistent with the direction of the magnetic field, which proves that the diffraction of the visible light is caused by the ordered structure caused by the magnetic field. However, this phenomenon does not appear in sepiolite@Fe_3O_4 system at the same concentration (**Figure 22(b)**). It indicated that Bragg diffraction is not only dependent on the solid content, but also on the size of structural elements.

In the previous content, we discussed in detail the microstructures of various magnetic substrates (**Figure 17**). Combined with **Figure 22**, it can be concluded that the solid content and size affect the spacing of ordered structures by influencing the intermolecular force, and then affect the Bragg diffraction of visible light. Although the orientation effect of various 1D clay mineral based magnetic structural elements on the solid base is not equal to the orientation characteristics in the colloidal state, the decisive influence of structure on optical properties is explained from the side. The similar optical effects of attapulgite@Fe_3O_4 and sepiolite@Fe_3O_4 indicate the universality of Bragg diffraction effect in 1D clay mineral@Fe_3O_4 based colloidal dispersion. In the colloidal dispersion system, although the structures of the two 1D clay mineral systems are different, the Bragg diffraction of the two mineral systems are yellow light, and they are also similar under the influence of magnetic field intensity, magnetic field direction and solid content: in a certain range of magnetic field, the greater the magnetic field intensity is, the stronger the Bragg diffraction light is; Different Bragg diffraction regions are obtained in different magnetic field directions; In a certain range of solid content, the Bragg diffraction effect decreases with the decrease of solid content. In the colloidal system, the magnetic field strength and direction determine the magnetic force, while the solid content determines the intermolecular force. The interaction of the two forces

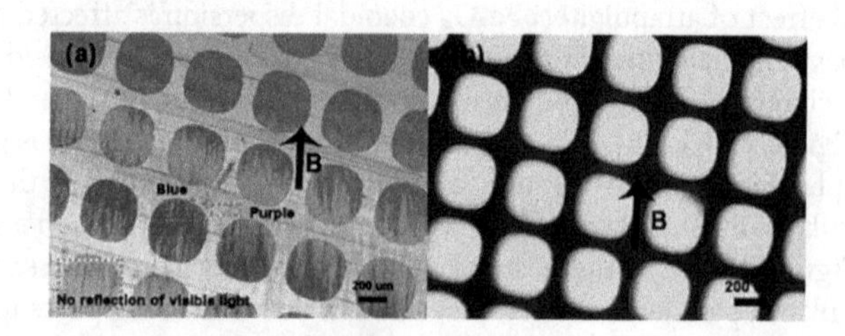

Figure 22.
Optical microscope images on the substrate (in reflected light): (a) aligned attapulgite@Fe_3O_4; (b) aligned sepiolite@Fe_3O_4.

DOI: http://dx.doi.org/10.5772/intechopen.98908

determines the orientation structure spacing, and then affects the diffraction effect of the structure on visible light.

6. Application prospect of one-dimensional nano magnetic functional minerals

The similar optical effects of attapulgite@Fe_3O_4 and sepiolite@Fe_3O_4 colloidal dispersions under magnetic field indicates that the universality of instant controllable liquid crystal phase and photonic crystal prepared by magnetization of one dimensional clay mineral dispersed in dilute acid solution. Magnetic one

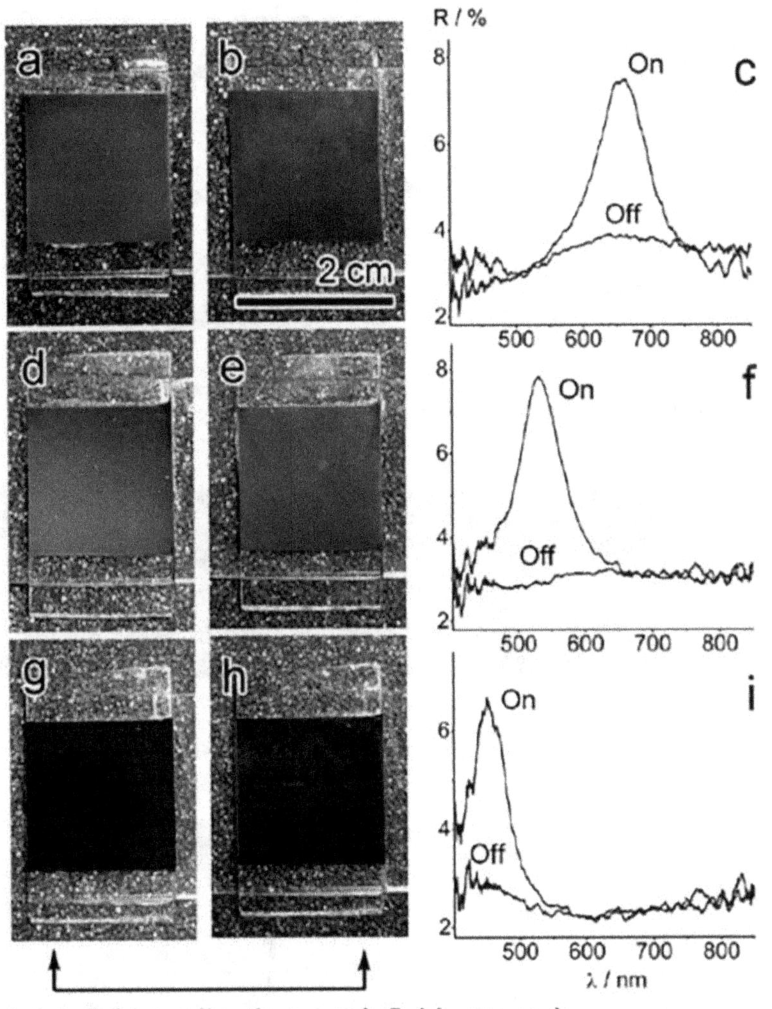

Figure 23.
Digital photos and reflection spectra of three types of Fe_3O_4@SiO_2/PEGDA microspheres loaded in $1.8 \times 1.8 \times 0.1$ cm^3 glass cells filled with PEG (M_w) = 1500). The diffraction is switched on (a, d, g) or off (b, e, h) by melting the PEG matrix, rotating the microspheres with a magnetic field, and finally cooling down the PEG matrix to lock the sphere orientation. Bistable states can therefore be maintained in the absence of magnetic fields. The corresponding reflection spectra (c, f, i) display diffraction peaks at the "on" stage and none at the "off" stage.

dimensional clay mineral is a material with great potential. Like other common magnetically controlled liquid crystals and photonic crystals, it can be applied in magnetically tunable nanostructures for security and sensing devices, high resolution patterning of multiple structural colors, display device and so on.

Jianping Ge [20] demonstrated a simple switchable color display system in which the color information can be rewritten multiple times by means of a magnetic field using superparamagnetic $Fe_3O_4@SiO_2$ core/shell particles as shown in **Figure 23**. The matrix material melts when heated, allowing the colors display by

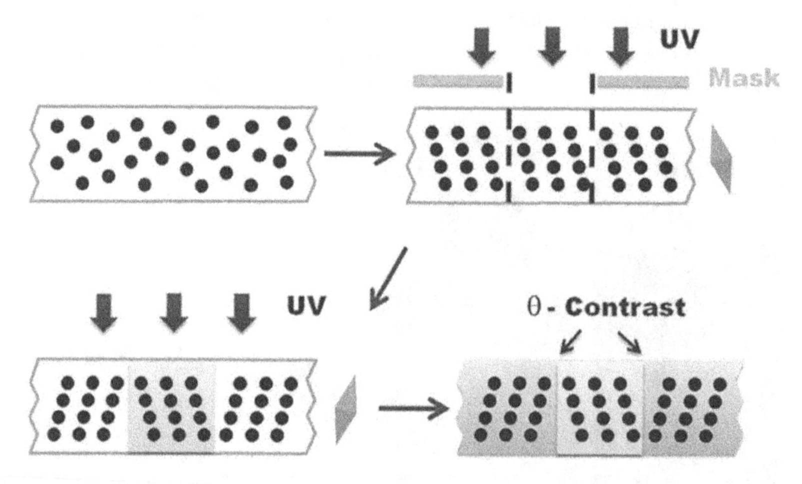

Figure 24.
Printing process based on the orientational tuning of photonic structures.

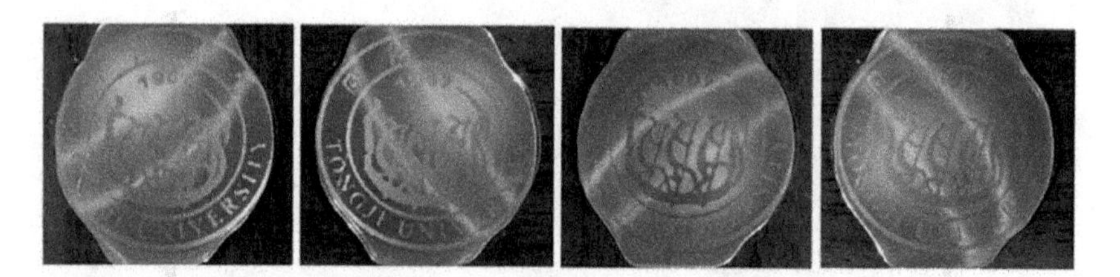

Figure 25.
Digital photographs of the logo as the incident light is projected from different angles.

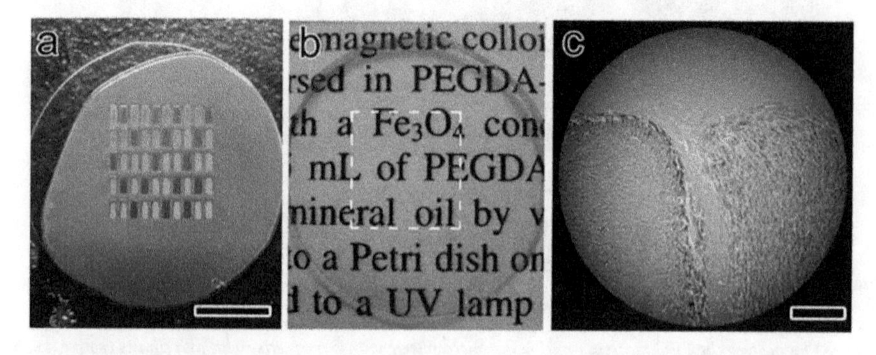

Figure 26.
(a) Colorimetric binary codes array and (b) an invisible replica printed with an orientational printing process. (c) Optical microscope image of two neighboring code chips in part b. scare bars: (a, b) 5 mm and (c) 200 μm.

aligning the microspheres under magnetic fields. When the system is cooled to room temperature, the matrix solidifies and the orientation of microspheres is frozen so that the color information remains for a long time without the need of additional energy.

Ruyang Xuan [21] developed a novel photonic printing technique using orientational tuning of photonic structures. In the printing process, the θ-contrast pattern is produced by magnetic alignment, orientational tuning, and lithographical photopolymerization (**Figure 24**). When the angle of incident light is changed or samples are tilted, labels printed with two mirror-symmetric or multiple axially symmetric photonic orientations show a switchable color distribution or dynamic color halo (**Figure 25**). This printing method can fabricate colorimetric or invisible codes, which can be decoded by visual observation or a spectrometer (**Figure 26**).

Mingsheng Wang [22] used ferrimagnetic inorganic nanorods as building blocks to prepare liquid crystals (**Figure 27**). The optical properties of the liquid crystals can be instantly and reversibly controlled by manipulating the orientation of the nanorods using considerably weak external magnetic fields (1 mT). They exhibit an

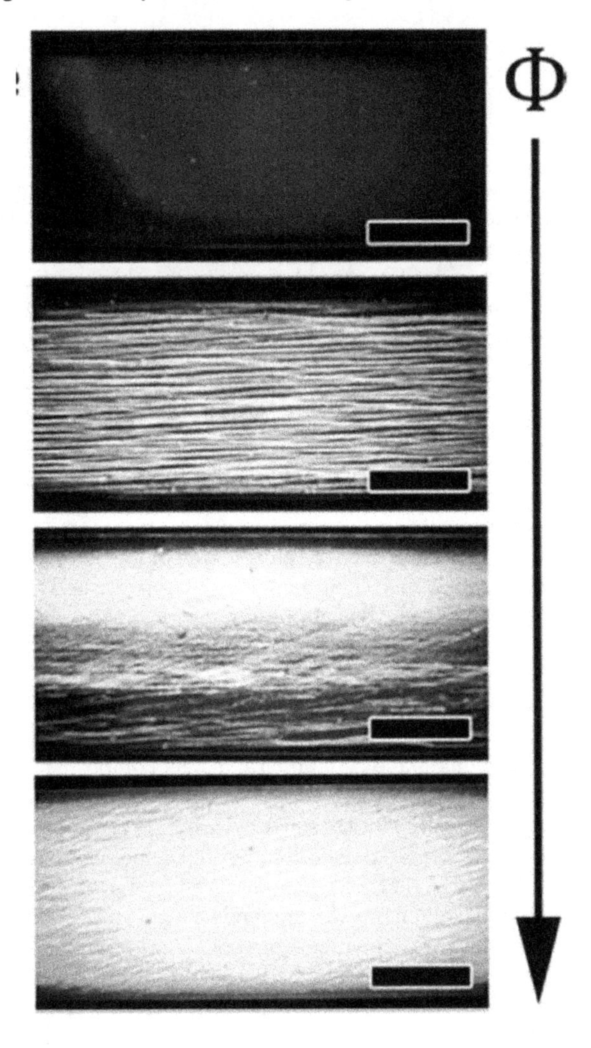

Figure 27.
POM images of aqueous dispersions of $Fe_3O_4@SiO_2$ nanorods in a capillary tube at different volume fractions (Φ) of 1%, 3%, 5%, and 10% (from top to bottom). Scale bars: 500 μm.

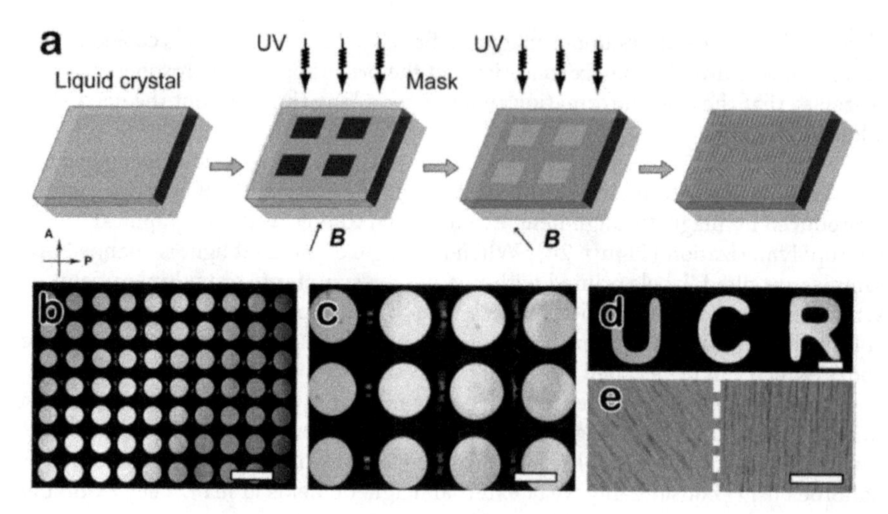

Figure 28.
(a) Scheme showing the lithography process for the fabrication of thin films with patterns of different polarizations; (b-d) POM images of various polarization-modulated patterns; (e) enlarged OM image shows the arrangement of nanorods in the pattern (left) and surrounding area (right). Scale bars: (b – d) 500 μm; (e) 10 μm.

optical switching frequency above 100 Hz under an alternating magnetic field. It is comparable to the performance of commercial liquid crystals using electrical switching. By combining magnetic alignment and lithography processes, it is also possible to create patterns of different polarizations in a thin composite film and control over the transmittance of light in particular areas (**Figure 28**). Developing such magnetically responsive liquid crystals opens the door toward various applications, which may benefit from the instantaneous and contactless nature of magnetic manipulation.

7. Conclusion and outlook

This chapter mainly describes the related research of one-dimensional nano clay minerals in the field of optics, including the following four parts: The first part is the composition, structure and properties of one-dimensional nano clay minerals; The second part is the magnetic assembly of one-dimensional nano clay minerals represented by halloysite and sepiolite; The third part is how to prepare colloidal dispersion based on one-dimensional magnetically assembled nano clay minerals; The fourth part is about the liquid crystal properties and photonic crystal properties of magnetic one-dimensional nano clay mineral matrix composites and their application prospects. One dimensional nano clay minerals show great development potential in the field of security and sensing devices, high resolution patterning of multiple structural colors, display device etc., but in the process of research, there are mainly five problems: (1) A broader system stability should be established so that magnetic one dimensional nano clay minerals have a strong stability in a wider pH range, which is conducive to the practical application of materials; (2) Better optical properties need to be obtained by better coating form and more regular coating; (3) It is possible to obtain better Bragg diffraction effect and realize the full range control of the visible region by synthesizing the structural elements with uniform particle size; (4) The magnetic particles coated on the surface of one-dimensional nano clay minerals are easy to fall off; (5) The color of liquid crystal formed by one-dimensional magnetic nano clay mineral colloid is limited by the color of Fe_3O_4. In the future, researchers can try to synthesize one-dimensional nano clay minerals with more uniform size instead of natural production, so that the magnetic colloidal system could have more regular building blocks. Try other electrolytes or solvents to get more stability of colloidal system. Therefore, there is still a long way to go for one-dimensional nano clay minerals to realize industrial application in optical field.

Acknowledgements

This work was supported by the Maoming Science and Technology Plan Project (2020580) and the Project of Talents Recruitment of Guangdong University of Petrochemical Technology.

Conflict of interest

The authors declare no conflict of interest.

Author details

Meng Fu[1*], Zepeng Zhang[2], Rui Jiang[2] and Hongbao Liu[2]

1 School of Materials Sciences and Technology, Guangdong University of Petrochemical Technology, Maoming, China

2 Beijing Key Laboratory of Materials Utilization of Nonmetallic Minerals and Solid Wastes, National Laboratory of Mineral Materials, School of Materials Science and Technology, China University of Geosciences, Beijing, China

*Address all correspondence to: fumeng19930731@163.com

References

[1] Li XZ, Shi HY, Zuo SX, et al. Lattice reconstruction of one-dimensional mineral to achieve dendritic heterojunction for cost-effective nitrogen photofixation. Chemical Engineering Journal. 2021. DOI: 10.1016/j.cej.2021.128797.

[2] Pei ML, Pan CG, Wu Dan, et al. Surface hydrophilic-hydrophobic reversal coatings of polydimethylsiloxane-palygorskite nanosponges. Applied Clay Science. 2020. DOI: 10.1016/j.clay.2020.105546.

[3] Papoulis D, Somalakidi K, Todorova N, et al. Sepiolite/TiO_2 and metal ion modified sepiolite/TiO_2 nanocomposites: synthesis, characterization and photocatalytic activity in abatement of NO_x gases. Applied clay science. 2019. DOI: 10.1016/j.clay.2019.105156.

[4] Tang J, Mu B, Zong L, et al. Facile and green fabrication of magnetically recyclable carboxyl-functionalized attapulgite/carbon nanocomposites derived from spent bleaching earth for wastewater treatment. Chemical Engineering Journal. 2017; 322: 102-114. DOI: 10.1016/j.cej.2017.03.116.

[5] Li LX, Li BC, Fan L, et al. Palygorskite@Fe_3O_4@polyperfluoroalkylsilane Nanocomposites for Superoleophobic Coatings and Magnetic Liquid Marbles. Journal of Materials Chemistry A. 2016; 16: 5859-5868. DOI: 10.1039/C6TA00758A.

[6] Ren HD, Wang S, Lian W, et al. Preparation of Coral-like Palygorskite-dispersed Fe_3O_4/polyaniline with Improved Electromagnetic Absorption Performance. Applied Clay Science. 2021. DOI: 10.1016/j.clay.2021.106009.

[7] Zhu J, Zhou S, Li M, et al. PVDF mixed matrix ultrafiltration membrane incorporated with deformed rebar-like Fe_3O_4-palygorskite nanocomposites to enhance strength and antifouling properties. Journal of Membrane Science. 2020. DOI: 10.1016/j.memsci.2020.118467.

[8] Ruiz-Hitzky E, Darder M, Alcântara ACS, et al. Recent Advances on Fibrous Clay-Based Nanocomposites. In: Kalia S, Haldorai Y, editors. Organic-Inorganic Hybrid Nanomaterials. Advances in Polymer Science. Springer; 2014. p. 39-86. DOI: 10.1007/12_2014_283.

[9] Chen LF, Liang HW, Lu Y, et al. Synthesis of an attapulgite clay@carbon nanocomposite adsorbent by a hydrothermal carbonization process and their application in the removal of toxic metal ions from water. Langmuir the Acs Journal of Surfaces & Colloids. 2011; 27: 8998-9004. DOI: 10.1021/la2017165.

[10] Yuan M, Gao G, Hu X, et al. Premodified Sepiolite Functionalized with Triethylenetetramine as an Effective and Inexpensive Adsorbent for CO_2 Capture, Industrial & Engineering Chemistry Research. 2018; 57: 6189-6200. DOI: 10.1021/acs.iecr.8b00348.

[11] Yuan B, Yin XQ, Liu XQ, et al. Enhanced Hydrothermal Stability and Catalytic Performance of HKUST-1 by Incorporating Carboxyl-Functionalized Attapulgite. Acs Applied Materials & Interfaces. 2016; 8: 16457-16464. DOI: 10.1021/acsami.6b04127.

[12] Corma A, Fornés V, Mifsud A, et al. Aluminum-Exchanged Sepiolite as a Component of Fluid Cracking Catalysts. Acs Symposium Series. 1991; 293-307. DOI: 10.1021/bk-1991-0452.ch018.

[13] Zhuang G, Zhang Z, Jaber M, et al. Comparative study on the structures

and properties of organo-montmorillonite and organo-palygorskite in oil-based drilling fluids. Journal of Industrial & Engineering Chemistry. 2017; 56: 248-257. DOI: 10.1016/j.jiec.2017.07.017.

[14] Wang AQ, Wang WB, Zheng YA, et al. Attapulgite Rod Bundle Dissociation and its Nano Functional Composites. Beijing, 2014. ISBN: 978-7-03-041706-0.

[15] Shan Q. Structure Mineralogy. Beijing, 2011. ISBN: 978-7-301-16157-9/P·0073.

[16] Fu M, Li XM, Zhang ZP. Comparative study of optical properties by clay minerals with magnetic coating in colloidal dispersion under an external magnetic field. Applied Clay Science. 2019; 181. DOI: 10.1016/j.clay.2019.105224.

[17] Fu M, Li XM, Jiang R, et al. One-dimensional Magnetic Nanocomposites with Attapulgites as Templates: Growth, Formation Mechanism and Magnetic Alignment, Applied Surface Science. 2018; 441: 239-250. DOI: 10.1016/j.apsusc.2018.02.028.

[18] Jiang R, Zhang ZP, Chen HW, et al. Preparation of one-dimensional magnetic nanocomposites with palygorskites as temples after inorganic modification, Colloids and Surfaces A: Physicochemical and Engineering Aspects. 2021. DOI: 10.1016/j.colsurfa.2021.126520.

[19] Fu M, Zhang ZP. Highly Tunable Liquid Crystalline Assemblies of Superparamagnetic rod-like Attapulgite@Fe_3O_4 nanocomposite. Materials Letters. 2018; 226: 43-46. DOI: 10.1016/j.matlet.2018.04.128.

[20] Ge JP, Lee H, He L, et al. Magnetochromatic Microspheres: Rotating Photonic Crystals. Journal of the American Chemical Society. 2009; 131:15687-15694. DOI: 10.1021/ja903626h.

[21] Xuan RY, Ge JP. Photonic printing through the orientational tuning of photonic structures and its application to anticounterfeiting labels. Langmuir the Acs Journal of Surfaces & Colloids. 2011; 27: 5694-5699. DOI: 10.1021/la200571y.

[22] Wang MS, He L, Zorba S, et al. Magnetically actuated liquid crystals. Nano Letters. 2014; 14: 3966-3971. DOI: 10.1021/nl501302s.

Section 2

Clay Properties and Applications

Chapter 6

Clay Minerals Effects for Metal Reclamation from Leached Solution

Murugesan Manikkampatti Palanisamy, Akilamudhan Palaniappan, Venkata Ratnam Myneni, Kannan Kandasamy, Minar Mohamed Lebbai and Padmapriya Veerappan

Abstract

The recent advancements in technology play a pivotal role in mankind's life and have a significant stint in the generation of E-waste. The present investigation focuses on the recovery of heavy metals from Printed Circuit boards (PCBs) by applying two efficient techniques viz., leaching and adsorption. A combination of leaching and adsorption is a novel and productive approach to recovering heavy metals from like PCBs. After the phases of chemical leaching, the solution was recovered through adsorption and is eco-friendly. The process is carried out to increase the separation rate, reduce the time spent and reach the limits of incineration and pyrolysis methods. Adsorption provides the recovery of heavy metals with respect to the required adsorbent since it is a surface phenomenon. The optimum condition of process variables was found through response surface methodology (RSM). The maximum recovery of copper ions (97.33%) was obtained at the optimum operating conditions such as adsorbent size of 0.04 mm, adsorbent dosage of 3.5 gm L^{-1} and the temperature of 80°C with 0.845 desirability. This investigation was found to be an eco-friendly way to recover copper ions and does not cause any environmental issues.

Keywords: E-waste, leached solution, bentonite clay, EDXs, aqua regia, response surface methodology

1. Introduction

Electronic waste or e-waste is designated as the discarded electrical or electronic devices which are intended for reuse, recycle, resale, or disposal. Technological innovation, market expansion, economic growth and the short life of electrical and electronic equipment (EEE) have led to significant growth in waste of EEE (WEEE). PCBs are the main component of this equipment which generally contains 40% of metals, 30% of ceramics and 30% of plastics [1–3]. The metallic composition consists primarily of 10–30% of copper (Cu) and other metals such as Tin (Sn), Zinc (Zn), Lead (Pb), Nickel (Ni), Iron (Fe), Silver (Ag), Cadmium (Cd), Gold (Au), etc. depending on sources of printed circuit boards

(PCB) [4]. Informal processing of e-waste in developing countries can lead to adverse effects on human health and environmental pollution. In 2016, 44.7 million metric tons of e-waste were produced worldwide [5, 6]. If the e-waste was directly disposed of by filling the soil without removing metal ions from PCBs, the pollution of land and water supplies would result. These metals adopt mediums such as dust, air, water and soil to meet the human framework. Exposure to metals such as Pb and Cd affects reproductive health, development, mental instability and damage to human DNA [7–9]. Health symptoms like headache, dizziness, irritation in the eye, nose, mouth, etc. are caused by exposure to Cu which is present in landfills [10, 11]. The methods that can be used to recover metals from PCBs are essentially physical/mechanical and chemical separations. Several studies on the feasibility of metal recovery from PCBs have been investigated in the last decade. Hydrometallurgical procedures, such as leaching, are very intentional in these studies. Several leaching reagents demonstrate major improvements in metal recovery. When treated with different acidic media, HNO_3, HCl and H_2SO_4, PCBs were cut to extract Cu^{2+} ions, the recovery percentage of Cu^{2+} was 97.5 percent, 65 percent and 76.5 percent respectively [12].

A novel ultrasonically assisted treatment process assisted in the reduction, recovery and higher separation from homogeneous heavy metals waste. The studies showed the complete recovery of copper and iron from PCB waste sludge by converting them into separated copper sulfate and ferric chloride solutions. The process has a high separation and recovery efficiency to extract metals. The results indicate that a metal recovery facility treating PCB waste sludge containing 3.14–4.85% copper and 3.71–4.23% iron achieved a copper recovery efficiency of 95.2–97.5% and iron recovery efficiency of 97.1–98.5%. However, because they were fully used in chemical leaching reagents, this process had some limitations in terms of waste emission and effects [13].

Many more studies were performed and reported the various operating conditions on the recovery of heavy metals such as Ag, Au, Ni, and copper found in PCBs. About 80% of the precious metals in the PCB are contained in the particle size ranges from 3.33 mm to 0.43 mm. Column leaching outcome shows that the gold dissolution rate is higher than those of the silver and copper during the first 10 days of the process. From the day 11 there is a reduction in the gold and silver recovery rate due to the copper oxide and copper hydroxide layers on the material surface. The cyanidation of PCBs provides the recovery rates such as 47.9% of Au, 51.6% of Ag, 48.1% of Ni and 77.2% of Cu in a column leaching using NaCN reagent whereas, the activated carbon adsorption process provides 97.3% of Au, 99.3% of Ag, 98.2% of Ni, and 80.7% of Cu [14]. Other useful metals remain as traces in the leaching solution. The deposition of extracted metals possesses different dendritic growth with respect to leaching reagent used. The copper recovered by leaching of PCBs with H_2SO_4 solution presented a fine dendritic structure with branches of about 80–100 μm [15, 16]. Significant recovery rates of copper through chemical leaching was reported in our previous researches [13, 14]. The hydrometallurgical method is a great concern to reseachers because it has low consumption of reagents, energy, less environmental pollution. The study deals with the extraction of copper ions Cu^{2+} from PCBs by two stage leaching technology [17] under various conditions of particle size, time, pulp density and temperature of the PCBs and find the optimum value for the maximum recovery of metals in both as well as experimental and predicted value through response surface methodology (RSM).

Researchers employed heavy metals retrieving methods such as electro wining, electro refining, cementation and the ion exchange techniques. These methods have some defects causing release of secondary pollutants, etc. So for this study, adsorption technique with natural adsorbents was introduced. Heavy metals have been acknowledged as potential health and environmentally hazardous materials. Many studies have been shown that these metals are toxic even at low concentrations. The presence of these toxic metals can cause in turn accumulative poisoning, destroy liver cancer, and brain damage when found above the tolerance level. Two locally available adsorbents namely bentonite clay and roasted date pits were collected. The date pits were roasted in an oven at 130°C for 4 hr. and ground in a mill to obtain powder for experimentation. The two adsorbents were analysedby surface area analyzer. The adsorbents are a mixture of heavy metal ions such as copper, cobalt, zinc, lead, arsenic, cadmium and chromium in the industrial waste water. The heavy metal concentration levels in the industrial waste water were above the permissible concentration levels. In addition the minimum removal efficiency of metal ions by adsorption using bentonite clay and the roasted date pits was 97% [18]. 15 g granules of the mobile PCB sample were leached in the 250 ml solution using 500 ml glass beaker which contained the pre determined amount of the ammonium thiosulfate and copper sulfate at various pH values. All leaching experiments were carried out at an agitation speed of 250 rpm and temperature. After 8 hrs leaching the solution was removed and was filtered by the Whitman 40 filter paper to separate the residual PCBs from the solution. The residue was then dried in the vacuum oven for 2 hr. at 130°C to remove all the moisture from the sample and the samples were weighed and the weight of the residue was calculated. In case PCB granules 56.7% gold could be leached under the optimized conditions viz., ammonium thiosulfate 0.1 M, stirring speed 250 rpm and at room temperature in 8 hr. time duration. In case of complete PCB unit the maximum gold leaching was 78.8% at thiosulfate 0.1 M, copper sulfate 40 mm, Ph 10–10.5, stirring speed 250 rpm at room temperature in 8 hr. time duration [19].

The residual mercury is to be treated and deposited in a geological repository with a clay barrier between the waste and the rock. In reality, hazardous chemical waste is for the most part deposited at the surface under drained conditions, while long-lived and high level nuclear waste in most programmes is intended to be deposited in geological formations below the ground water level. For sodium based bentonites, two modes of swelling exist: crystalline and osmotic. Crystalline swelling takes place only during the addition of low fractions of water. While osmotic swelling can take place for much larger additions. In the present work, the feasibility of applying nuclear long-lived waste disposal concepts to chemical hazardous substances is being tested. The elements needed for at least a simple safety analysis are identified and described in the present paper and will be tested experimentally and theoretically. In addition to mobility tests, the experiment included demonstration of a technique for compacting a mixture of spent batteries and bentonite clay. From the experiment, the sufficient extraction of chemicals was taken [20].

Based on previous researchers copper recovering techniques from various wastes and to overcome the drawbacks, the researchers opt for a new method such as adsorption by bentonite clay. Clays and clay minerals are of great importance due to the unique properties including hardness, durability, strong plasticity and plasticitythat make them ideal for industrial applications [21, 22]. Due to their complex shapes, clays have limited particle sizes and highly specific surface areas. They have been recognized as one of the most suitable low-cost adsorbents and standard components in a variety of industrial applications. Bentonite is an aluminum phyllosilicate adsorbent derived from montmorillonite. It is a sedimentary rock composed primarily of clays with a typical 2:1 layer structure and high concentrations of Na^+, Ca^{2+}, and K^+ ions found between the layers. Acid treatment on clay minerals has additional mineralogical and mineralogical impacts on a mineralogical system [23]. Due to its cation capacity, greater surface area and adsorption capacity for various organic and inorganic ions, acid-activated bentonite has been a traditional commodity for removing metal ions. In this present study, Copper recovery from PCB leached solution with treated bentonite clay has been studies thoroughly and the experimental results are optimized through RSM.

2. Materials and methods

2.1 Sample collection and preparation

The waste PCBs are obtained from e-waste disposal units in India. For experimental use, 500 g scraps of PCBs are broken into 15–20 cm particles and shredded using pliers and four blade cutting shredder into small pieces around 50 x 50 mm to 30 x 30 mm [12, 17, 24]. Metals and non-metals need to be separated [15, 16]. This separation is not as simple due to the difference in the physical characteristics of metals and non-metals. Hence, different separation methods, such as pneumatic separation, magnetic separation, filtering, eddy current separation, electrostatic separation, etc., are used to enrich metals and non-metals [12, 17].

The crushed PCBs obtained from the crusher are then pulverized and further exposed for milling operation for better size reduction using a ball mill and particles of different mesh sizes are analyzed. The weight fraction of crushed PCBs obtained from the lower screens of jaw crushers with a capacity of 80 kg $hr.^{-1}$ and a clearance of 10 mm is much lower, making better ion recovery impossible. Thus, it is subjected to 5 mm clearance in the same jaw crusher, yielding samples weighing 65, 53, 48, and 36 grams for sieves with mesh sizes of 0.3, 0.18, 0.05 mm, and pan, respectively, when screened using a rotary sieve shaker at a speed of 60 rpm with a power of 0.25 HP and a single phase 80 volt supply. As the reduction in size increases the rate of recovery of metal ions [8], the resulting crushed samples are processed into powder form using a pulverizer with a disk diameter of 175 mm operated by a 3-phase motor at 1400 rpm in a 225–445 V supply. The resulting powder samples are screened under different mesh sizes and the weight fraction of the bottom products (Sieves from 52 B.S.S. to pan) is increased but not adequate for the anticipated recovery. The pulverized PCB powder is milled in a ball mill having a ball weight of 500 grams at a speed of 60–120 rpm with a mill diameter of 200 mm driven by a 0.25 HP 3 phase motor which results in a size reduction and the highest weight fraction is obtained at lowest sieves. The weight fractions obtained at each sieve are collected separately and subjected to leaching (**Figure 1**).

2.2 Chemical leaching experimentation with aqua regia

2.2.1 Aqua regia preparation

The metal recovery from PCBs is carried by two stages of leaching media (first stage HCl and HNO_3 and second stage HCl and H_2SO_4). It is prepared by mixing HCl and HNO_3 in a 3:1 ratio under specified conditions of temperature, time and surrounding conditions. In previous studies (**Table 1**) with aqua regia as a leaching reagent, Copper was extracted from PCBs with a high recovery rate [15, 16, 19, 21, 22].

Aqua regia preparation involves mixing of strong acids. The two concentrated acids were mixed in 3:1 ratio (HCl:HNO_3), Concentrated HCl (35%) and HNO_3 (65%). The solutions should be keptaway from organic contaminants, because it leads to vigorous or violent reaction and low temperature should be maintained.

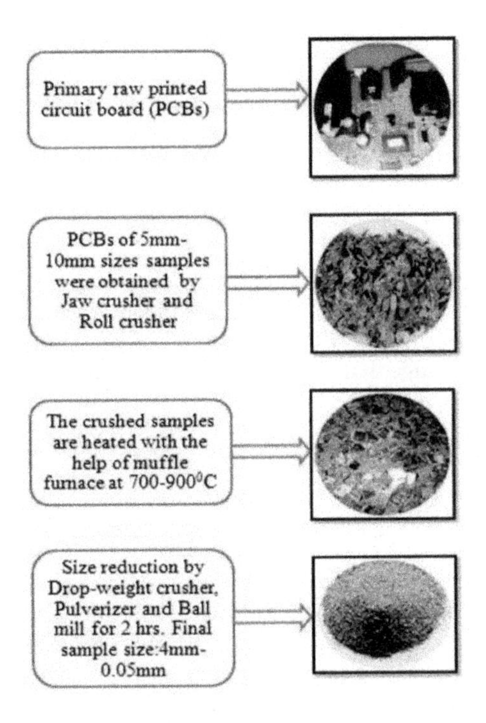

Figure 1.
Schematic diagram of primary raw PCBs; in to stepwise size reduction under the various mechanical operations (jaw crusher, roll crusher, thermal heater and pulverized mills produced small sizes between 4 and 0.05 mm).

Leaching media used	Cu recovery %	References
$H_2SO_4 + H_2O_2$	96.72	[15]
HNO_3 and $HCl + HNO_3$	86.9	[16]
NaCN	77.7	[19]
$(NH_4)_2S_2O_3$ and $CuSO_4$	78.8	[21]
$H_2SO_4 + NH_3$	88.6	[22]

Table 1.
Recovery data of copper with different leaching agents.

2.2.2 Experimentation with various parameters on copper recovery

All the experiments were conducted in a conical flask with a temperature controlled shaker. Primary analysis was conducted by applying specific conditions to obtain a standard recovery rate. 20 g of PCB samples are allowed to mix with 0.5 liters of leaching media at 80°C and shaken in a mechanical shaker at a shaking speed of 120 rpm for 3 hours. At the end of this contact time, the shaker is stopped and solutions in the conical flask are filtered using filter paper. After complete filtration and metal composition retained is determined. The leaching rate depends on various parameters such as shaking intensity, size, contact time, pulp density and temperature. Different values for the recovery rate and the composition of heavy metals are obtained by varying these parameters. The samples are then tested and time results are analyzed over the recovery rate. The leached copper was reclaimed with the help of bentonite clay.

2.3 Copper ion reclaimation by adsorption

Adsorption operation is extensively applicable in chemical operations for the reclamation of copper ions from the leached solution. Some other techniques have been used in previous studies, like precipitation, cementation process, liquid membrane techniques and ion exchange process. These methods have their specific advantages and disadvantages. Some of the methods are:

- Precipitation methods were used in precipitating reagents such as carbonate, sulfide and hydroxide which are precipitated from leached solution to insoluble form [25]. The disadvantage of this precipitation method is the formation of a huge quantity of sludge that contains toxic compounds.

- To overcome this defect, the copper metal reclaiming process was done by another method called the cementation process, which involves metal displacement reactions [26]. The disadvantage of this process is the need for high contact time. The copper solution necessitates a slow flow rate.

To overcome all these downsides, a new technique has to be developed for the separation of copper ions (Cu^{2+}) from the leached solution. The stability of adsorption operation compared to other separation operations is the major reason for the recent renovation for selective separation and recovery of copper ions from the leached solution. Therefore, a suitable technique has to be selected so that the highest rate of copper recovery can be achieved. Cu^{2+} ions are recovered more effectively with these A-Bent adsorbent.

2.3.1 Physical activation method

250 grams of both adsorbents were taken in the thermal crucible and were dried for about 5 hr. for thermal activation at 900°C. The samples obtained are from 1 μm to 5 μm. The higher specific surface area is obtained due to the removal of unwanted gaseous molecules from the Non-Activated Adsorbents (NAA). The activated adsorbents are shown in **Figure 2a,b**.

Figure 2.
(a) The schematic diagram for bentonite clay thermal activation at 600°C. (b) Chemical activation by used concentrated HCl and HNO_3.

2.3.2 Chemical activation method

The chemical activation involves the chemical reaction of the precursor with the activating agent at temperature 600°C. Initially, the Bentonite clay is washed with tap water and undergoes solar drying until the complete moisture content is removed. Once the moisture is completely removed from the adsorbent again, it will be washed with tap water and again dried under sunlight. The materials were mixed with a Nitric acid solution (85 percent of purity) at a ratio of 1:2 by mass (materials: HNO_3 solution) and they are stirred well for 2 h and then conveyed to a stainless steel plate which is placed in a muffle furnace and heated at 550°C for 2 h. By natural cooling, the temperature is brought down to room temperature. Then, the adsorbent samples (C-A Bent) were crushed to less than 1 μm size and all the adsorbent samples were weighted and washed with 0.1 mol L^{-1} HCl to remove the surface ash.

Then, the adsorbent samples were washed with de-ionized water to remove the HCl and dried for 24 h at 150°C. After drying, both samples were ground and sieved. Chemically activated samples of both adsorbents are found favorable surface properties like C-A Bent have the maximum specific surface area 817 m^2 g^{-1}, less than 0.5 μm sizes and Pore volume is 0.1 cm^3 g^{-1}. Then, the adsorbent samples of C-A PSC have the specific surface area of 1026 m^2 g^{-1}, pore volume 0.37cm^3 g^{-1} and pore size 0.5 μm. The prepared samples were tested with the help of the Scanning Electron Microscope (SEM-FEI-Quanta FEG 200F) which is shown in **Figure 3a,b**.

2.3.3 Adsorbent characterization and studies

The feed to adsorption is copper solution recovered by leaching. Adsorption of copper ions on Bent was carried out in a batch system in both activated and NA-Adsorbents. 2 gram of adsorbent was added to 20 ml of the leached solution in a conical flask. The mixture was to be shaken at 200 rpm for 5 h at 80°C. After complete adsorption is done, the samples were filtered and copper concentration was analyzed by using EDXs which is used for the analysis of the elemental characterization of a sample in conjunction with SEM. The energy of the beam current is typically in the range of 100Na, Schottky emitter ranges between(−200v to 30 kV), magnifications range 12X–105X, and resolution of 2 Nanometer (Gold Nano-particles suspended on carbon substrate). Then, the adsorption efficiency of an adsorbent (Bent) was determined by the following Eq. (1).

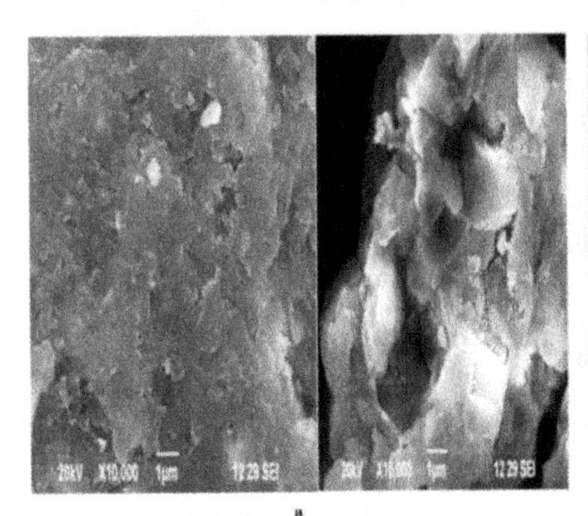

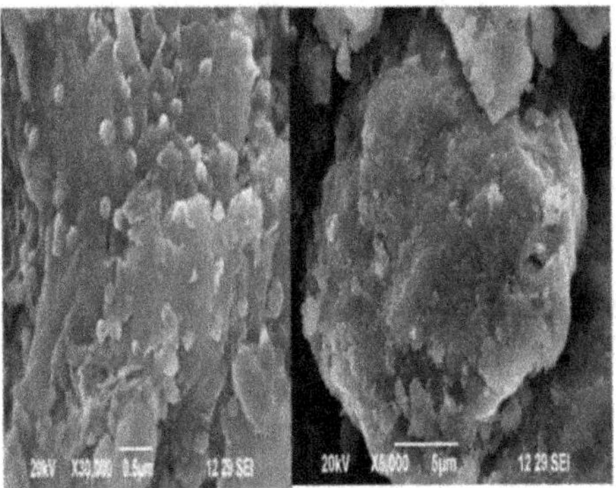

Figure 3.
(a) The SEM images of bentonite clay thermal activation at 600°C. (b) Chemical activation by used concentrated HCl and HNO_3.

Variable	Name of the process variable	Range and levels		
		−1	0	1
A	Temperature, °C	40	60	80
B	Adsorbent dosage gm L^{-1}	2	3	5
C	Adsorbent sizeμm	0.4	2	5

Table 2.
Levels of different process variables in coded and un-coded form chemical leaching % of copper ions (box-Benhken method).

$$\text{Removal Efficiency}\,(\%) = (C_o - C_e)/C_o \times 100 \quad (1)$$

C_o is the initial concentration of metal ions from leached samples. C_e is the metal ions concentration after adsorption operation [27].

2.4 Response surface methodology (RSM)

Studies were conducted in order to obtain the optimum valves of various parametersfrom the recovery of copper ions from leached solution by Response surface methodology. The influence of various parameters (Size of adsorbent, adsorbent dosage and temperature) were studied for copper ions recovery. In this analysis, input parameters were taken into account aretemperature, adsorbent dosage and temperature. Based on the ideal experimental conditions for the shaking intensity and dimensions of the metals optimum recovery percentage the leaching variable input parameters were calculated (**Table 2**).

3. Results and discussion

3.1 Sample analysis of PCBs (sizes and metal elements)

The graphical representation of the size analysis reveals that, subject to size decrease sequence, the fraction of sample generated on the screens with larger mesh sizes has decreased. The total weight collected in the sieves is, however, maintained similar roughly with marginal loss. The sample collected at the ball mill is much less than 0.05 mm from the analytical data of each procedure. Numerous experiments have used a shredded sample dimension less than 0.5 mm, contributing to an elevated copper recovery rate [25]. Present findings consist of 0.05 mm of the sample held above the pan for the liquidation used particle scale. EDXs have been used to analyze the copper concentrations of preliminary samples. To ensure uniformity and to obtain results of copper by EDXs, samples were randomly mixed (**Figure 4**) and the final composition of metals by weight % (Cu 3.15%, Sn 42.4%, Zn 1.16%, Pb 27.81% and others metals 25.48%).

3.2 Maximum copper recovery of leaching by optimization study

Experiments carried out based on RSM results. In addition to that ANOVA, response surface plots, quadratic model equation and CCD were analyzed for experimental conditions. Hence, the results obtained for Optimum removal of Cu 95.33%, with a desirability of 0.761 were obtained at Time 5 hours, Temperature 90.01°C, pulp density 25 g L^{-1}.

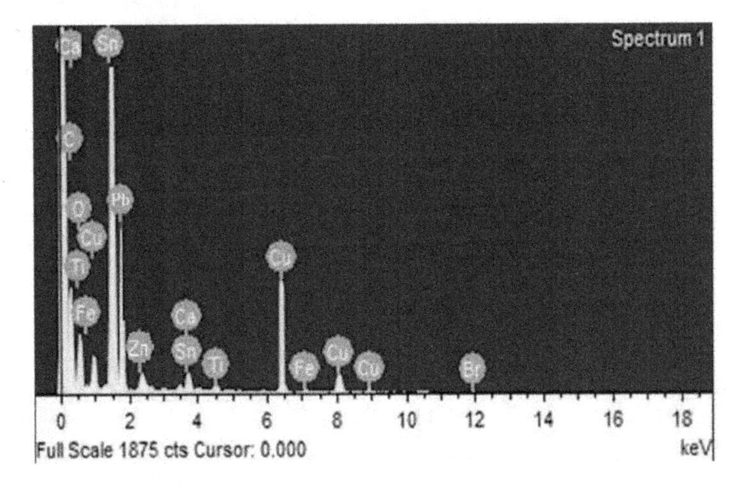

Figure 4.
Presents of copper ions from PCBs sample by EDXs.

The optimum values were found under the studied parameters at which the maximum recovery is obtained. Therefore, The experiments done above optimized three parameters with two experimental parameters (80 rpm of speed and 0.05 mm particle size). Therefore, the optimized gives 20 grams of the sample treated with 0.5 liter of aqua regia at this optimum condition, metal compositions present in to the PCBs by after leaching (Cu 0.09 weight percentage) are shown in EDXs results (**Figure 5**). The results obtained at optimum condition shows that the recovered rate of copper is 97.06%.

3.3 Adsorption studies for copper recovery from leached solution

Adsorption studies are explained for the recovery of coppers from leached solution with the help of Bentonite clay as an adsorbent. Hence, all the adsorption results for recovery concerning various parameters are evaluated and studied as

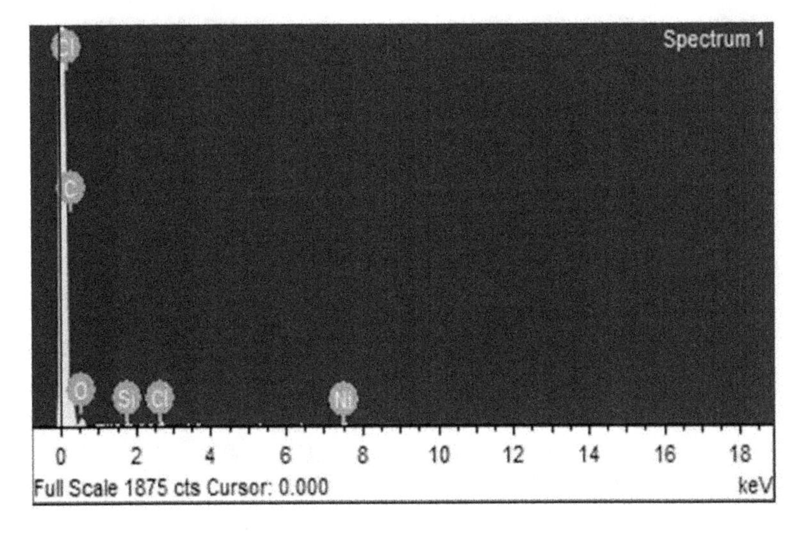

Figure 5.
EDXs spectrum analysisfor copper ions removal after leaching treatment of (PCBs).

explained based on previous research [28] and compared; we get the optimum condition to obtain maximum recovery of metals. The optimum condition is the value of concentration, size, temperature and time at which the maximum recovery is obtained. The optimum conditions are 4 g of adsorbent dosage, 0.05 μm particle size of adsorbent, 80°C of temperature and 4 hours of contacting time. Under these conditions, chemically activated bentonite clay gives maximum adsorption rate when compare to other adsorbents. Therefore, the present study was experimented to recover the copper ion (Cu^{2+}) from the leached solution with the use of optimal parameters and constructive results obtained in chemically activated adsorbents.

The results show (**Figure 6**) that at optimum condition, the recovery is 97% of Copper. This is the most favorable condition to obtain the maximum recovery of copper ions which was found initially 3.119 weight percentage of copper and after copper present in adsorbent 3 weight percent therefore copper were recoverd 97.33%. The optimal values are tested the specified parameters by response surface methodology.

3.4 Optimization parameters by design of experiments (DOE)

Optimize and evaluate individual process variables for better recovery rates by analyzing operating parameters and reducing the number of tests. The CCD (Central Composite Design) for Cu, adsorption was calculated with optimized operating parameters and RSM maximum copper recovery. The CCD results shown in **Table 3** experimental and predicted copper adsorption were analyzed.

3.4.1 RSM for copper reclaimation from leached solution

Statistical modeling methods were used to evaluate the multiple regression of the experiments designed to determine the multivariable equation (**Table 3**). RSM concept data plots collected in the final regression equation in terms of coded recovery variables for Cu recovery. The final equation in terms of the coded factors equation discussed Eq. (2). The equation in terms of coded factors can be used to make predictions about the response for given levels of each factor. By default, the high levels of the factors are coded as +1 and the low levels are coded as −1. The

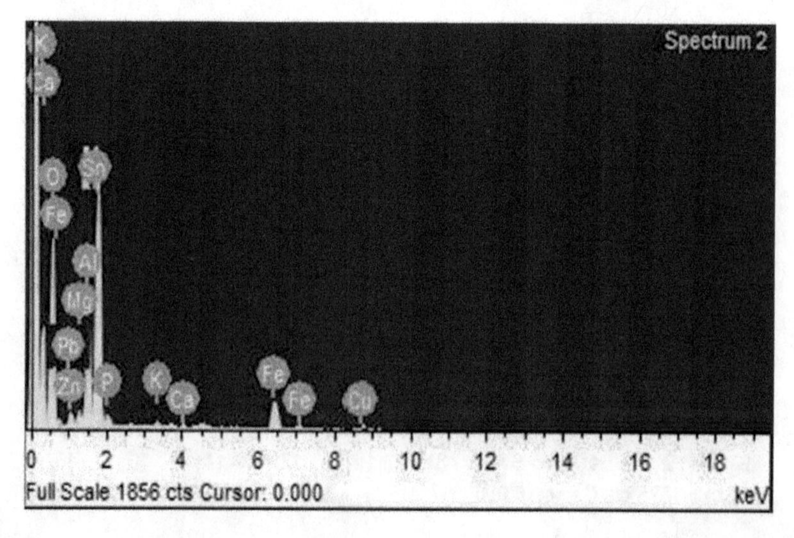

Figure 6.
EDXs images in metal compositions for after adsorption.

Run No.	A	B	C	Experimental	Predicted
1.	1	−1	0	92.88	92.85
2.	−1	1	0	89.24	89.15
3.	1	1	0	94.16	93.96
4.	−1	0	−1	92.16	92.19
5.	1	0	−1	90.23	90.06
6.	−1	0	1	88.34	88.43
7.	1	0	1	96.24	96.33
8.	0	−1	-1	94.88	96.33
9.	0	1	-1	93	92.71
10.	0	-1	1	96.8	96.33
11.	0	1	1	94.6	94.49
12.	0	0	0	86.2	86.37
13.	0	0	0	91.36	91.47
14.	0	0	0	93.7	93.9
15.	0	0	0	96.17	96.46
16.	0	0	0	97.33	96.33

Table 3.
Experimental and predicted results from CCD with optimal parameters for copper adsorption.

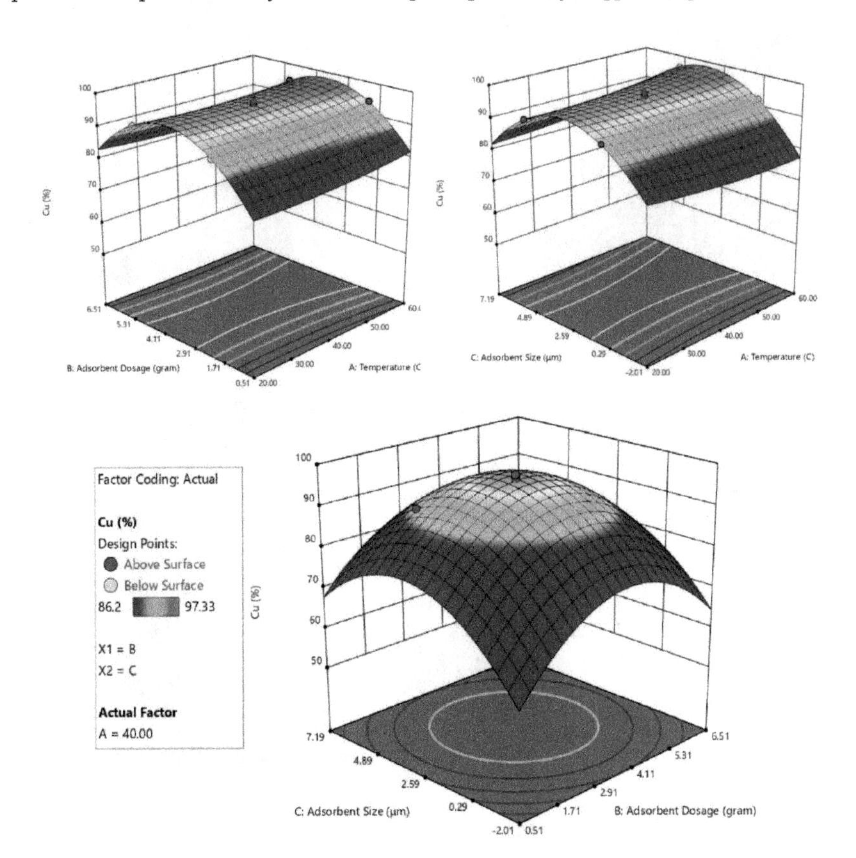

Figure 7.
RSM plots and interactions between the the temperarure, adsorbent dosage and size of adsorbent by Cu recovery.

coded equation is useful for identifying the relative impact of the factors by comparing the factor coefficients.

$$\begin{aligned}\%\text{of } Cu = &+96.33 + 0.7688 \times A + 0.7388 \times B + 1.10 \times C \\ &- 0.4750 \times A \times B + 1.03 \times A \times C - 0.287 \times B \times C \\ &+ 1.09 \times A^2 - 3.96 \times B^2 - 3.86 \times C^2\end{aligned} \quad (2)$$

The response of each parameter was Predicted within the limits through the model in function of coded factor. Here, the maximum and minimum coded factor termed as +1 and −1. The response surface were visualized in three dimensional plots that exhibit two factors functions while keeping the other factors constant. The predicted design plots, shows the above red zones were found at 97.33% of Cu and above yellow zones confirms 93% of Cu, and above blue colors confirms 88.95% of Cu. It shown in **Figure** 7 and contour plots for copper recovery (**Figure 8**).

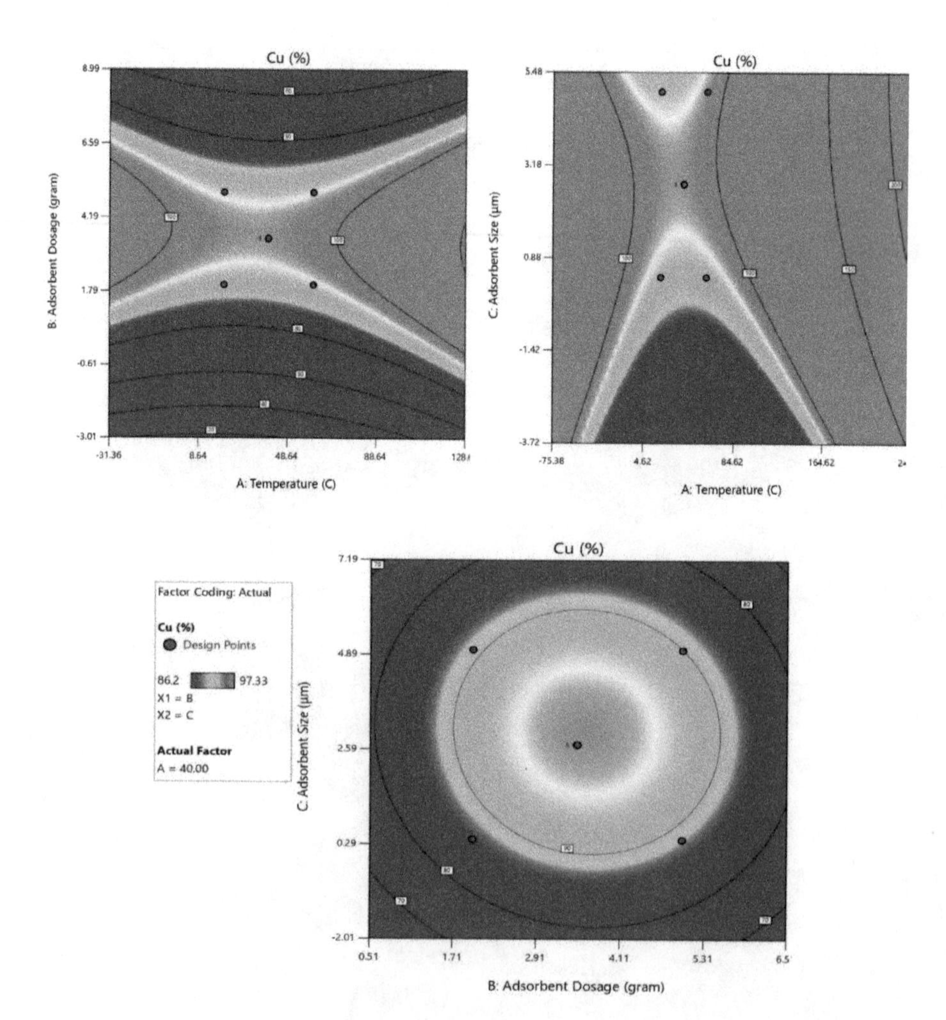

Figure 8.
Contour plots and interactions between the temperarure, adsorbent dosage and size of adsorbent by Cu recovery.

3.4.2 Evaluation of the model

P-values less than 0.0500 indicate model terms are significant. In this case A, B, C, AC, A^2, B^2, C^2 are significant model terms. Analysis of variance correspond to experimental results were presented in **Table 4**. The Model F-value of Cu 34.28 implies the model is significant. There is only a 0.01% chance that an F-value this large could occur due to noise. Also, the acceptable and reasonable value of lack of fit with F-value of Cu 0.9321, with probability (>0.05) indicates the suitability of the method for good presentation of experimental data. Implied that the model was accurate. Also, the acceptable and reasonable value of lack of fit with F-value of Cu 0.02322, with probability (>0.05) indicates the suitability of the method for good presentation of experimental data.

As presented in **Table 5**, the model presents the high R^2 value of Cu0.9778 indicates that there was a good agreement between the experimental and predicted

Source	Sum of squares	df	Mean square	F value	p-value Prob > F
Model	162.29	9	18.03	34.28	< 0.0001
A-Temperature	4.73	1	4.73	8.99	0.02
B-Adsorbent Dosage	4.37	1	4.37	8.3	0.0236
C-Adsorbent Size	9.72	1	9.72	18.49	0.0036
AB	0.9025	1	0.9025	1.72	0.2316
AC	4.26	1	4.26	8.11	0.0248
BC	0.3306	1	0.3306	0.6285	0.4539
A^2	4.98	1	4.98	9.47	0.0179
B^2	66.11	1	66.11	125.68	<0.0001
C^2	62.9	1	62.9	119.57	<0.0001
Residual	3.68	7	0.526	—	—
Lack of Fit	0.3458	3	0.1153	0.1382	0.9321
Pure Error	3.34	4	0.831	—	—
Cor Total	165.98	16	—	—	—

Table 4.
ANOVA table for model to predict % of leaching of copper.

Parameters	Cu
Standard Deviation (SD)	0.7253
Mean	93.16
Coefficient of Variation (CV%)	0.7785
Predicted residual error sum of squares (PRESS)	3.68
R-Squared (R^2)	0.9778
Adj R-Squared (R^2)	0.9493
Pred R-Squared (R^2)	0.9353
Adequate precision (AP)	18.125

Table 5.
Quality of the quadratic model for the adsorption of copper.

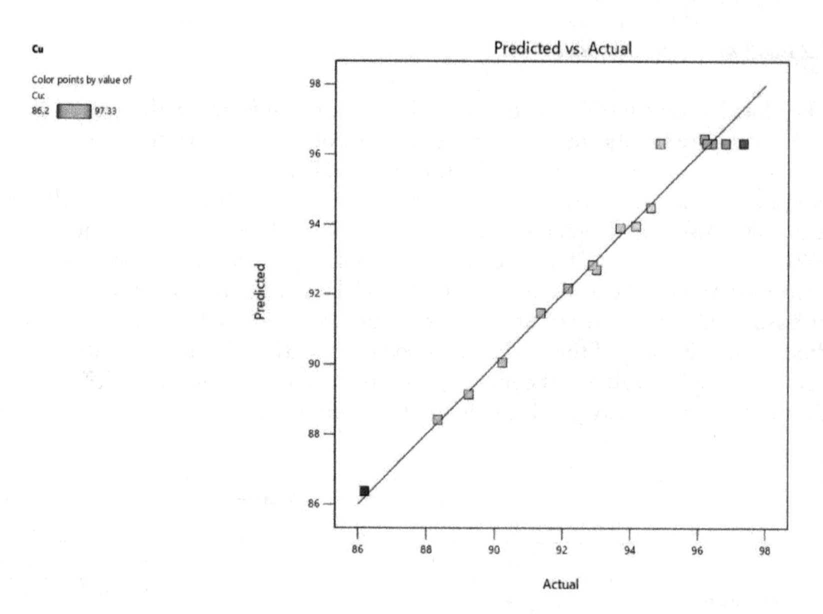

Figure 9.
Comparison plot between the experimental and predicted data.

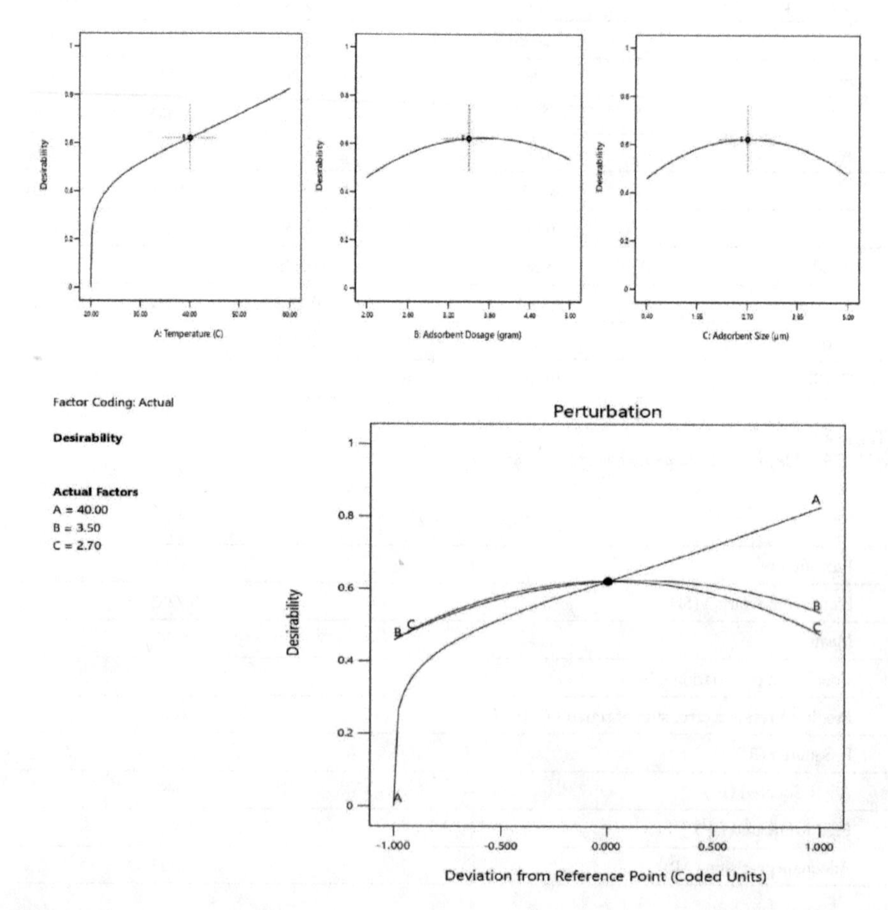

Figure 10.
Desirability plot for recovery of copper from leached solution.

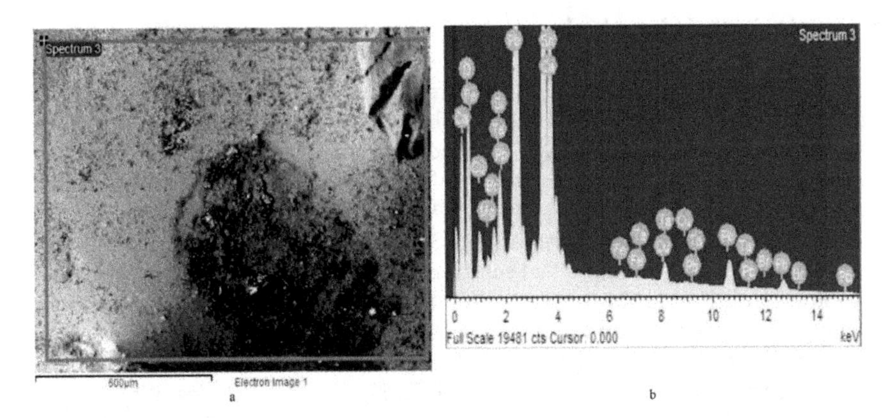

Figure 11.
EDXs spectrum analysis for metal ions obtained for after adsorption.

results. Also, the predicted R^2 value Cu 0.9353was which were in reasonable agreement with the adjusted R^2 value of Cu 0.9493. Adeq Precision measures the signal to noise ratio. A ratio greater than 4 is desirable. Your ratio of Cu 18.125 indicates an adequate signal. This model can be used to navigate the design space. Predicted value were Showed (**Figure 9**) of the responses from model was in agreement with observed values over the selected range of independent variables with reasonable higher values of coefficient of determination (R^2).

3.4.3 Desirability plot for recovery of copper from leached solution

The desirability profile for the removal percentage of copper versus the variables is shown in **Figure 10**. The desirability varies from 0.0 to 1.0 corresponds to approaching from undesirable to the very desirable condition. Optimum removal of Cu 97.33%, has been obtained with the desirability of 0.845 which was obtained at adsorbent dosage 2 gm L^{-1}, size of adsorbent 0.4 mm temperature 90°C.

Therefore, this design has been analyzed for experimental and predicted valves of metal separations' of chemical leaching, the values of desirability rate was found in the range of prediction is 0.845. Since the optimum values are predicted then optimal parameters are used to run the copper recovery process.

3.5 Maximum copper recovery by optimization study

Experiments carried out based on RSM results. In addition to that ANOVA, response surface plots, quadratic model equation and CCD were analyzed for experimental conditions. Hence, the results obtained for Optimum removal of Cu 97.33%, with a desirability of 0.845 were obtained at adsorbent dosage 2 gm L^{-1}, size of adsorbent 0.4 mm temperature 90°C.

The optimum values were found under the studied parameters at which the maximum recovery is obtained. Therefore, The experiments done above optimized three parameters with two experimental parameters (size of adsorbent 0.4 mm temperature 90°C). Therefore, the optimized gives 2 grams of the sample treated with 0.5 liter of leched solution at this optimum condition, metal compositions present in to the PCBs by after leaching (Cu 0.09 Weight percent) are shown in SEM with EDXs results (**Figure 11**). The results obtained at optimum condition shows that the recovery of copper are 97.06% of copper.

4. Conclusions and outlook

In summary, copper in waste PCBs were leached into corresponding reagents during the two-stage chemical leaching. The effectiveness of two-stage chemical leaching media (HCl and HNO_3, H_2SO_4 and HCl) was employed for the separation of copper ions during the treatment of PCBs is evaluated. The results of this study, C-A Bent adsorbents assist in the 97% of effective copper separation for Chemical leached solution Therefore, the Study concluded that, copper ions are recovered effectively from leached solutions by using adsorption techniques under optimum conditions in the presence of C-A Bent adsorbent. These types of metal leaching operations are promoted in order to reduce the environmental problems caused by these kinds of heavy metals. The analysis demonstrates the dependency of the recovery rates. Optimum removal of Cu 97.33% with a desirability of 0.845 was achieved at adsorbent dosage 2 gm L^{-1}, Size of adsorbent 0.4 mm temperature 90°C. Hence this form of heavy metal leaching and adsorption reclamation process is proposed with a view to reducing environmental impacts (caused by heavy metals). It was concluded that the combination of aqua regia leaching and bent adsorption is an effective and economic way for the recovery of copper from leached solution.

According to studies, modifying the surface of the clay increases the rate of adsorption, but this raises the total cost and results in the introduction of additional chemicals into the atmosphere. As a result, attempts will be taken in the future to resolve these issues. Only a few field trials have been performed, and more systematic studies are needed to decide the best conditions for using clay minerals as adsorbents.

Acknowledgements

This study was carried out with utilization of the laboratory facilities in Erode Sengunthar Engineering College and Kongu Engineering College. The corresponding author would like acknowledge and thank to his parents and brother P. Selvarasu, PG Assist Zoology, Govt Higher Secondary school, Vellore for their kind support.

Nomenclature

CCD	central composite design
Cu	copper
EEE	electrical and electronic equipment
E-Waste	electronic waste
EDXs	energy-dispersive X-ray spectroscopy
HCl	hydrochloric acid
Pb	lead
HNO_3	nitric acid
PCBs	printed circuit boards
RSM	response surface methodology
SEM	scanning electron microscopy
H_2SO_4	sulfuric acid
Sn	tin
WEEE	waste of electrical and electronic equipment
Zn	zinc

Highlights

- The heavy metals in PCBs were leached with two-stage aqua regia (first stage-HCl and HNO_3 and second stage-HCl and H_2SO_4) in order to get more recovery rate.

- A multi response optimization procedure based on the response surface methodology has been applied. The task of the optimization problems has been the maximization of the recovery of copper.

- Adsorption (Bent) clay minerals as an adsorbing media to recover copper from a chemically leached solution of PCBs.

- The overall leaching efficiency of copper (Cu) was found at 97.06%.

- Since this kind of extraction has proved to be successful in the separation and recovery of copper ions, it is not advisable to extract specific metals in a targeted manner, even though they are economically viable.

Author details

Murugesan Manikkampatti Palanisamy[1*], Akilamudhan Palaniappan[2], Venkata Ratnam Myneni[3], Kannan Kandasamy[4], Minar Mohamed Lebbai[2] and Padmapriya Veerappan[5]

1 Centre for Education, Council of Scientific and Industrial Research–Central Electro Chemical Research Institute (CSIR–CECRI), Karaikudi, Tamil Nadu, India

2 Department of Chemical Engineering, Erode Sengunthar Engineering College, Erode, Tamil Nadu, India

3 Department of Chemical Engineering, Mettu University, Mettu, Ethiopia

4 Department of Chemical Engineering, Kongu Engineering College, Erode, Tamil Nadu, India

5 Department of Applied Electronics, Erode Sengunthar Engineering College, Erode, Tamil Nadu, India

*Address all correspondence to: engineermurugesh@gmail.com

References

[1] Yang, H., Liu, J., Yang, J., 2011. Leaching copper from shredded particles of waste printed circuit boards. J. Hazard. Mater. 187 (2011) 393-400.

[2] Wei, L and Liu, Y 2012,'Present status of e-waste disposal and recycling in China', Ministry of Environmental Protection of China, vol. 16, pp. 506-514.

[3] Yang, H, Liu, J and Yang, J 2011, 'Leaching copper from shredded particles of waste printed circuit boards', Journal of Hazardous Materials, vol. 187, pp. 393-400.

[4] Bari, F, Begum, MN, Jamaludin, B and Hussi, K 2009,'Selective leaching for the recovery of copper from PCB', Proceedings of the Malaysian Metallurgical Conference '09, Pp. 1-4.

[5] Manikkampatty Palanisamy Murugesan, Kannan Kandasamy Venkata Ratnam Myneni 2021, Two phase leaching for metal recovery from waste printed circuit boards: Statistical optimization, Chemical Industry and Chemical Engineering Quarterly. Vol. 27 (3) https://doi.org/10.2298/CICEQ210115022M

[6] Wei, L and Liu, Y 2012, 'Present status of e-waste disposal and recycling in China', Ministry of Environmental Protection of China, vol. 16, pp. 506-514.

[7] Frazzoli, C, Ebere, O, Dragone, R and Mantovani, A 2010, 'Diagnostic health risk assessment of electronic waste on the general population in developing countries scenarios', environmental impact assessment review, Elsevier Inc., vol. 30, no. 6, pp. 388-399.

[8] Xu, X, Yang, H, Chen, A, Zhou, Y, Wu, K, Liu, J, Zhang, Y and Huo, X 2012, 'Birth outcomes related to informal e-waste recycling in Guiyu, China', reproductive toxicology, Elsevier Inc., vol. 33, no. 1, pp. 94-98.

[9] Huo, X, Peng, L, Xu, X, Zheng, L, Qiu, B, Qi, Z, Zhang, B, Han, D and Piao, Z 2007,'Research | children' s health elevated blood Lead levels of children in Guiyu, an electronic waste recycling town in China', Environmental Health Perspectives, vol. 115, no. 7, pp. 1113-1117.

[10] Li, Y, Huo, X, Liu, J, Peng, L, Li, W and Xu, X 2011, 'Assessment of cadmium exposure for neonates in Guiyu, an electronic waste pollution site of China', Environmental Monitoring and Assessment, vol. 177, pp. 343-351.

[11] Masavetas, I, Moutsatsou, A, Nikolaou, E, Spanou, S, Zoikis-Karathanasis, A and Pavlatou, EA 2009, 'Production of copper powder from printed circuit boards by Electrodeposition', Global NEST Journal, vol. 11, no. 2, pp. 241-247.

[12] Xie, F, Cai, T, Ma, Y, Li, H, Li, C, Huang, Z and Yuan, G 2009, 'Recovery of Cu and Fe from printed circuit board waste sludge by ultrasound: Evaluation of industrial application', journal of cleaner production, Elsevier Ltd, vol. 17, no. 16, pp. 1494-1498.

[13] Montero, R, Guevara, A and De La Torre, E 2012, 'Recovery of gold, Silver, Copper and Niobium from Printed Circuit Boards Using Leaching Column Technique', Journal of Earth Science and Engineering, vol. 2. pp. 590-595.

[14] Vijayaram, R and Chandramohan, K 2013, 'Chemical Engineering and Process Technology Studies on Metal (Cu and Sn) Extraction from the Discarded Printed Circuit Board by Using Inorganic Acids as Solvents', vol. 4, no. 2, pp. 2-4.

[15] Vijayaram, R, Nesakumar, D and Chandramohan, K 2013, 'Copper

extraction from the discarded printed circuit board by leaching.', Research Journal of Engineering Sciences, vol. 2, no. 1, pp. 11-14.

[16] Murugesan Manikkampatty Palanisamy and Kannan Kandasamy 2020, "Comparative studies on Bentonite clay and peanut shell carbon recovering heavy metals from printed circuit boards" Journal of Ceramic Processing Research. vol. 21, pp. 75-85.

[17] Saad, A 2010, 'Removal of heavy metals from industrial wastewater by adsorption using local Bentonite clay and roasted date pits in Saudi Arabia', Trends in Applied Sciences Research, vol. 5, pp. 138-145.

[18] Tripathi, A., Kumar, M., Sau, D. C., Agrawal, A., and Chakravarty, S. (2012). "Leaching of gold from the waste Mobile phone printed circuit boards (PCBs) with ammonium Thiosulphate, Int. J. Metallurgical Engg. 1 (2012) 17-21.

[19] Sjöblom, R, Bjurström, H and Pusch, R 2003, 'Feasibility of compacted bentonite barriers in geological disposal of mercury-containing waste', Applied Clay Science, vol. 23, pp. 187-193.

[20] Gu, S., Kang, X., Wang, L., Lichtfouse, E., Wang, C., 2019. "Clay mineral adsorbents for heavy metal removal from wastewater: A review". Environ. Chem. Lett. 17, 629-654.

[21] Ahmadi, A., Foroutan, R., Esmaeili, H., Tamjidi, S., 2020. "The role of bentonite clay and bentonite clay @ MnFe2O4 composite and their physico-chemical properties on the removal of Cr (III) and Cr (VI) from aqueous media". Environ. Sci. Pollut. Res. 27 (2020) pp. 14044-14057.

[22] Amari, A., Gannouni, H., Khan, M.I., Almesfer, M.K., Elkhaleefa, A.M., Gannouni, A., 2018. "Effect of structure and chemical activation on the adsorption properties of green clay minerals for the removal of cationic dye". Appl. Sci. 8 (2018) 1-18

[23] Yazici, EY and Deveci, H 2013, 'Extraction of metals from waste printed circuit boards (WPCBs) in H2SO4-CuSO4-NaCl solutions', Hydrometallurgy, vol. 139, pp. 30-38.

[24] Li, C., Xie, F., Ma, Y., Cai, T., Li, H., Huang, Z., Yuan, G., 2010. "Multiple heavy metals extraction and recovery from hazardous electroplating sludge waste via ultrasonically enhanced two-stage acid leaching". J. Hazard. Mater. 178, 823-833

[25] Abdennebi, N, Bagane, M and Chtara, C 2013, 'Removal of copper from phosphoric acid by adsorption on Tunisian Bentonite', Journal of Chemical Engineering Process Technology, vol. 4, pp. 166-170.

[26] N. Abdennebi, M. Bagane, C. Chtara, Removal of copper from phosphoric acid by adsorption on Tunisian Bentonite. J Chem Eng Process Technol. 4 (2013) 166-170.

[27] Karra, SB, Haas, CN, Tare, V and Allen, HE 1985, 'Kinetic limitations on the selective precipitation treatment of electronic waste', Wasp, Air and soil pollution, vol. 24, pp. 253-265

[28] Ping, Z, Zeyun, F, Jie, L, Qiang, L, Guangren, Q and Ming, Z 2009, 'Enhancement of leaching copper by electro-oxidation from metal powders of waste printed circuit board', Journal of Hazardous Materials, vol. 166, pp. 746-750.

Chapter 7

Towards the Use of Yellow Clay in Fired Bricks

Maryam Achik, Boutaina Moumni, Hayat Benmoussa, Abdellah Oulmekki, Abdelhamid Touache, Gil Gonzalez Álvaro, Francisco Guitián Rivera, Antonia Infantes-Molina, Dolores Eliche-Quesada and Olga Kizinievic

Abstract

This chapter deals with the study of the possibility of using yellow clay - which was only used in pottery so far- in the civil engineering field as building materials, especially in the field of fired bricks. With the aim to improve the technological properties of yellow clay based bricks, two wastes were used as secondary raw materials. The first one is a mineral waste - pyrrhotite ash - this waste was neither characterized nor valued before by any other author. While the second waste is an organic waste - cedar sawdust - which is from the artisanal sector. Clay bricks containing yellow clay and different content of wastes were prepared and tested to evaluate their technological properties: water absorption, bulk density, porosity and mechanical strength... The test results indicate that the addition of wastes to clay bricks improves their technological properties and highlights the possibility of wastes reuse in a safe and sustainable way.

Keywords: clay, bricks, mineral waste, organic waste, mechanical strength, clay bricks, waste, pyrrhotite ash, recycling

1. Introduction

Recently, the study of the reuse of industrial solid waste in the fields of construction materials (fired bricks, tiles, etc.), pavement materials and concrete has received considerable attention across the world. The recovery of wastes is used to develop environmentally friendly technologies, to reduce negative impact on the environment and landfill waste in large storage and disposal areas, and to reduce production costs for new products. However, the recovery of wastes depends on their chemical composition, their microstructure and their physical and hydrodynamic properties. For example, industrial waste containing iron oxide, silicon oxide, aluminum oxide - in the form of major oxides with various contents - such as fly ash (with major oxides: SiO_2, Al_2O_3, Fe_2O_3), pyrite ash (major oxide: Fe_2O_3), red mud (major oxides: Fe_2O_3, TiO_2, Al_2O_3, SiO_2), as well as biomass ash, were studied and reused in various fields. There are many applications for these wastes:

IntechOpen

- Fly ash is mainly used in the production of concrete, road bedrock materials, cement clinkers and geopolymer concrete [1, 2];
- The red mud is used to produce ceramic blocks which store heat [3, 4]. It is also used in the plastics industry and for the production of pigments and bricks for the construction industry, road construction and agriculture [5];
- Pyrite ash is used to produce high density materials for heat storage materials and road construction materials [6];
- Biomass ash such as bagasse ash from sugar cane, rice husk ash and wood ash [7–9] for the production of bricks based clay.

On the other hand, the reuse of wastes in the field of terracotta is not the only reason to conduct research on the addition of certain solid residues in a clay matrix, even though it was the ultimate goal of this research. Other reasons can be taken into consideration. In fact, waste can:

- Economize energy in the manufacturing process by increasing the temperature at certain stages of the firing process in a tunnel kiln. Their higher calorific values cause self-combustion within the clay matrix so that a minimum of energy is required to firing the bricks;
- Reduce water requirements while improving the plasticity of the mixture;
- Improve - according to its chemical and mineralogical composition - certain technological properties of clay bricks.

Therefore, the reuse of wastes as additives in the ceramics sector has more reason to be than recycling. So, various research has focused on improving the performance of clay bricks. Some authors have studied the effect of wastes on manufacturing processes - and more specifically the firing process - and others have estimated the amount of waste that can be added to meet masonry standards. It consists of the evaluation of the technological properties of bricks versus the nature of the waste and the rate of its incorporation into the clay matrix.

The literature shows that the addition of waste glass improves the compressive strength, water absorption and porosity rates of bricks. Also, this waste increases the shrinkage of bricks [10, 11].

The addition of other additives such as sawdust and marble residue resulted in bricks with good compressive strength, especially for 15–20 wt.% of marble powder content [12]. The water absorption of these bricks was very high to be used in the field of civil engineering [13].

Another example of organic waste concerns the addition of biomass ash such as sugar cane bagasse and rice husk ash to clay bricks. These wastes reduce mechanical strength and increase the ability of bricks to absorb water [7, 8]. These two types of bricks have interesting thermal insulation properties and are also lighter which is an advantage in terms of transportation and use in the areas affected by the earthquake [8, 14].

The performance of clay-based bricks containing various amounts of rice husk ash or wood ash was also evaluated. The study has shown that bricks containing up to 10 wt.% of the rice husk ash and those containing 30 wt.% of the wood ash respect the standard requirements of clay masonry units [15]. Other work on the same waste has shown that 20 wt.% of the wood ash can be added to the ceramic matrix as a natural, economical and environmentally friendly pigment, thus allowing the lightening of bricks [16]. Another study has shown that adding sawdust to clay bricks improves porosity and results in lightweight bricks [17].

Among the ash waste category, there is another industrial waste, rich in hematite Fe_2O_3, which is the pyrrhotite ash. Few studies were carried out for this waste to explore areas of its recovery in industry [18–22]. It was generated between 1964 and 1982 [1] by the sulfuric acid manufacturing process from the combustion of pyrrhotite ore extracted from the Kettara mine in Marrakech (Morocco). Pyrrhotite ash is currently stored in large quantities in a large open space in the southwest of Morocco.

The present work is a contribution to evaluate the effect of the addition of two types of wastes on the technological properties of fired bricks-based yellow clay. This clay, whose main components are silica, calcium carbonate and kaolinite, was only used in pottery so far. The two wastes used are the pyrrhotite ash, which is a mineral waste, and the cedar sawdust, which is an organic waste from the artisanal sector.

2. Method and materials

The approach followed throughout this study is presented in **Figure 1**. The chemical, physical, mineralogical, environmental, thermal and mechanical characterization were carried out. Many analytical techniques were used, namely: X-ray diffraction (XRD), X-ray fluorescence (FRX), Fourier transform infrared (IR) spectroscopy, reservoir, Inductively Coupled Plasma Spectrometry (ICP),

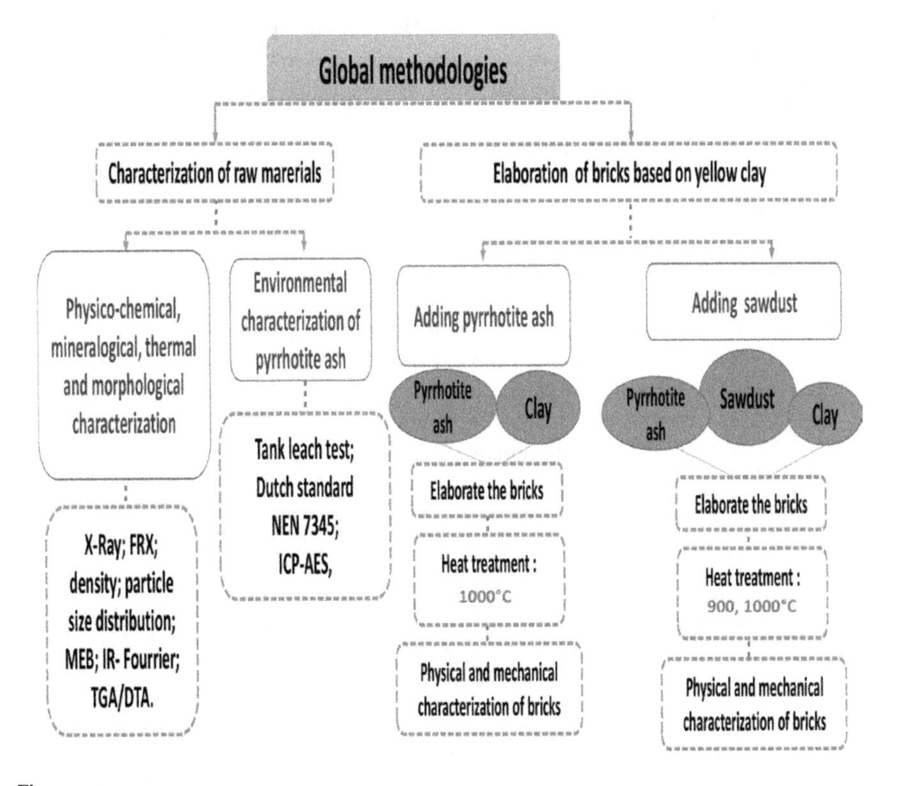

Figure 1.
Global methodologies used to carry out this study.

Thermogravimetric Analysis (TGA), Differential Thermal Analysis (DTA), Hydrogen potential (pH), Scanning Electron Microscopy (SEM), distribution particle size, bulk density, apparent porosity, shrinkage, weight loss, water absorption, three-point flexural strength and compressive strength.

Three raw materials were used, namely:

- The yellow clay extracted from the region of Fez city, and used as a matrix to make bricks;
- Pyrrhotite ash produced during the manufacture of sulfuric acid from pyrrhotite ore extracted from the Kettara mine which is located in south west of Morocco. The sample used in this study was retrieved from the depth of 0.5 m. It is a mineral waste that was used as an additive to improve the mechanical properties of the produced bricks;
- Sawdust from cedar wood, organic waste which is a waste of the artisanal sector of the old medina of Fez. It was incorporated into the ceramic body to adjust the physical properties of bricks.

The characterization of the raw materials concerns the identification of:

- The particle size distribution of pyrrhotite ash was carried out using the Sifting machine DIGITAL FI-FTL0150 & FIFTL0200. To achieve this analysis, sample was grinded with a wooden roller. The median diameter of particles was determined using the SediGraph 5100 instrument;
- The mineralogical phases using X-ray diffraction using Siemens D500 Diffractometer. The XRD patterns were performed in the range of 2θ between 2° and 60° with operating conditions of 40 kV and 50 mA;
- The functional groups using infrared Fourier transform spectroscopy (JASCO 4000 Fourier Transform Spectrometer) in wave number range of 4000–400 cm−1;
- The major and minor elements by means of X-ray fluorescence;
- The thermal behavior through thermogravimetric and differential thermal analysis (TGA - DTA) was performed with a TA Instruments balance model STA-1640. It allows obtaining simultaneous DTA and TGA diagrams under similar experimental conditions. Experiments were performed under N2 flow, from 25–1000°C at a heating rate of 5°C /min.

The **Figure 2** shows the steps of making bricks and the characterization of the fired bricks with different contents of pyrrhotite ash and sawdust.

- The morphological characteristics were determined by scanning electron microscopy (SEM) using a SEMHitch S-2500 microscope operating with an acceleration voltage of 16kv.
- The porosity and bulk density measured by the mercury porosimeter using Micromeritics AutoPore IV 9500 Series, and interpreted according to Swiss standards SIA 266 and ASTM C62 standards for porosity, and NF P 94–093 standard for density.

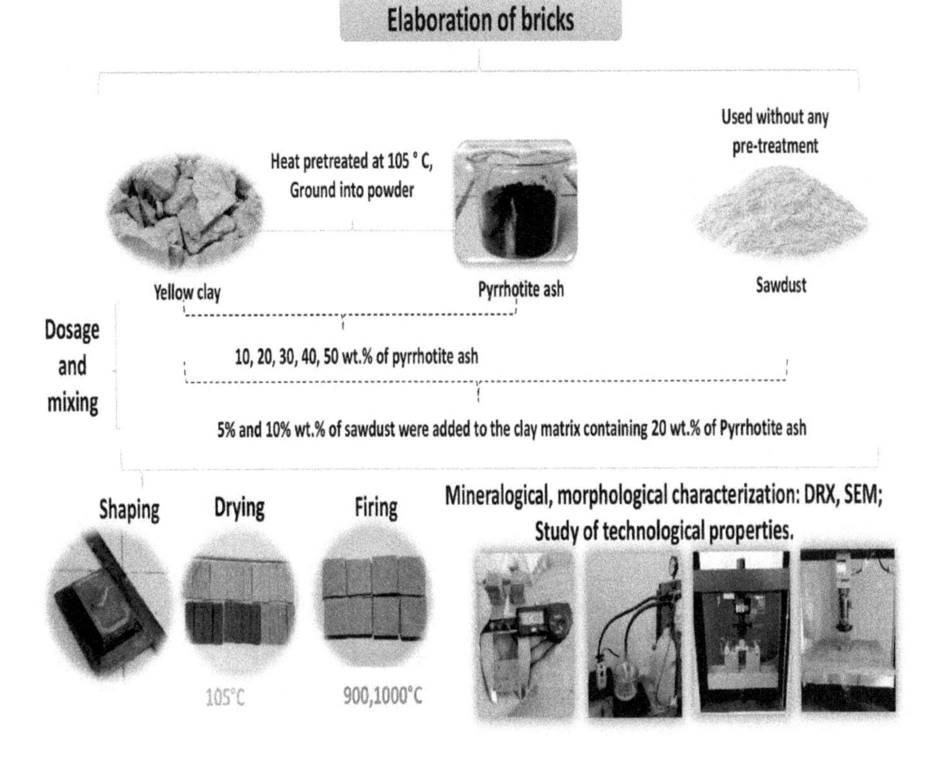

Figure 2.
The procedure adopted to carry out this work from the raw materials to the final bricks.

- The flexural properties have been carried out according to standard EN 771–1.
- The water absorption in accordance with ASTM C62.
- The shrinkage and weight loss according to ASTM and CNS 382.R2002 (Chinese National Standard).

3. In-depth study of the clay matrix

3.1 Summary of the chemical and physical properties of the yellow clay

The **Figure 3** shows the percentages of metal oxides obtained by XRF analysis. The **Table 1** shows the physicochemical characteristics of the clay with the main remarks drawn from this analysis.

The X-ray fluorescence analysis of yellow clay (**Figure 3**) shows the presence of several chemical elements [22]. According to the literature [23–25] this clay seems to be a calcareous clay which can be used in the production of low refractory building bricks.

As shown in **Table 2**, analysis by infrared spectroscopy of the clay reveals the presence of characteristic bands of silica, calcium carbonate and kaolinite. These results were confirmed by the X-ray analyzes which show the presence of crystalline phases of silica, calcite and kaolinite [22].

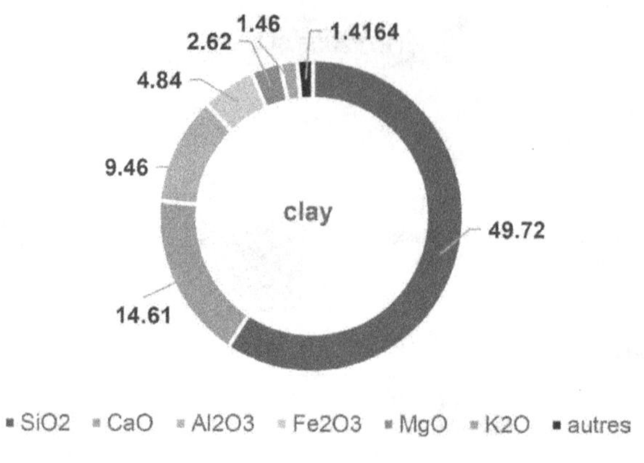

Figure 3.
X-ray fluorescence of clay raw.

Clay used for construction	Yellow clay	Interpretation
50 < SiO_2 wt.% < 60	49,72	Can be used for the production of bricks
CaO wt.% > 6%	14,61	Limestone clay
ΣFeO, CaO, MgO > 9%	4,84 + 14,61 + 2,62 = 22.07% > 9%	Low refractory material

Table 1.
The main chemical properties of yellow clay.

	Yellow clay
Predominant crystalline phase (XRD analysis)	Silica, calcite, kaolinite, dolomite and albite
Characteristics bands (infrared spectroscopy analysis)	Silica, calcium carbonate and kaolinite

Table 2.
The main characteristics of yellow clay.

3.2 Thermal study of clay bricks

The chemical analysis of the clay highlights the possibility of using it to develop terracotta bricks. Given that this clay has never been used as a clay bricks, and in order to understand its behavior at different temperatures to establish a firing program, a thermal study was realized.

3.2.1 Thermal expansion test

This measurement was studied by the DIL 402 Expedis dilatometer with a heating rate of 3°C/min. The test was carried out on bricks made of clay with percentages of pyrrhotite ash: 0 wt.%, 30 wt.% and 60 wt.%. The expansion curves obtained are shown in **Figure 4**.

L0: Length of the brick before thermal expansion;

L: Length of the brick during thermal expansion;

dL / L0: the thermal expansion factor.

From the results of the thermal expansion illustrated in **Figure 4**, and DTA / TGA detailed in a previous publication [22], two aspects are noted:

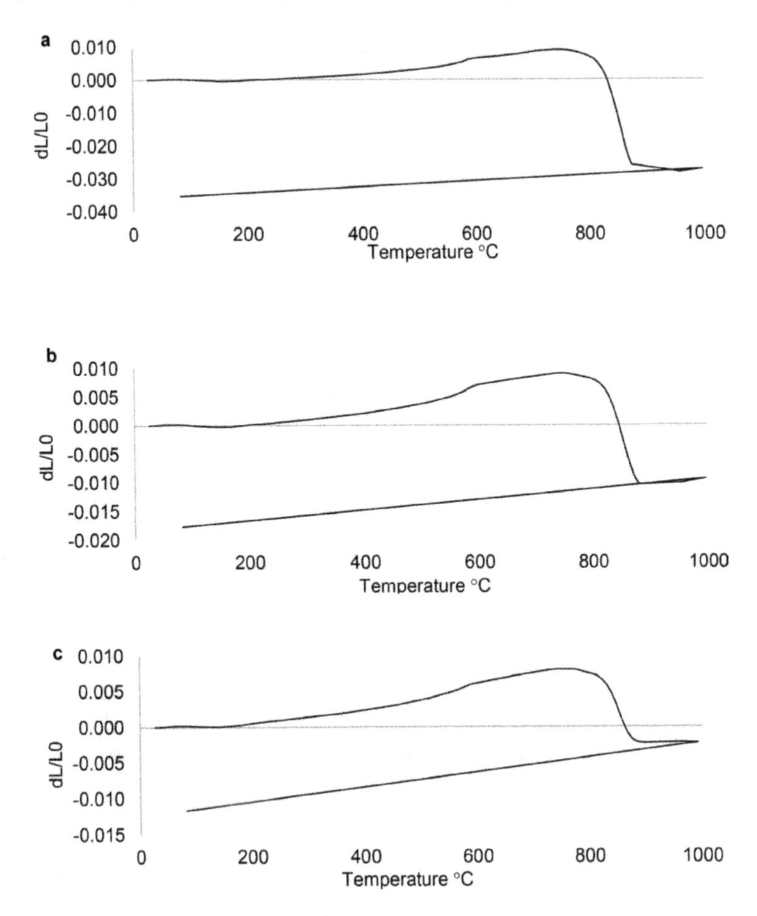

Figure 4.
Expansion curves for clay-based bricks with different pyrrhotite ash content: (a) 0 wt.%; (b) 30 wt.% and (c) 60 wt.%.

- Firstly, the expansion profile gives an idea of the shrinkage of bricks produced depending on the pyrrhotite ash content. **Figure 5** shows that the addition of ash decreases the dL/ L0 factor, which makes bricks able to keep their original shapes and improves their physical properties. Indeed, the decrease in dimensional variations reduces the risk of cracking that can affect the physical and mechanical properties of the ceramic body, namely porosity, density, resistance to mechanical force, etc.

- Secondly, dilatometric analysis allows to define the firing program, which is essential to approach the elaboration of any ceramic material, giving information on the temperature ranges where the material expands continuously without undergoing any deformation.

In this case, thermal expansion analysis (**Figure 4**) shows that all samples expand continuously without any deformation detected up to 750°C.

3.2.2 Brick heat treatment program

Based on the DTA/TGA analysis [22] and the dilatometry test, four temperature ranges can be identified. These areas are illustrated in **Table 3**. The identification of

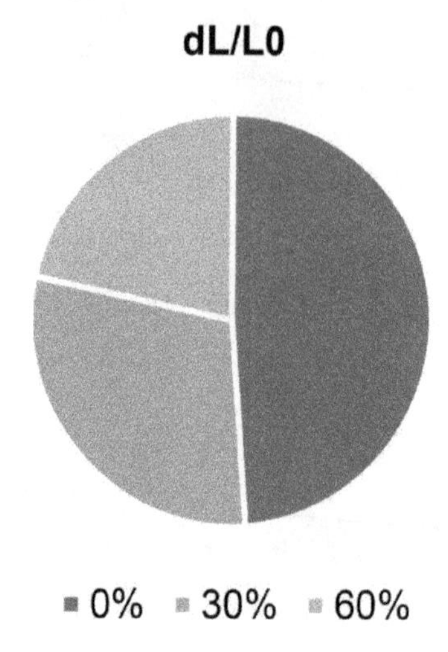

Figure 5.
Brick expansion profiles for bricks with 0, 30 and 60 wt.% pyrrhotite ash.

Temperature range °C	Heating rate °C/min	Observations
20–200	8	Moisture removal: hygroscopic water (100 ° C);
200–350	2	Slow speed so that the combustion of the organic matter takes place without the appearance of micro cracks which can be caused by the release of gases from combustion; (260–347°C);
350–750	8	Fast speed where the material expands continuously;
750–1000	2	Slow speed for better decomposition of carbonates (813.31° C);
1000–20	1	Slow speed to avoid any structural deformation.

Table 3.
Justification of the adopted firing program.

these areas allowed to establish the most suitable heat treatment program for firing bricks made from yellow clay and pyrrhotite ash. This firing program highlights the treatment temperature as a function of time as well as the heating rate. **Figure 6** shows the established program.

After studying the possibility of making terracotta bricks-based on yellow clay from Fez, new elements are sought to be used as additives in order to improve the technological properties of bricks. Pyrrhotite ash was chosen to this end. It is a mineral waste that was studied and valorized for the first time in our previous work [19, 21]. The physicochemical characterization of the pyrrhotite ash showed that it is a mineral waste rich in hematite, silica and alumina. It is also weakly hygroscopic and exhibits a low loss on ignition (3.4%) with a density around of 4.33 g/cm^3.

Morphological analysis by the scanning microscope shows that the pyrrhotite ash particles have a spherical shape with a relatively smooth surface. Obviously, the particles having a spherical shape and a smooth surface retain a small quantity of water, which confers to the pyrrhotite ash a weakly hygroscopic character.

The particle size of the pyrrhotite ash is continuous and contains grain fractions having a diameter between 1 μm and 125 μm. It is well known that mixing different fractions generally led to a compact material because the relatively small particles can get lodged in the interstices between the larger ones. So the material

DOI: http://dx.doi.org/10.5772/intechopen.99009

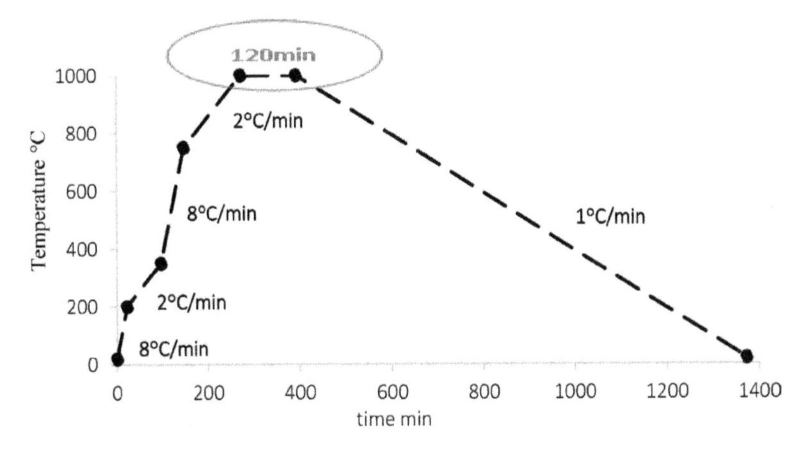

Figure 6.
Clay firing program.

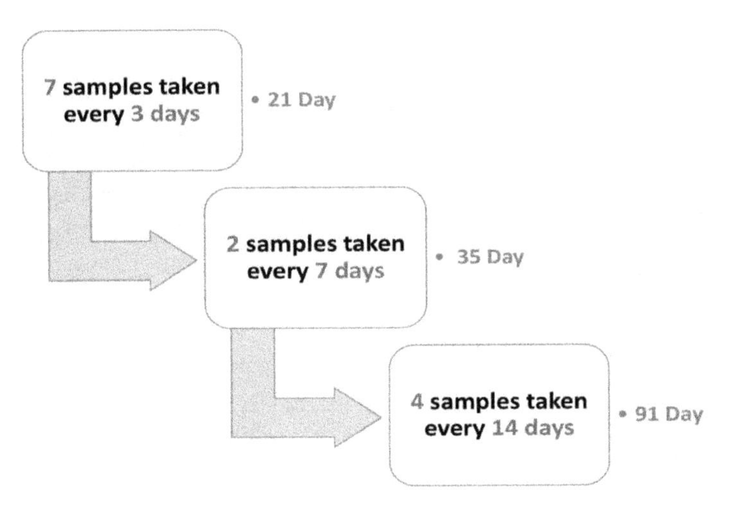

Figure 7.
Leaching test in a tank or tank with renewal of the lixiviant.

fills the volume more compactly [19]. Another work dedicated to the study of the behavior of pyrrhotite ash towards the environment has been published [21]. The main steps (**Figure 7**) and results (**Figure 8**) of this environmental study are shown below.

The test protocol is taken from the Dutch Standard NEN 7345 adapted to the Moroccan hydrological context. (MBMD: Modified Building Materials Decree) [1]. It is a Standard used to highlight the polluting potential of the fly ash recovered in construction materials.

Test protocol and conditions are the following:

- Spring ambient temperature;
- Bricks of dimensions 35 * 15 * 70 mm, aged for 28 days;
- Pure water as a washing agent with a ratio $V_L / V_S = 3.00$, (V_L: Volume of water, V_S: Volume of brick).

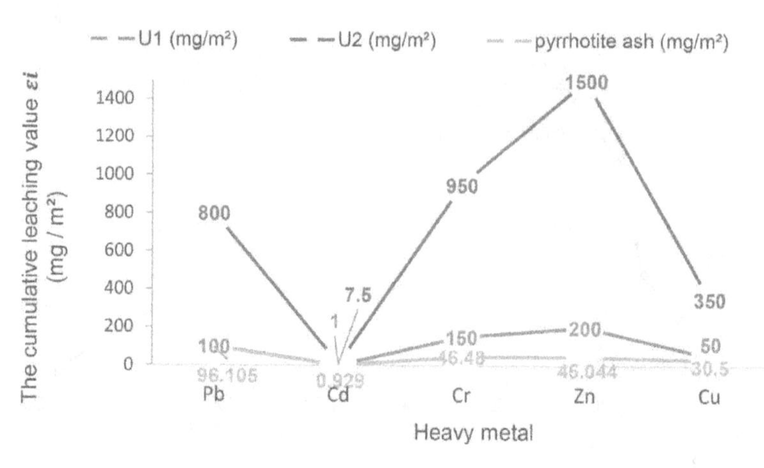

Figure 8.
The cumulative results of the heavy metals studied.

The leachates obtained were filtered using a 0.45 μm membrane filter, and after measuring the pH, they were acidified to pH 0.9–1.1 with a concentrated HNO_3 solution. After determining the concentration of heavy metals (Cr, Zn, Cd, Pb and Cu) using an Inductively Coupled Plasma Spectrometry, the εi (Σmg / m^2) value was calculated and compared with limits U_1 and U_2 to identify the category of this waste. The **Figure 8** shows that all cumulative of the heavy metals studied are below the limit U_1 [26–28], so the pyrrhotite ash can be classified as waste that can be reused in construction materials.

4. Elaboration of yellow clay-based bricks

Currently, the unique application of the yellow clay is the pottery. So, this study aims to valorize the yellow clay differently. The feasibility to elaborate bricks for construction based on the yellow clay was more detailed in an article previously published [22].

4.1 The effect of adding a mineral waste: case of pyrrhotite ash

The study of bricks treated at 1000°C shows that substituting up to 30 wt.% natural clay with pyrrhotite ash has a positive effect on the technological properties of bricks.

A notable variation of all these properties was observed namely: shrinkage, weight loss, porosity, bulk density, water absorption capacity and mechanical strength. **Table 4** summarizes the results obtained for the brick containing 0 wt.%, 20 wt.%, 30 wt.% and 40 wt.% ash as well as the requirements of certain standards for building bricks available in the literature.

In order to better respond to the imperatives of the sustainable development that requires the respect of the environment and the rational use of resources and energy, it was deemed necessary to further study the manufacture of bricks-based clay and ash by seeking to optimize the manufacturing conditions using minimum of energy. For this reason, the evaluation of the technological properties of bricks containing ash was also made for bricks fired at 900°C. The **Table 5** summarizes results of this study.

At 900°C, the brick containing 20 wt.% of pyrrhotite ash exhibits the best flexural strength (28.69 MPa). Since it reveals a low porosity, it was decided to improve

Test	Standard	Requirement	Bricks with 0 wt.% of ash	Bricks with 20 wt.% of ash	Bricks with 30 wt.% of ash	Bricks with 40 wt.% of ash
Shrinkage (%)	ASTM et CNS 382.R2002	< 8	10	6	5	2
Weight loss (%)	CNS 382 (Chinese National Standard)	<15	20	11.98	11.13	10
Porosity (%)	SIA 266 ASTM C62	[20–55] <40	36	36.41	39.4	42.11
Water absorption (%)	ASTM C62	< 22	13.8	16.16	21.6	23.2
Bulk density (g/cm^3)	NF P 94–093	[1.5–1.8]	1.63	1.79	1.87	2.04
Flexural strength (Mpa)	EN 771–1	> 7	7.65	23.88	31.16	28.53

Table 4.
Summary of the clay bricks study with 0, 20, 30 and 40 wt.% content of pyrrhotite ash fired at 1000°C.

Percentage	Shrinkage %	Weight loss %	Porosity %	Flexural strength MPa
20 wt. %	11	14.74	19.69	28.69
30 wt. %	10	13.94	20.38	18.05
Standards requirements	<8	<15	[20–55] and <40	>7

Table 5.
Summary of the clay bricks study with 20 wt.% and 30 wt.% content of pyrrhotite ash fired at 900°C.

Temperature	Shrinkage %	Water absorption %	Porosity %	Density g/cm^3	Compressive strength MPa
900	1.34	20.65	50.14	1.806	11.82
1000	0.89	19.88	50.78	1.797	10.78
Standards requirements	<8	<22	[20–55]	[1.5–2]	>7

Table 6.
The technological properties of the best formulation of clay-ash-sawdust bricks fired at 900 and 1000°C.

this formula (20 wt.% of pyrrhotite ash – 80 wt.% of yellow clay), by adding an organic element which evaporates during firing, leaving pores which will lighten the brick thus produced. For this purpose, cedar sawdust was chosen to be added to yellow clay bricks incorporating 20 wt. % of pyrrhotite ash.

4.2 The effect of adding an organic waste: case of cedar sawdust

Table 6 shows that bricks containing 20 wt.% of pyrrhotite ash, 80 wt.% of clay and 5 wt.% of sawdust of the total mass has characteristics corresponding to the requirements of international standards for terracotta bricks, whether fired at 900°C or 1000°C. However, those fired at 900°C are more resistant to compression with a value of 11.82 MPa against 10.78 MPa for those fired at 1000°C.

5. Discussion

The technological evaluation of bricks containing pyrrhotite ash was mainly carried out by measuring shrinkage, weight loss, bulk density, porosity, dilatometery and mechanical strength.

About bricks containing yellow clay and pyrrhotite ash, the results (**Table 4**) shows that the addition of the mineral waste increases the bulk density and flexural strength. However, the addition of up to 30 wt.% of waste enhances the flexural strength. This property decreases when 40 wt% of waste is added. Bricks containing pyrrhotite ash up to 30 wt.% exhibits a good bulk density with an increase of the flexural strength. Such a behavior was attributed in our previous work [22] to:

- The low decomposition of organic matter from the waste sample [19], thus low generating pores in the fired structure;

- The presence of a high content of iron particles in the waste sample, which do not induce flaws in the fired ceramic matrix;

- The high density of waste particles [19].

The maximum of flexural strength is obtained for the brick containing 30 wt.% of waste. The flexural strength decreases for bricks containing more than 30 wt.% of waste. This behavior was attributed in our previous work [20] to the firing temperature that should be higher than 1000°C, as well as the complex mineralogical transformations, occurring during the firing and cooling process, that depend on the content of Fe_2O_3 and fluxing oxides.

The evolution of porosity is in accordance with the water absorption values but is not in accordance with the bulk density and flexural strength values especially for the percentage of 40 wt.%. This behavior was explained in our previous work [22] by the fact that the increase of the waste content causes the coalescence of pores which leads to generating regions of weakness, which, in turn, weakened the mechanical properties of the bricks when the content of pyrrhotite ash is higher than 30 wt.%.

The bricks with 20 wt.% of pyrrhotite ash and 80 wt.% of clay - fired at 900°C - have the best mechanical properties with a flexural strength of the order of 28.69 MPa (**Table 5**). Knowing that the bricks intended for construction must have a mechanical strength which exceeds 7 MPa [29]. However, this type of bricks have a shrinkage of 11% (which exceeds the limit <8%) [30], a weight loss near the limit 14.75% (<15%) [31] and also a porosity around the lower limit 19.6% (> 20%), which makes the bricks with 20 wt.% of pyrrhotite ash and 80 wt.% of clay dense and heavy. In order to improve all these properties, another element has been added to bricks containing 20 wt.% of pyrrhotite ash. This element should promote the formation of pores, which will reduce the bulk density of the bricks and obviously make them lighter. To remain around the concept of recycling waste to protect and serve the environment, the element chosen is an organic waste which is cedar sawdust from the artisanal sector in the city of Fez.

Adding sawdust to the bricks has the effect of reducing their weight so that the brick becomes light. The addition of organic waste results in light bricks or porous bricks. The bricks become more porous [20% -55%] and meet European standards [15, 30] and the compressive strength remains above 7 MPa.

Experience has shown that bricks with a sawdust content of up to 5 wt.% of the mixture consisting of 20 wt.% of pyrrhotite ash and 80 wt.% of clay treated at 900° C, exhibits compressive strength of the order of 11.82 MPa, a porosity of 50.14% and a bulk density of 1.8 g/cm^3, and thus meet European standards for building bricks.

6. Conclusions and outlook

The main objective of this study has been satisfactorily achieved. Yellow clay used in pottery field so far was valorized in a field in high demand around the world, that of the building bricks. By adding mineral and organic wastes, pyrrhotite ash and sawdust, the technological properties of yellow clay based bricks were improved.

This study has demonstrated the feasibility of using by-products (pyrrhotite ash and sawdust) as a partial clay substitute in fired clay products. Waste's content affected all technological fired brick properties significantly. Based on the results of the physical-mechanical properties evaluations of the end products and the environmental evaluation industrial waste is recommended as a raw material (pyrrhotite ash and sawdust) in the manufacture of fired clay products. Use of this waste could have practical implications as a means of recycling and for achieving costs savings in brick production, as fewer raw clay materials would be required. Most importantly, the added value of this study is the reuse of two wastes at a time in a brick with good technological performance that should be economically and environmentally beneficial.

On the other hand, this study made it possible to determine the optimal formulation and favorable conditions for the production of bricks based on yellow clay and wastes. With the view to make it exploitable, it is necessary to apply it on an industrial scale to verify the reproducibility of the results obtained in the laboratory. Even to build a prototype (typical house) in order to study the durability of the bricks in real conditions while following the parameters influenced by the properties of the bricks, namely the climate and the air quality inside the typical house.

Finally, this work opens the way to lead the reflection in order to expand the range of products where it will be possible to valorize the yellow clay and develop other materials used in the fields of buildings and civil engineering.

Acknowledgements

This work would not have been possible without collaboration with universities at international level. Note that the majority of the experimental part was carried out in Spain and the rest between Morocco and Lithuania.

Institute of Ceramics of Galicia, the University of Santiago, Compostela, Spain;

Department of Inorganic, Crystallographic and Mineralogical Chemistry of the Faculty of Sciences of the University of Malaga in Spain;

Department of Environmental Chemistry and Materials Engineering of the University of Jaén in Spain;

Composite Materials Laboratory at the Building Materials Institute of Vilnius Gediminas Technical University in Lithuania;

Author details

Maryam Achik[1], Boutaina Moumni[1], Hayat Benmoussa[1*], Abdellah Oulmekki[1], Abdelhamid Touache[2], Gil Gonzalez Álvaro[3], Francisco Guitián Rivera[3], Antonia Infantes-Molina[4], Dolores Eliche-Quesada[5] and Olga Kizinievic[6]

1 Laboratory of Processes, Materials and Environment, Faculty of Sciences and Techniques, Sidi Mohamed Ben Abdellah University, Fez, Morocco

2 Laboratory of Mechanical Engineering, Faculty of Science and Techniques, Sidi Mohamed Ben Abdellah University, Fez, Morocco

3 Galician Institute of Ceramics, University of Santiago de Compostela, Spain

4 Department of Inorganic Chemistry, Crystallography and Mineralogy, Faculty of Sciences, University of Malaga, Spain

5 Department of Chemical Environmental, and Materials Engineering, Advanced Polytechnic School of Jaén, University of Jaén, Spain

6 Institute of Building Materials, Vilnius Gediminas Technical University, Vilnius, Lithuania

*Address all correspondence to: hayat.benmoussa@usmba.ac.ma

References

[1] S. El Moudni El Alami, M. Monkade, Valorisation des cendres volantes de la centrale thermique de jorf lasfar dans les ciments: Etude mecanique et environnementale, Physical and Chemical News. 51 (2010) 38-45.

[2] T. Hemalatha, A. Ramaswamy, A review on fly ash characteristics – Towards promoting high volume utilization in developing sustainable concrete, Journal of Cleaner Production. 147 (2017) 546-559. https://doi.org/10.1016/J.JCLEPRO.2017.01.114.

[3] G.A.P. RODRIGUEZ, Obtencion de Ladrillos Acumuladores de Calor a partir de Lodos Rojos, Universidade De Santiago, Instituto De Ceramica De Galicia, 1999.

[4] G. Rivera, Procediminiento para la obtencion de bloques ceramicos acumuladores de calor a partir de barros rojos del Proceso Bayer, UNIVERSITY OF SANTIAGO COMPOSTELA, 1997.

[5] G.A. Pérez Rodríguez, F. Guitián Rivera, S. De Aza Pendás, Obtención industrial de materiales cerámicos a partir de lodos rojos del proceso Bayer, Boletín de La Sociedad Española de Cerámica y Vidrio. 38 (1999) 220-226. https://doi.org/10.3989/cyv.1999.v38.i3.962.

[6] T.C.P. Rivera G., Mesa F. G., Procedimiento de obtencion de materiales ceramicos de alta densidad a partir de cenizas de piritas, (1999) 126 478.

[7] S.M.S. Kazmi, S. Abbas, M.A. Saleem, M.J. Munir, A. Khitab, Manufacturing of sustainable clay bricks: Utilization of waste sugarcane bagasse and rice husk ashes, Construction and Building Materials. 120 (2016) 29-41. https://doi.org/10.1016/J.CONBUILDMAT.2016.05.084.

[8] E.G. C.Viruthagiri, S. Sathiya Priya, N. Shanmugam, A. Balaji, K. Balamurugan, Spectroscopic investigation on the production of clay bricks with SCBC waste, Spectrochimica Acta Part A: Molecular and Biomolecular Spectroscopy. 149 (2015) 468-475.

[9] G.H.M.J. SubashiDe Silva, B.V.A. Perera, Effect of waste rice husk ash (RHA) on structural, thermal and acoustic properties of fired clay bricks, Journal of Building Engineering. 18 (2018) 252-259. https://doi.org/10.1016/j.jobe.2018.03.019

[10] S.E. Chidiac, L.M. Federico, Effects of waste glass additions on the properties and durability of fired clay brick, Canadian Journal of Civil Engineering. 34 (2007) 1458-1466. https://doi.org/10.1139/L07-120.

[11] C.N. Djangang, E. Kamseu, A. Elimbi, G.L. Lecomte, P. Blanchart, Net-shape clay ceramics with glass waste additive, Materials Sciences and Applications. 05 (2014) 592-602. https://doi.org/10.4236/msa.2014.58061.

[12] D. Eliche-Quesada, S. Martínez-Martínez, L. Pérez-Villarejo, F.J. Iglesias-Godino, C. Martínez-García, F.A. Corpas-Iglesias, Valorization of biodiesel production residues in making porous clay brick, Fuel Processing Technology. 103 (2012) 166-173. https://doi.org/10.1016/J.FUPROC.2011.11.013.

[13] F. Saboya, G.C. Xavier, J. Alexandre, The use of the powder marble by-product to enhance the properties of brick ceramic, Construction and Building Materials. 21 (2007) 1950-1960. https://doi.org/10.1016/J.CONBUILDMAT.2006.05.029.

[14] M. V Madurwar, S.A. Mandavgane, R. V Ralegaonkar, Development and feasibility analysis of bagasse ash bricks,

Journal of Energy Engineering. 141 (2014) 04014022. https://doi.org/10.1061/(asce)ey.1943-7897.0000200.

[15] D. Eliche-Quesada, M.A. Felipe-Sesé, J.A. López-Pérez, A. Infantes-Molina, Characterization and evaluation of rice husk ash and wood ash in sustainable clay matrix bricks, Ceramics International. 43 (2017) 463-475. https://doi.org/10.1016/J.CERAMINT.2016.09.181.

[16] O. Kizinievic, V. Kizinievic, Utilisation of wood ash from biomass for the production of ceramic products, Construction and Building Materials. 127 (2016) 264-273. https://doi.org/10.1016/J.CONBUILDMAT.2016.09.124.

[17] P. Turgut, H. Murat Algin, Limestone dust and wood sawdust as brick material, Building and Environment. 42 (2007) 3399-3403. https://doi.org/10.1016/j.buildenv.2006.08.012.

[18] B. Hatimi, J. Mouldar, A. Loudiki, H. Hafdi, M. Joudi, E.M. Daoudi, H. Nasrellah, I.-T. Lançar, M.A. El Mhammedi, M. Bakasse, Low cost pyrrhotite ash/clay-based inorganic membrane for industrial wastewaters treatment, Journal of Environmental Chemical Engineering. 8 (2020) 103646. https://doi.org/10.1016/j.jece.2019.103646.

[19] M. Achik, A. Oulmekki, M. Ijjaali, H. Benmoussa, N.E.L. Moudden, F.G. Rivera, Physicochemical characterization of an industrial waste: A case study of the pyrrhotite ash from south west of Morocco ., 8 (2017) 2738-2746.

[20] M. Achik, H. Benmoussa, A. Oulmekki, M. Ijjaali, N. EL Moudden, O. Kizinievic, V. Kizinievic, Evaluation of Physical and Mechanical Properties of Fired-Clay Bricks Incorporating both Mineral and Organic Wastes, the Proceedings of the 13th International Conference "Modern Building Materials, Structures and Techniques" (MBMST 2019). (2019). https://doi.org/10.3846/mbmst.2019.004.

[21] M Achik, A Oulmekki, M Ijjaali, H Benmoussa, O. Kizinievic, environmental study and valorization of an ashy waste: Case of pyrrhotite ash, IOP Conf Series. 606 (2019). https://doi.org/10.1088/1757-899X/660/1/012075.

[22] M. Achik, H. Benmoussa, A. Oulmekki, M. Ijjaali, N. El Moudden, A. Touache, G.G. Álvaro, F.G. Rivera, A. Infantes-Molina, D. Eliche-Quesada, O. Kizinievic, Evaluation of technological properties of fired clay bricks containing pyrrhotite ash, Construction and Building Materials. 269 (2021) 121312. https://doi.org/10.1016/j.conbuildmat.2020.121312.

[23] P. Muñoz Velasco, M.P. Morales Ortíz, M.A. Mendívil Giró, L. Muñoz Velasco, Fired clay bricks manufactured by adding wastes as sustainable construction material - a review, Construction and Building Materials. 63 (2014) 97-107. https://doi.org/10.1016/j.conbuildmat.2014.03.045.

[24] S. Abbas, M.A. Saleem, S.M.S. Kazmi, M.J. Munir, Production of sustainable clay bricks using waste fly ash: Mechanical and durability properties, Journal of Building Engineering. 14 (2017) 7-14. https://doi.org/10.1016/j.jobe.2017.09.008.

[25] A.M. Musthafa, K. Janaki, G. Velraj, Microscopy, porosimetry and chemical analysis to estimate the firing temperature of some archaeological pottery shreds from India, Microchemical Journal. 95 (2010) 311-314. https://doi.org/10.1016/J.MICROC.2010.01.006.

[26] N Alba, E Vázquez, S Gassó, J.M Baldasano. Stabilization/solidification

of MSW incineration residues from facilities with different air pollution control systems. Durability of matrices versus carbonation. Waste Management. Volume 21, Issue 4, July 2001, Pages 313-323. https://doi.org/10.1016/S0956-053X(00)00082-9

[27] J. Beleña-Pozo, I , Ordoñez-Belloc, L.M., Aliques-Granero, LEACHING STUDY OF ALKALI ACTIVATED MATERIALS FOR THEIR USE IN ROAD BUILDING, Materials Research Technical Unit, AIDICO, Paterna (Spain). (2014) 8.

[28] H.. van der Sloot, Comparison of the characteristic leaching behavior of cements using standard (EN 196-1) cement mortar and an assessment of their long-term environmental behavior in construction products during service life and recycling, Cement and Concrete Research. 30 (2000) 1079-1096. https://doi.org/10.1016/S0008-8846(00)00287-8.

[29] M. Sutcu, S. Akkurt, The use of recycled paper processing residues in making porous brick with reduced thermal conductivity, Ceramics International. 35 (2009) 2625-2631. https://doi.org/10.1016/J.CERAMINT.2009.02.027.

[30] Y. Taha, M. Benzaazoua, R. Hakkou, M. Mansori, Natural clay substitution by calamine processing wastes to manufacture fired bricks, Journal of Cleaner Production. 135 (2016) 847-858. https://doi.org/10.1016/j.jclepro.2016.06.200.

[31] C. Bories, M.-E. Borredon, E. Vedrenne, G. Vilarem, Development of eco-friendly porous fired clay bricks using pore-forming agents: A review, Journal of Environmental Management. 143 (2014) 186-196. https://doi.org/10.1016/J.JENVMAN.2014.05.006.

Chapter 8

Fire Resistant Geopolymers Based on Several Clays Mixtures

Ameni Gharzouni, Clément Alizé and Sylvie Rossignol

Abstract

This chapter aims to highlight the effect of clay mixture mineral composition and alkali concentration of potassium alkaline solutions on the thermal behavior of geopolymer materials. For this, three mixtures composed of kaolin (pure, impure kaolin or mixture of both), calcium carbonate, sand and potassium feldspar and three potassium alkaline silicate solutions with different concentrations were used (5, 6 and 7 mol.L^{-1}). At first, the effect of rotary calcination parameters at 750°C such as the dwell time (30, 60, 120 and 180 min) and weight powder (100, 400 and 500 g) was investigated. It was demonstrated that the kaolin dehydroxylation is quasi complete (> 90%) and do not significantly depend on the dwell time and powder weight. Whereas the carbonate decomposition degree increases with the increase of dwell time and the decrease of powder weight but still not complete (<80%). These differences influence the feasibility of consolidated materials. Indeed, a flash setting occurs for samples based mixtures with high calcium carbonate decomposition degree (> 50%) and low wettability values (500 µL/g) for the three used alkaline solutions. The thermal behavior at 1000°C depends on the chemical composition of the aluminosilicate source and the concentration of alkaline solution. A conservation of the compressive strength at 43 MPa after thermal treatment at 1000°C of geopolymers based on mixture of pure and impure kaolin and a low potassium concentration solution (5 mol.L^{-1}) was evidenced.

Keywords: geopolymers, kaolin, rotary oven, thermal properties, compressive strength

1. Introduction

Thermal resistance is an essential property for different applications. Inorganic refractory materials are generally used. However, the preparation of these materials requires high-temperature solid state reactions [1]. As an alternative, geopolymer materials, synthetized at low temperature (less than 100°C), are known to have good thermal stability. The term geopolymer was introduced by Davidovits [2] to design amorphous three-dimensional materials resulting from the activation of an aluminosilicate source by an alkaline solution [3]. They are generally synthesized from metakaolin [4, 5] or other more abundant and low-cost clays or industrial co-products [6, 7]. The thermal stability of metakaolin based geopolymers is due to the densification resulting from viscous sintering and pore network collapse [8]. The effect of calcium on the thermal behavior was also highlighted [9]. It was proven that the addition of low amount of calcium increases the densification temperature and improves the mechanical strength after thermal treatment. Dupuy et al. [10], have shown that geopolymers based on argillite (mainly composed of interlayered illite/smectite and 22% of calcite) exhibit a good thermal resistance that depends on the argillite calcination process. Indeed, a higher resistance is obtained for furnace-calcined argillite compared to flash calcined one due to the complete dehydroxylation of clay minerals and decomposition of carbonates. Tognonvi et al., [11] have also shown that the addition of argillite improved significantly the thermomechanical properties of kaolin-based geopolymers due to the in-situ formation of wollastonite, leucite and zeolite-type phases. Rashad and Zeedan [12] found that for fly ash based materials, the concentration of the activator had a significant effect on and residual strength after heating. As the concentration of the activator increases, the initial strength compressive strength increases. However, as the concentration of the activator increases, the residual compressive strength after firing decreases. Barbosa et al. [13], have also evidenced the crystallization of feldspar, kalsilite and leucite at 1000°C in potassium based gopolymers. Consequently, the mineralogy and thermal treatment of the used aluminosilicate is an important parameter controlling the thermal behavior of geopolymers. Raw clays contains naturally clay minerals, carbonate and feldspar. Calcium carbonate decomposes between 600 and 800°C into free lime and carbon dioxide. However, depending on the relative humidity, the produced CaO can react with H_2O to form $Ca(OH)_2$ [14]. The carbonate thermal decomposition depends on different parameters such as the nature and crystalline structure, the sample weight, the particle size, the purge gas... [15]. Furthermore, the calcination process can also influence the carbonate decomposition. For example, it was demonstrated that the limestone calcination in a pilot-scale rotary kiln calcination depends essentially on heat transfer and feed rate, whereas rotational speed and inclination angle are less important [16]. The calcination process have also an important role on the chemical, physical and structural properties of clays. San Nicolas et al. [17] have undertaken a comparative study between rotary and flash calcinations of kaolin and have shown that the method of thermal treatment influences the physical properties of resulting metakaolins and therefore and their reactivity for geopolymer synthesis. That is why it is necessary to understand the effect of mixture of kaolin, calcite and feldspar. The interaction between kaolinite and calcite upon thermal treatment was also studied [18, 19]. It was evidenced that calcite decomposition was influenced by the ratio of kaolinite to calcite, the CO_2 flow rate, the mixing, the heating rate and the volatiles during the dehydroxylation of kaolinite.

To understand the thermal behavior of geopolymer based on clays, it is necessary to understand the role played by each constituent of the clay. Thus, fundamental research on clay mixtures should be undertaken. The objective of this study is to exacerbate the effect of rotary furnace on the physical and chemical properties of clay mixtures and on the thermal behavior at 1000°C of the resulting geopolymers.

2. Effect of rotary furnace on clay mixtures properties

Three clay mixtures, named F1, F2 and F3, were studied as detailed in **Table 1.** They are composed of 40 wt. % of kaolin (pure and/or impure kaolin), 15% of calcium carbonate, 35% of sand and 10% of potassium feldspar. The difference between the two kaolins is the purity. In fact, impure kaolin has a Si/Al molar ratio of 1.44 and contains mo quartz, calcite and hematite. However, the pure metakaolin has a Si/Al molar ratio equal to 1. The mixtures were thermally treated at 750°C in a laboratory-scale rotary furnace (HTR 11/150 + 301 controller, Carbolite Gero) with different parameters. The dwell time was varied at 30, 60, 120 and 180 min. Furthermore, for the same dwell time of 60 min, the powder weight was

Constituent (wt. %)	Mixtures		
	F1	F2	F3
Pure kaolin	40	0	20
Impure kaolin	0	40	20
Calcium carbonate		15	
Sand		35	
Feldspar		10	

Table 1.
Nomenclature and the weight percentage of each constituent of the mixtures.

varied at 100, 400 and 500 g. The effect of these parameters on the calcined powder was investigated.

2.1 Dehydroxylation and carbonate decomposition degree

Thermal analysis (DTA-TGA) were performed on raw and calcined mixtures. An example of the obtained curves for raw F1 mixture is plotted in **Figure 1**. Three endothermic pics accompanied with three weight losses are observed in the temperature ranges 30–200°C, 400–600°C and 600–800°C. The first one is attributed to the release of adsorbed and free water [20]. The second weight loss between 400 and 600°C corresponds to the dehydroxylation of kaolin [21]. The weight loss, between 600 and 800°C, is due to the decomposition of calcium carbonate [22]. The comparison between the raw and calcined mixtures permits to calculate the kaolin dehydroxylation degree or the calcium carbonate degree (A) as Eq. (1)

$$A = 1 - \frac{m2}{m1} \times 100 \tag{1}$$

where, m2 is the mass fraction of the residual hydroxyl groups or CO_2 in the calcined mixture and m1 is the mass fraction of the hydroxyl groups or CO_2 in the raw mixture.

In order to understand the effect of dwell time and powder weight, the kaolin dehydroxylation degree and the carbonate decomposition rate were plotted in function of the dwell time in **Figure 2A**. No significant change of the dehydroxylation degree can be observed in function of the dwell time (**Figure 2A.a**). Regardless of the mixture, the dehydroxylation degree varies between 92 and 99% revealing a quasi-complete dehydroxylation of kaolin. However, lower values of carbonate decomposition degree and varying in function of the dwell time are noticed (**Figure 2A.b**). In general, the decomposition degree increases with the increase of the dwell time. For F1 mixture, the decomposition degree increases from 32 to 49% at 30 and 180 min, respectively. F2 mixture shows the highest decomposition degree of 80% after 180 min. F3 mixture exhibits similar results as F1 mixture with a decomposition degree of 50% after 180 min.

Consequently, the kaolin dehydroxylation is quasi-complete whatever the dwell time. However, depending on the mixture, the carbonate decomposition is partial and increases for longer dwell time. This result reveals than more energy is needed for calcium carbonate decomposition.

Similarly, the kaolin dehydroxylation degree and the calcium carbonate decomposition degree were plotted in function of the powder weight in **Figure 2B**. The

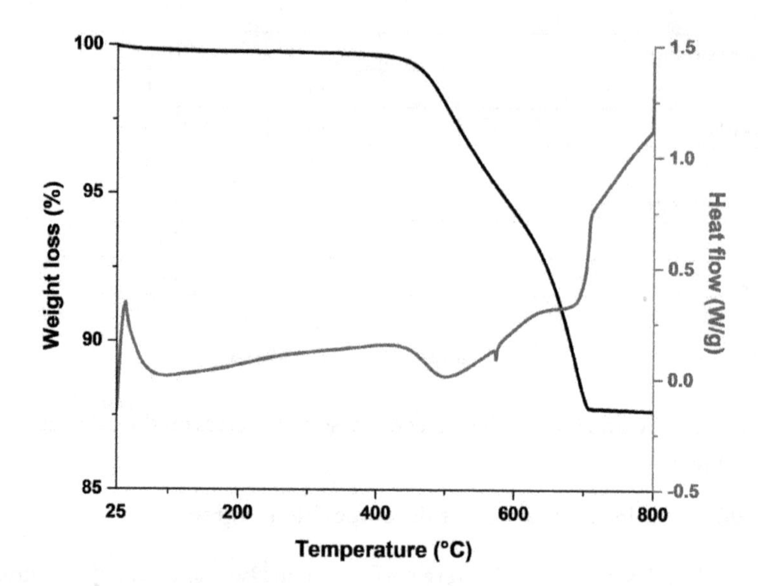

Figure 1.
Thermal curves (—) weight loss and (—) heat flow of raw F1 mixture.

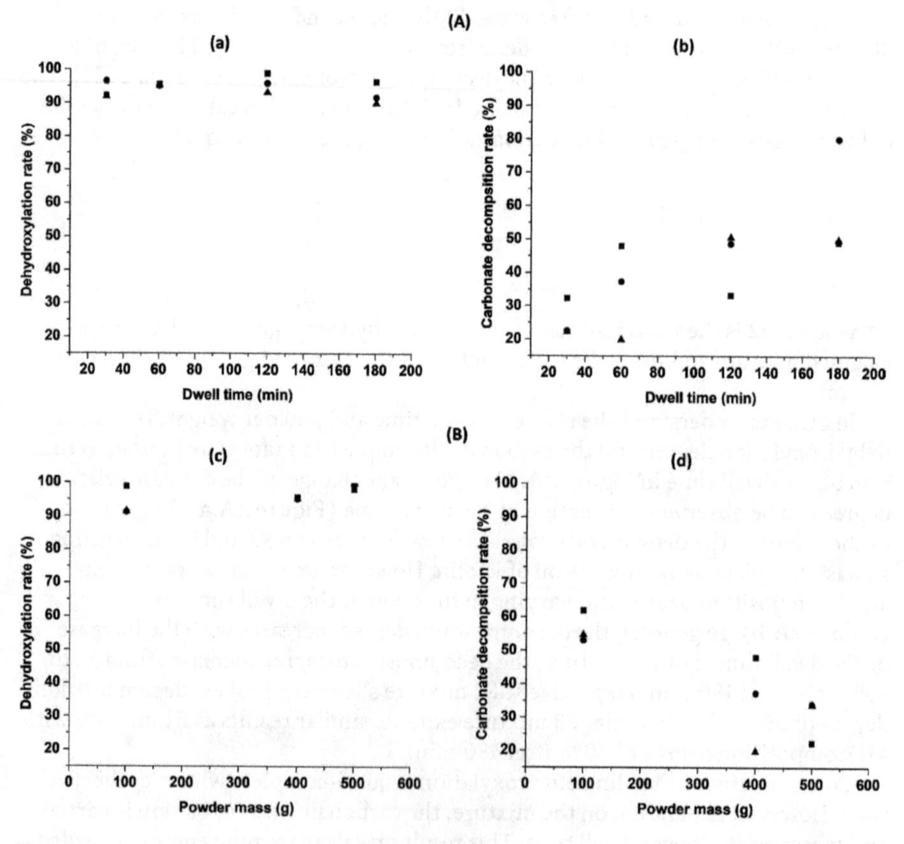

Figure 2.
Evolution of (a, c) kaolin dehydroxylation and (b, d) carbonate decomposition degrees in function of the (A) dwell time and (B) powder mass for ■ F1 • F2 and ▲ F3 calcined mixtures.

dehydroxylation degree values are very high, similar and varying between 91 and 99% (**Figure 2B.a**). A more significant difference can be observed in the carbonate decomposition degree. Indeed, it decreases with the increase of powder weight (**Figure 2B.b**). For F1 mixture, it decreases from 61 to 22% for 100 and 500 g, respectively. F2 and F3 mixtures show similar result with a decrease from 53 to 33% for 100 and 500 g, respectively. Consequently, the smaller powder weight, the higher decomposition degree. This result is in accordance with literature [23, 24].

Thus, the rotary thermal treatment parameters and more precisely the dwell time and the powder weight influence the calcium carbonate decomposition in kaolin and carbonate mixtures. Indeed, it increases with the increase of dwell time and the decrease of powder weight but remains not complete.

2.2 Wettability value

No significant differences were detected in the particle size of the different powders. Indeed, the median diameter is equal to 9, 60 and 60 μm for F1, F2 and F3 mixtures respectively, regardless if the used calcination parameters. So, a focus

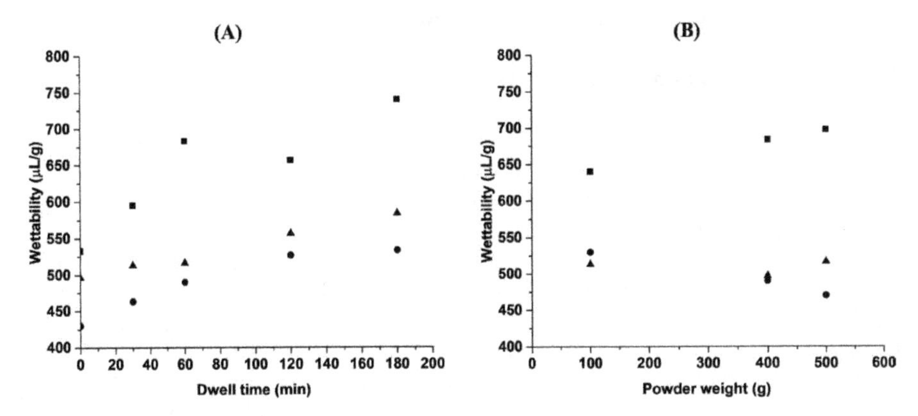

Figure 3.
Evolution of wettability values in function of the (A) dwell time and (B) powder mass for ▪ F1 • F2 and ▲ F3 calcined mixtures.

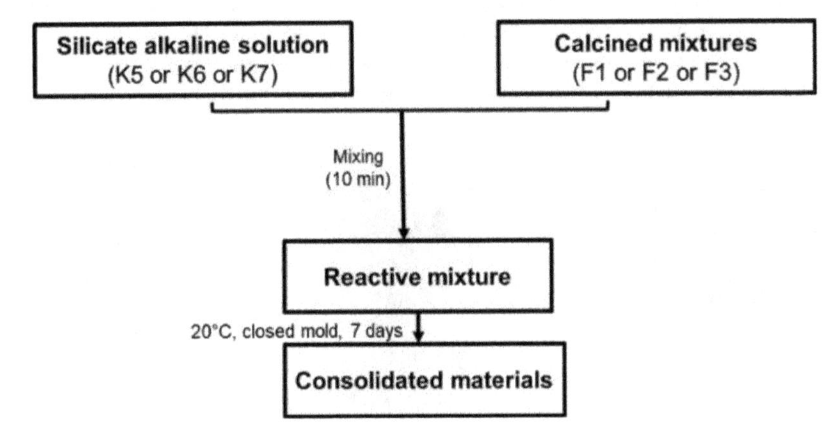

Figure 4.
Protocol of geopolymer sample preparation.

has been put on the wettability value which is an indicator of the aluminosilicate reactivity for geopolymer synthesis [5]. It corresponds to the volume of water that can be adsorbed by one gram of powder until saturation. In order to determine the calcination parameters effect, the wettability values were also plotted in function of the dwell time and the powder weight in **Figure 3**. At first the raw mixtures have different wettability values (533, 430 and 497 μL/g for F1, F2 and F3 mixtures respectively. Whatever the mixture, the wettability values increase with the increase of dwell time. The highest values are obtained for F1 mixture due to the higher purity of the used kaolin (740, 533 and 583 μL/g for F1, F2 and F3 mixtures, respectively). Less impact can be observed of the powder weight on the wettability values (**Figure 3B**). Quite similar values are observed whatever the mixture for the different powder weight. Thus, the wettability values are more sensitive to the dwell time and the chemical composition of the initial mixtures. Consequently, rotary calcination parameters induces differences in chemical composition and properties of the clay mixtures. This fact will induce different reactivity in alkaline media (**Figure 4**).

3. Thermal properties evaluation of geopolymer materials

3.1 Feasibility of geopolymer materials

Feasibility tests of consolidated materials were carried out for all the studied mixtures. Sample were prepared by mixing calcined mixtures with three potassium alkaline solution with different potassium activation solution with different concentration (5, 6 and 7 mol.L^{-1}). The samples were cast in closed polysterene mold and kept at room temperature. Examples of the visual aspect of the different obtained samples are presented in **Figure 5**. Whatever the used solution, samples exhibit either flash setting (hardening after few seconds of mixing before total homogenization of the mixture) (**Figure 5A**) or a consolidated appearance and a reddich color due to the initial color of the used kaolin containing hematite [25] (**Figure 5B**). The flash setting seems to be only linked to the calcined mixtures and not to the used alkaline solution. That is why the feasibility of consolidated materials was plotted in function of the properties of the calcined mixtures i.e. the wettability value and the calcium carbonate decomposition degree in **Figure 6**. For F1 mixture, whatever the dwell time, the samples are feasible. This is due to low carbonate decomposition degree <49% and high wettability values (> 600 μL/g). For F2 mixture, for a dwell time exceeding 60 min, a flash setting is observed. It corresponds to high carbonate decomposition degree exceeding 40% and a wettability

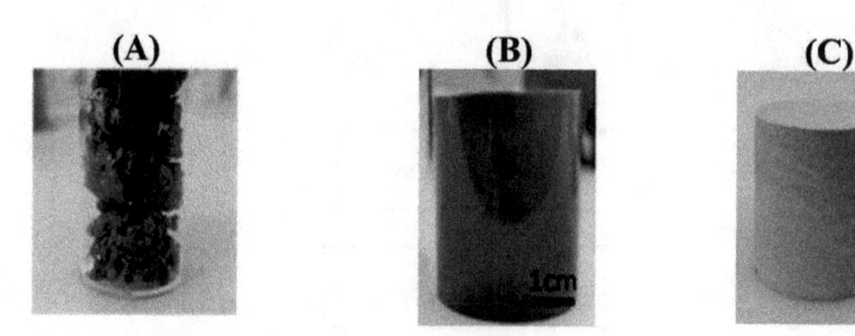

Figure 5.
Example of (A) flash consolidated sample (S1F2, dwell time = 180 min) and consolidated sample (S3F2, dwell time = 30 min) (B) before and (C) after thermal resistance at 1000°C.

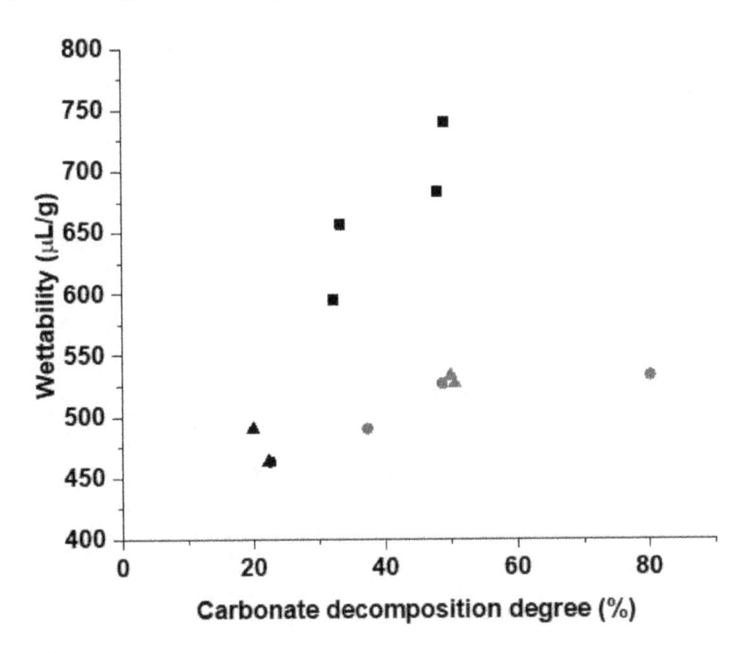

Figure 6.
Feasibility of consolidated materials in function of the wettability value and the calcium carbonate decomposition degree of the different calcined mixture for ▪ F1 • F2 and ▲ F3 mixtures (grey: flash setting).

value from 500 μL/g. Concerning F3 mixture, flash setting is obtained from a dwell time of 120 and 180 min corresponding to carbonate decomposition degree of 50% and a wettability values about 500 μL/g.

To sum up, flash setting occurred for mixtures with high calcium carbonate decomposition degree (>50%) and low wettability values about 500 μL/g. This result is in accordance with literature where flash setting was generally associated with high "CaO" content [26, 27].

3.2 Thermo-mechanical properties

In the following section, only the thermal behavior of the sample based on mixture with a dwell time of 30 min (no flash setting) with the different alkaline solutions was evaluated. Samples were heated at 1000°C during 1 hour in an oven. An example of the visual aspect of the thermally treated geopolymer is presented in **Figure 5**. C. It is shown a color lightening and no cracks. The samples were subjected to compression tests before and after thermal resistance at 1000°C. The obtained compressive strength values are given in **Table 2**. Before thermal treatment, the highest compressive strength values are obtained with K7 solution (from 47 to 54 MPa for K7F1 and K7F2, respectively). This fact can be explained by the higher reactivity of this solution due to its higher alkali concentration permitting to favor the geopolymer reaction and to reinforce the final structure [28]. After thermal treatment, with K6 and K7 solution, whatever the mixture, a decrease of the compressive strength is noticed especially with F1 mixture (based on pure kaolin) showing a drastic decrease from 30 to 3 MPa and from 46 to 20 MPa with F2 and F3 mixtures, respectively. With K5 solution, a decrease of compressive strength is obtained for F1 and F2 mixtures. However, the mechanical strength are conserved using F3 mixture (43 MPa). The reduction in strength is due to the dehydration of the geopolymer matrix creating internal stress, weakening the structure [29].

Sample	σ before thermal resistance (MPa)	σ after thermal resistance (MPa)
K5 F1	39	22
K5 F2	39	26
K5 F3	43	43
K6F1	30	3
K6 F2	42	28
K6 F3	38	20
K7 F1	47	20
K7 F2	54	46
K7 F3	49	24

Table 2.
Compressive strength value before and after thermal resistance at 1000°C.

Consequently, the compressive strength are governed by the reactivity of the alkaline solution. However, after thermal treatment, the compressive strength depend on the chemical composition of the aluminosilicate source.

3.3 Structural investigation

In order to explain the different mechanical behaviour and for more accurate information on the structural change of the samples after thermal treatment at 1000°C, XRD characterization was performed. Examples of XRD patterns for K7F1 ($\sigma_{after\ 1000°C}/\sigma_{before\ 1000°C}$ = 0.5), K7F2 ($\sigma_{after\ 1000°C}/\sigma_{before\ 1000°C}$ = 0.9) and K5F3 ($\sigma_{after\ 1000°C}/\sigma_{before\ 1000°C}$ = 1), before and after thermal resistance are presented in **Figure 7**. Before thermal treatment, similar phases are observed such as quartz, orthoclase and residual calcite. Impurities such as hematite are detected in F2 and F3 based samples and are due to the used kaolin. After thermal treatment, the patterns evidence the persistence of quartz and orthoclase and the formation of new crystalline phases such as leucite $K(AlSi_2O_6)$ [30], kalsilite ($KAlSiO_4$), potassium aluminium silicate ($KAl(SiO_4)$) and wollastonite ($CaSiO_3$) [31]. In fact, the amorphous phase crystallizes to form potassium aluminum silicate $KAl(SiO_4)$, kalsilite and leucite. Calcium reacts from silica of the amorphous phase to form wollastonite. These phases are refractory and are the origin of the thermal resistance of the samples [32, 33]. More leucite seems to be formed in detriment of kalsilite in K5F3 and K7F2 compared to K7F1 sample. This due to higher Si/Al ratio of this sample. Indeed, the formation of leucite is favored at higher Si/Al molar ratio [13]. This fact can explain the conservation of mechanical strength for this sample.

In summary, the thermal treatment at 1000°C leads to the formation of crystalline phases which depend on the initial chemical composition of the mixture. To correlate the thermal behaviour to the chemical composition, the compressive strength ratio ($\sigma_{after\ 1000°C}/\sigma_{before\ 1000°C}$) was plotted in function of the molar ratio (nCa + nSi)/nK in **Figure 8**. It is demonstrated that the compressive strength ratio increases from 0.1 to 1 with the increase of the molar ratio (nCa + nSi)/nK from 1 to 1.6. Indeed, the increase of this molar ratio means the increase of the availability of calcium and silica able to form crystalline phases at high temperature. The decrease of the potassium concentration seems also to favor the thermal resistance. Consequently, the thermos-mechanical behavior is related to the structural changes after thermal treatment which is intimately linked with the initial chemical composition of the used precursors.

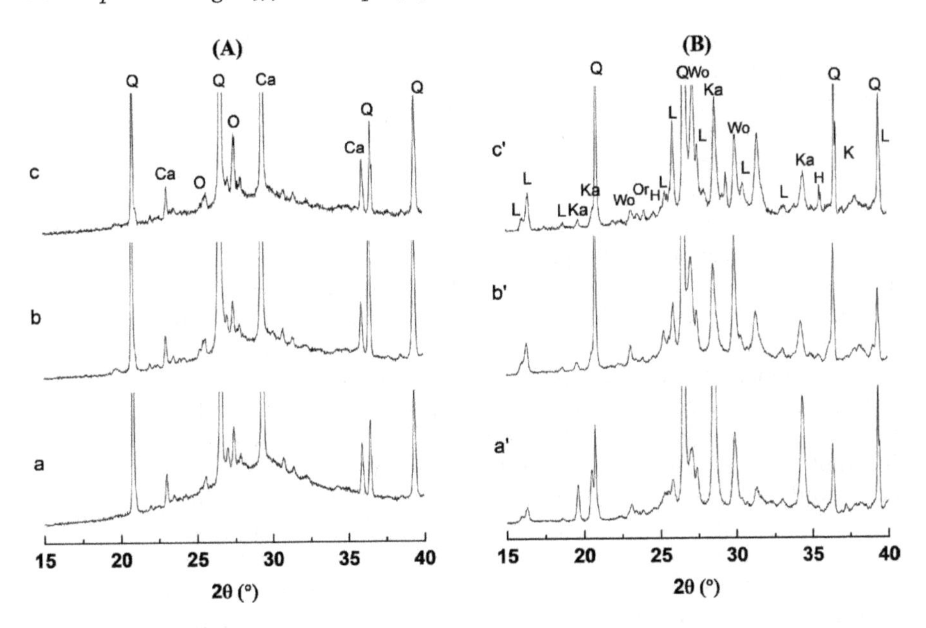

Figure 7.
XRD patterns of geopolymers (a, a') K7F1, (b, b') K7F2 and (c, c') K5F3, before (A) and after (B) thermal resistance at 1000°C (Q-quartz (01-070-3755), Ca-calcite (00-005-0586), A-anatase (00-021-1272), L-leucite (04-013-2099), Wo-wollastonite (00-043-1460), Ka-kalsilite (00-066-0070), Or-orthoclase (04-009-3610).

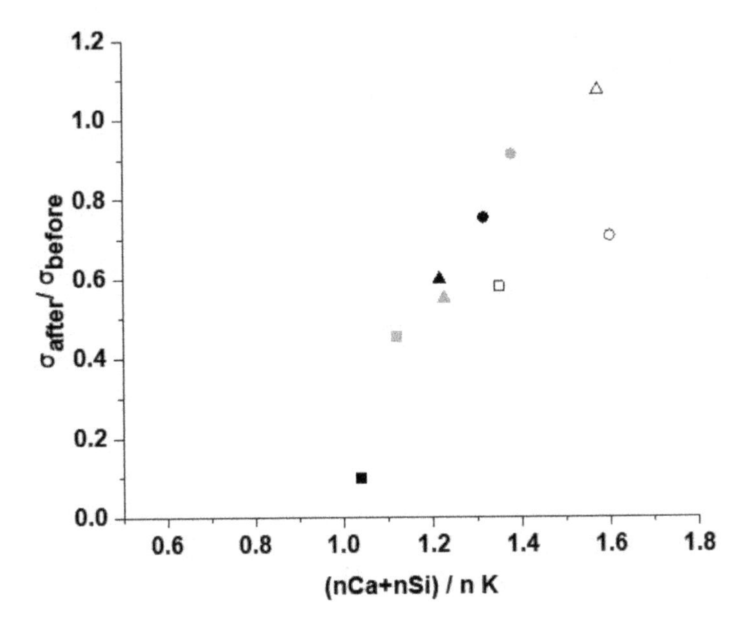

Figure 8.
Evolution of the compressive strength ratio (σ after thermal resistance/ σ before thermal resistance) in function of the molar ratio (nCa+nSi)/nK for ■ F1 • F2 and ▲ F3 mixtures with K5 (empty), K6 (black) and K7 (grey).

4. Conclusion

The objective of this study is to evaluate the thermal behavior of geopolymer materials based on different clay mixtures and potassium alkaline solution with different concentrations. Three clay mixtures composed of 40 wt. % of kaolin (pure or impure kaolin or mixture of both), 15% of calcium carbonate, 35% of sand and 10% of potassium feldspar, were studied. At first, the effect calcination parameters at 750°C in a rotary furnace was investigated. Indeed, the effect of dwell time (30, 60, 120 and 180 min) and weight powder (100, 400 and 500 g) on the kaolin dehydroxylation and the calcium carbonate decomposition degrees. It was shown that the kaolin dehydroxylation is quasi complete (> 90%) and varies very slightly with the dwell time and powder weight. However, more significant changes are observed for the carbonate decomposition degree which it increases with the increase of dwell time and the decrease of powder weight but still not complete (from 50 to 80%) even after 180 min of dwell time at 750°C. Consolidated materials were prepared based on the different mixtures and alkaline solutions with different concentrations (5, 6 and 7 mol.L^{-1}). A problem of flash setting has been encountered and was due to the properties of the calcined mixtures (high calcium carbonate decomposition degree (> 50%) and low wettability values about 500 μL/g) and not the used alkaline solution. The thermal behavior at 1000°C of the sample based on mixture with a dwell time of 30 min with the different alkaline solutions was evaluated. Before thermal treatment, the highest compressive strength were obtained for the highest alkali concentration of the used solution (54 MPa). However, after thermal treatment, the compressive strength depend on the chemical composition of the aluminosilicate source. A general decrease of the mechanical strength was observed a drastic decrease was obtained with mixture based on pure kaolin. A slight decrease for sample based on impure kaolin. A conservation of the compressive strength with mixture based on mixture of pure and impure kaolin. Formation of new crystalline refractory phases such as leucite, kalsilite, potassium aluminium silicate and wollastonite was evidenced. Thus, in order to obtain thermal resistant materials with conservation or increase of residual strength after 1000°C, it is recommended to use a low concentrated potassium alkaline solution and an aluminosilicate rich of calcium.

Conflict of interest

The authors declare no conflict of interest.

Author details

Ameni Gharzouni, Clément Alizé and Sylvie Rossignol*
Institute of Research for Ceramics (IRCER, UMR CNRS 7315), Limoges Cedex, France

*Address all correspondence to: sylvie.rossignol@unilim.fr

References

[1] Dimitriev Y, Ivanova Y, Iordanova R. History of sol-gel science and technology. J. Univ. Chem. Technol. Metall. 2008;43:181-92.

[2] Davidovits J., Geopolymers, inorganic polymeric new materials. Journal of Thermal Analysis.1991; 37:1633-1656. DOI: 10.1007/BF01912193

[3] MacKenzie KJD. What are these things called geopolymers? A physico-chemical perspective. Adv. Ceram. Matrix Composites IX, Ceram. Trans. 2003;153:175-186. DOI: 10.1002/9781118406892.ch12

[4] Duxson P. The structure and thermal evolution of metakaolin geopolymers [thesis] Melbourne University; 2006.

[5] Autef A, Joussein E, Poulesquen A, Gasgnier G, Pronier S, Sobrados I, Sanz J, Rossignol S. Role of metakaolin dehydroxylation in geopolymer synthesis, Powder Technol. 2013;250:33-39. DOI: 10.1016/j.powtec.2013.09.022

[6] Buchwald A, Hohman M, Posern K, Brendler E. The suitability of thermally activated illite/smectite clay as raw material for geopolymer binders. Appl. Clay Sci. 2009; 46: 300-304. DOI:10.1016/j.clay.2009.08.026

[7] Essaidi N, Samet B, Baklouti S, Rossignol S. Feasibility of producing geopolymers from two different Tunisian clays before and after calcination at various temperatures. Appl. Clay Sci. 2014; 88-89: 221-227. DOI:10.1016/j.clay.2013.12.006

[8] Duxson P, Lukey GC, and van Deventer J.S. J. Evolution of Gel Structure during Thermal Processing of Na-Geopolymer Gels. Langmuir. 2006;22: 8750-8757. DOI: 10.1021/la0604026

[9] Bernal SA, Rodríguez ED, Mejía de Gutiérrez R, Gordillo M, Provis JL. Mechanical and thermal characterisation of geopolymers based on silicate-activated metakaolin/slag blends. J Mater Sci. 2011;46:5477-5486. DOI: 10.1007/s10853-011-5490-z

[10] Dupuy C, Gharzouni A, Texier-Mandoki N, Bourbon X, Rossignol S, Thermal resistance of argillite-based alkali-activated materials. Part 1: Effect of calcination processes and alkali cation, Materials Chemistry and Physics. 2018;217:323-333. DOI:10.1016/j.matchemphys.2018.06.079

[11] Tognonvi M, Petlitckaia S, Gharzouni A, Fricheteau M, Texier-Mandoki N, Bourbon X, Rossignol S, High-temperature, resistant, argillite based, alkali activated materials with improved post-thermal treatment mechanical strength. Clays Clay Miner. 2020;68:211-219. DOI:10.1007/s42860-020-00067-9

[12] Rashad AM and Zeedan SR, the effect of activator concentration on the residual strength of alkali-activated fly ash pastes subjected to thermal load. Construction and Building Materials. 2011;25:3098-3107. DOI: 10.1016/j.conbuildmat.2010.12.044

[13] Barbosa VFF, MacKenzie KJD. Synthesis and thermal behaviour of potassium sialate geopolymers. Materials Letters. 2003;57:1477-1482. DOI:10.1016/S0167-577X(02)01009-1

[14] Karunadasa KSP, Manoratne CH, Pitawala HMTGA, Rajapakse RMG. Thermal decomposition of calcium carbonate (calcite polymorph) as examined by in-situ high-temperature X-ray powder diffraction. J. Phys. Chem. Solids. 2019;134:21-28. DOI:10.1016/j.jpcs.2019.05.023

[15] Romero Salvador A, Garcia Calvo E, Beneitez Aparicio C. Effects of sample

weight, particle size, purge gas and crystalline structure on the observed kinetic parameters of calcium carbonate decomposition, Thermochimica Acta. 1989;143:339-345 DOI:10.1016/ 0040-6031(89)85073-7

[16] Watkinson AP, Brimacombe JK. Limestone calcination in a rotary kiln. Metall Mater Trans B. 1982;13:369-378. DOI:10.1007/BF02667752

[17] San Nicolas R, Cyr M, Escadeillas G, Characteristics and applications of flash metakaolins, Applied Clay Science.2013;83-84:253262. DOI:10.1016/j.clay.2013.08.036.

[18] Mackenzie RC, Rahman AA, Interaction of kaolinite with calcite on heating: I. instrumental and procedural factors for one kaolinite in air and nitrogen,Thermochimica Acta. 1987;121:51-69. DOI:10.1016/0040-6031 (87)80161-2

[19] Macenzie RC, Rahman AA, Moir HM. Interaction of kaolinite with calcite on heating. II. mixtures with one kaolinite in carbon dioxide, Thermochimica Acta. 1988;124:119-127.

[20] Perera DS, Vance ER, Finnie, KS, Blackford, MG, Hanna, JV, Cassidy, DJ and Nicholson CL. Disposition of water in metakaolinite-based geopolymers. Ceramic Transactions, 2005; 185: 225-236. DOI: 10.1002/9781118407844. ch20

[21] Buchwald A, Hohman M, Posern K. and Brendler E. The suitability of thermally activated illite/smectite clay as raw material for geopolymer binders. Applied Clays Science. 2009; 46: 300 -304. DOI: 10.1016/j.clay.2009.08.026

[22] 3] Dupuy C, Gharzouni A, Sobrados I, Texier-Mandoki N, Bourbon X, Rossignol S. Thermal resistance of argillite based alkali-activated materials. Part 2: identification of the formed crystalline phases, Materials Chemistry and Physics. 2018;218:262-271. DOI: 10.1016/j. matchemphys.2018.07.036

[23] Salvador AR, Calvo EG, Aparicio CB, Effects of sample weight, particle size, purge gas and crystalline structure on the observed kinetic parameters of calcium carbonate decomposition, Thermochim. Acta. 1989;143:339-345. DOI: 10.1016/ 0040-6031(89)85073-7

[24] Close PK. Gallagher DW. Johnson, The effects of sample size and heating rate on the kinetics of the thermal decomposition of CaCO3, Thermochim. Acta. 1973;6:67-83. DOI: 10.1016/ 0040-6031(73)80007-3

[25] Gharzouni A, Sobrados I, Joussein E, Baklouti S, Rossginol S. Control of polycondensation reaction generated from different metakaolin and alkaline solution, J. Ceram. Sci. Technol., 2017;8:365-376, DOI: 10.4416/ JCST2017-00040

[26] Antoni A, Wijaya SW, Satria J, Sugiarto A, Hardjito D. The use of borax in deterring flash setting of high calcium fly ash based geopolymer, Materials Science Forum, Trans Tech Publ. 2016; 857:416-420. DOI: 10.4028/www.scientific.net/msf.857.416

[27] Antoni SW, Wijaya Hardjito D, Factors Affecting the Setting Time of Fly Ash-Based Geopolymer Mater. Sci. Forum. 2016;841:90-97, DOI: 10.4028/www.scientific.net/MSF.841.90

[28] Gharzouni A, Joussein E, Samet B, Baklouti S, Rossignol S, Effect of the reactivity of alkaline solution and metakaolin on geopolymer formation, Journal of Non-Crystalline Solids, 2015; 410: 127-134. DOI: 10.1016/j. jnoncrysol.2014.12.021

[29] Kohout J and Koutník P. Effect of Filler Type on the Thermo-Mechanical Properties of Metakaolinite-Based

Geopolymer Composites. Materials. 2020;13:2395.,DOI: 10.3390/ma13102395.

[30] Duxson P, Lukey GC, van Deventer JSJ, The thermal evolution of metakaolin geopolymers: Part 2 – Phase stability and structural development. J. Non-Cryst. Solids. 2007;353:2186-2200. DOI: 10.1016/j.jnoncrysol.2007.02.050

[31] Yu Q, Sawayama K, Sugita S, Shoya M, Isojima Y. The reaction between rice husk ash and $Ca(OH)_2$ solution and the nature of its product. Cement Concr. Res.1999; 29:37-43. DOI: 10.1016/S0008-8846(98)00172-0

[32] Perera DS and Trautman RL. Geopolymers with the Potential for Use as Refractory Castables. AZojomo. 2006;2. DOI: 10.2240/azojomo0173

[33] Zhang Y, Ming Lv, Chen D, Wu J, Leucite crystallization kinetics with kalsilite as a transition phase. Materials Letters. 2007; 61:14-15. DOI: 10.1016/j.matlet.2006.10.057

Chapter 9

Activated Clays and Their Potential in the Cement Industry

Carlos Hernando Aramburo Varela, Luiz Felipe de Pinho, César Pedrajas Nieto-Márquez and Rafael Talero Morales

Abstract

The thermal activation of clays to produce highly reactive artificial pozzolans on a large scale is one of the most important technologies developed on an industrial scale to reduce CO_2 emissions in cement manufacture. This technical document deals with the scientific basis for the thermal activation of clays to produce an extraordinarily high quality supplementary cementitious material (SCM) based on the contents of its hydraulic factors, reactive silica (SiO_2^{r-}) and reactive alumina ($Al_2O_3^{r-}$). The production process and the optimization of its use in the new cements offers better performance, features and durability. Furthermore, its mixture with Portland cement is much more appropriate when carried out in a blending station after both components, activated clay and Portland cement, are ground separately and not jointly in a single mill.

Keywords: cement, activated clays, calcined clays, pozzolanic additions, low carbon

1. Introduction

Currently, the cement industry is working on the search and use of new SCMs that allow the reduction of the clinker/cement factor in a significant way. The traditionally ones used are mainly blast furnace slags, natural pozzolans and fly ashes. In the case of the latter, and in view of the requirement to reduce "greenhouse-effect" gas emissions, the commitments acquired from COP21, and the forthcoming closure of coal-based electricity generation plants will greatly affect and seriously compromise their availability soon.

In the field of cements, mineral additions are understood to be natural or artificial inorganic materials or products that, added to Portland cement (PC) in certain quantities, improve its normal behavior, and may also sometimes provide some additional and specific positive quality or improve some of the characteristics of PC. As already mentioned before, the traditional mineral additions that are used in the cement and concrete industry, we can mention the pozzolanic additions (natural and artificial) and blast furnace slags, both which are known as active additions, in order to differentiate them of non-active or misnamed inert additions. The latter can be of limestone or siliceous origin and receive the common name of "filler", and none can be considered pozzolanic.

Figure 1 shows the scarce availability of conventional SCMs in relation to the existence of limestone and clays. The availability of thermally activated clays on the

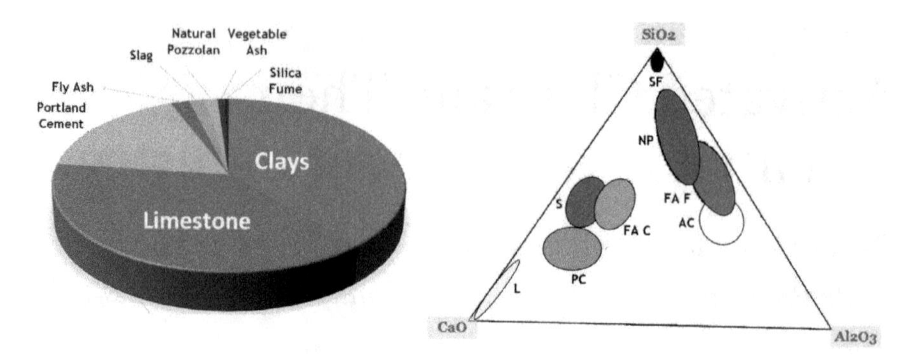

Figure 1.
Availability of MCSs worldwide. Their variability according to their composition.

globe is quite large, giving the SCM the greatest potential in the cement industry, even more so given the future drastic reduction in the supply of fly ash.

The need to activate clays thermally for an industrial scale manufacturing arises also because of its very high pozzolanic reactivity and the high quality that it implies. In addition, the cement producer has the control over production capacity and quality. Here it is necessary to clarify the difference of terms like "calcined clay" and " activated clay". The first term, which is the most frequently used in publications, also includes the calcined clays of the ceramic and brick industry, which have very low pozzolanic activity. The second term, "activated clay" (AC), which is a clay with a much higher pozzolanic activity, therefore it will be the term used instead of "calcined clay" from now on.

The new technology to produce AC implies an industrial development that will bring greater sustainability in the cement industry bringing not only due to the considerable reduction of CO_2 emission levels down to 70% compared to the Portland clinker manufacturing but also resulting in an important reduction in energy consumption.

2. Classification of pozzolanic additions by their chemical character

Classifying and cataloging pozzolans according to their origin or by their total oxide content that is, according to their chemical composition [1, 2], is insufficient and not at all significant for the characterization of their reactivity. Therefore, R. Talero proposed a very different classification based on the results and conclusions of his research carried out with or without other authors [3–15], which is based on its chemical character resulting from its corresponding reactive silica content, SiO_2^{r-}(%), and reactive alumina, $Al_2O_3^{r-}$(%) (Aluminum, Al, tetra- and/or penta-coordinated, which, in the case of the metakaolin is a metastable structure especially similar to the crystalline phase of the χ-alumina [16]). That is, under the same circumstances, capable of providing (depending on its amorphous or vitreous physical state and the average shape and size of its particles), every natural or artificial pozzolanic addition forming part of the cements and/or their derived products: concretes, mortars, pastes and prefabricated products.

Below are the chemical reactions (1)–(4) in which the hydraulic factors (reactive silica SiO_2^{r-}, and reactive alumina $Al_2O_3^{r-}$) of the pozzolans are involved when they react chemically with the portlandite in an aqueous medium at room temperature, much faster with the portlandite of the PC fraction mixed:

$$SiO_2^{r-} + CaO + H_2O = C?S?H + Q \quad (1)$$

$$Al_2O_3^{r-} + CaO + H_2O = C_3AH_6, C_4AH_{13}, C_4AH_{19} + Q \quad (2)$$

$$C_4AH_{13} + H_2O +_{gypsum} = AFm + Q \quad (3)$$

$$AFm + H_2O +_{gypsum} = AFt + Q \quad (4)$$

In this sense, it is very important to know the chemical character of pozzolans through the determination of the content of its hydraulic factors ((SiO_2^{r-}(%) and $Al_2O_3^{r-}$(%)).

Depending on its chemical character, pozzolans will have a very different influence on all the properties, performance and behavior of the PC base materials; starting from its fresh state to the recently hardened and the completely hardened: rheological behavior of its fresh pastes [3], to the heat of hydration [4–6], the mechanical-resistant performance [7] and durability against attack of sulfates [8–11] and chlorides [12–15] and other natural aggressive chemical attacks (sea water - aggregate-alkali reactivity and carbonation) in which the particle shape and average size can influence its nature like in the case of siliceous pozzolans and the silicic ones on its chemical character such as in silica fume and diatoms above all.

3. The clays. Its thermal activation and pozzolanic properties

The term "clay" refers to both a group of phyllosilicates and a granulometric division of the detritic rocks. This term also designates, in a not very precise way, a sediment or a rock constituted, in a great part, by minerals of the clay [17]. From a granulometric point of view, clay is any fraction smaller than 1/125 mm (≈ 4 µm) of a detritic rock, regardless of its composition. Although there is no precise size limit for clay minerals, most do not exceed 2 µm.

This crystalline structure is formed basically by two types of layers: tetrahedrons and octahedrons [18]. The tetrahedral layer has the group Si_2O_5 as basic unit, with

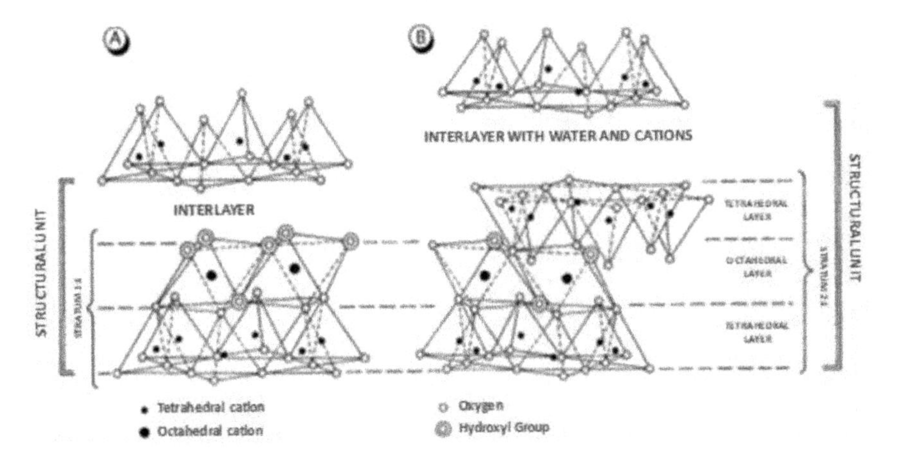

Figure 2.
Structure of the clay minerals. A) Type 1:1 stratum. B) Type 2:1 stratum [18].

the silicon in tetrahedral coordination and three oxygen of each tetrahedron shared with the adjacent ones forming a hexagonal structure (**Figure 2**). A part of the silicon atoms can be replaced by aluminum atoms and, occasionally, by Fe (III).

On the other hand, the octahedral layer has a cation, generally Al, Mg, Fe (II) or Fe (III), in octahedral coordination with oxygen or hydroxyl ions. The smallest tetrahedral structural unit of the octahedral layer consists of three octahedral and depending on the degree of occupation of the octahedral positions, the layers can be dioctahedral or trioctahedral. Dioctahedral minerals are those in which only two of the three octahedral of the structural unit have a cation in the center. When all the octahedral positions are taken, the minerals are called trioctahedral, and the cations occupying the octahedral positions are divalent (Mg, Fe (II)), while in the dioctahedral minerals the octahedral positions are occupied by trivalent cations (Al, Fe (III)).

The stacking of the layers and the substitutions of the ions determine different types of minerals in the clay. According to the layer stacking, they are divided in two big groups: those constituted by a tetrahedral layer and another octahedral layer, which share oxygen atoms (type 1:1) and those formed by two tetrahedral layers separated by an octahedral one (type 2:1).

Kaolinite, montmorillonite and illite clays, when undergoing adequate heating, can be activated as a result of a dihydroxylation process or loss of OH^- groups from their crystalline network, through the following chemical reaction:

$$-OH^- + -OH^- \xrightarrow{\uparrow Q} H_2O \uparrow + O^{2-} \quad (5)$$

The optimal temperature for this purpose usually ranges from 600–800°C, depending on the clay mineral composition itself. In synthesis, the clay thermal decomposition begins at 120°C with the loss of humidity (hygroscopic, colloidal and hydration water physically adsorbed, or absorbed in the material pores). As the process temperature increases, the hydroxyl groups begin to separate from the crystalline network (dihydroxylation stage). The increase in the vibration energy reaches a thermal agitation value adequate to enable the union with a nearby proton and form a water molecule that goes to the atmosphere to finally separate from the crystalline structure leaving it in an amorphous state that is not vitreous like that of fly ashes. At temperatures above 920° C, the AC becomes very unstable making the formation of spinel, pseudo-mullite or pre-mullite and even mullite possible [19]. **Figure 3** shows the thermal behavior of the most common clays [19]. The temperature values here given correspond to kaolinitic clays.

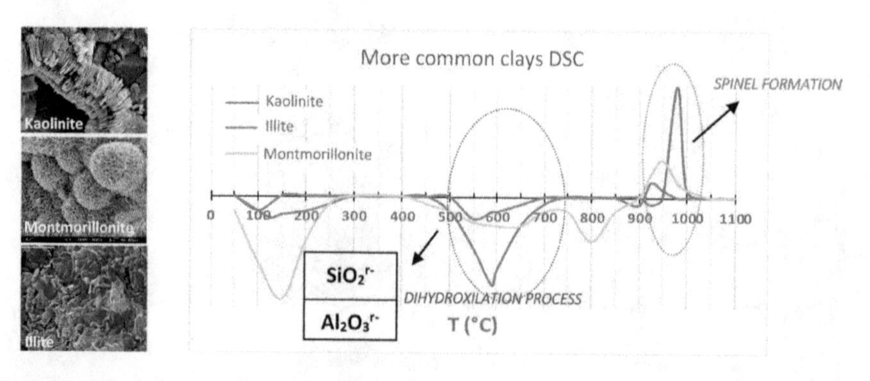

Figure 3.
Thermal behavior of the most common clays and its consequences for their resulting final pozzolanicity at each temperature.

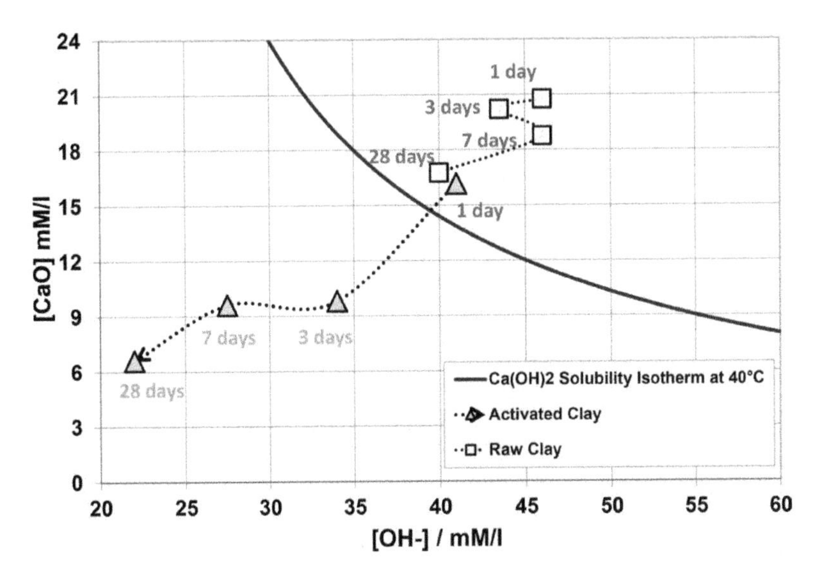

Figure 4.
Increased pozzolanic properties of clay after thermal activation. Frattini test [20]. Results. Ages: 1, 2, 7 and 28 days.

The thermal activation process of the clays produces an artificial pozzolan with an aluminic chemical character, according to R. Talero [3–15]. The chemically combined water of the clay released to the atmosphere acts on the coordination index of Al_2O_3 which was 6 [19]. After this thermal process, in optimum conditions (in coordination 4 or 5 [16]) it reacts chemically and very quickly with the portlandite of the liquid phase of the PC from the very first ages of its hydration. The physical state is amorphous and not vitreous like that of fly ash. On the other hand, the pozzolanic reaction of the latter, in the same circumstances and on an equal footing with everything else, is necessarily much slower.

Therefore, although kaolinitic clays have a higher content of Al_2O_3, a priori, it should not be a restriction as to which clay to use to produce an artificial pozzolan through thermal activation. Although finally and in any case, the suitability must be evaluated according to the content of SiO_2^{r-} (%) and $Al_2O_3^{r-}$ (%) in each mixture of clays that is possible to generate during its thermal activation process.

Figure 4 shows the pozzolanic activity of a kaolinitic clay, determined by the EN 196–5 standard [20] before and after its optimal thermal activation.

4. Pyro process technology

First, the clay must go through the drying, activation, and cooling processes. If the clay to be activated has a high content of iron (greater than 4%), it is important to ensure the change of color of the clay to gray during the thermal activation process to generate pozzolanic characteristics and thus promote its mixing with the PC.

The main parameters to obtain thermally AC and to guarantee its color change are the precise control of the adequate calcination temperature and the concentration of oxygen in the gases in the drying, activation, and cooling equipment.

The technology used for the combustion system of the drying and thermal activation processes allows operation with solid fuel, ensuring the stability of the flame even in a process with lower temperatures (less than 900°C).

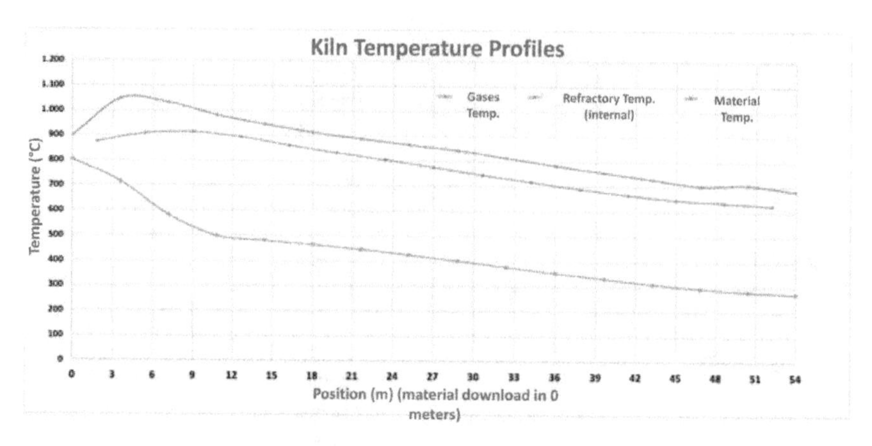

Figure 5.
T-profiles of gases, material bed and refractory.

The drying and thermal activation of the clays can be carried out by means of rotary kilns or with "flash technology". In the case of the use of rotary kilns, it is possible to reuse existing kilns in cement factories that are already out of service to adapt them, in any case, to their new condition of adequate heating of the clays for their activation.

Figure 5 shows the temperature profiles of the gases, the material bed and the refractory lining of a mathematical model developed for the simulation of rotary kilns for the thermal activation of clays. In this case, the material fed into the kiln has already been dried at ≈ 250°C.

The flash technology is based on the dragging of small solid particles by a concurrent flow of hot gases to obtain high coefficients of heat and mass transfer in a more compact equipment. This technology can be used for the drying or activation process. In the case of applying a flash calciner, the process must be staged in several stages in a cyclone tower to ensure the proper residence time of the material in the temperature range of 750 to 850°C or "transit time", necessary for the activation to take place.

The experience in rotary kilns at an industrial level is extensive in Brazil with kilns of up to 1,100 Tm/day. And at the present time in Colombia with a kiln with a capacity of 1,500 Tm/day. Its operation is relatively simple and easy to understand by control room operators. Its operation control, in terms of adjusting the activation temperatures according to the quality control variables hour by hour, is relatively easy to handle, even though the short activation range in terms of temperature makes this control very demanding in order to obtain an AC of high pozzolanic activity. Therefore, it is important to say that the experience of thermal activation of clays with rotary kilns has already been several decades and there is not, nowadays, an industrial activation in "flash calciner" of such an important industrial size.

Finally, after having achieved the thermal activation of the clayey material, it is necessary to cool it. In this last stage and in the case of clays with a high Fe_2O_3 (%) content, it is also important to control the atmosphere to avoid that the material at high temperatures comes into contact with high air flows and thus avoid that the gray color obtained in the previous heating stages is maintained and not lost by the oxidation of the new thermally activated material. A technology that is perfectly suited to these two objectives (cooling the material and maintaining its gray color) is the rotary cooler.

DOI: http://dx.doi.org/10.5772/intechopen.99461

5. Process control and verification variables

One of the aspects that takes on an extraordinary importance in the process of thermal activation of clays, is how to assure the quality of these after having them thermally activated because there is still no analytical method or mechanical test that determines the pozzolanic activity in a direct and immediate way as soon as the AC has left the rotary kiln or the flash Calciner.

Therefore, the clay thermal activation must be determined in an indirect way to guarantee the highest possible content of $Al_2O_3^{r-}$ (%) [21] and SiO_2^{r-} (%) [22] after the process of thermal activation of the kiln by quick kiln adjustments in case it will be necessary. This will undoubtedly translate into a higher pozzolanic activity of the same [20], as mentioned above.

During this stage, and for the same reason, it is highly recommended to determine parameters such as Loss of Ignition (LOI), content of Kaolinite (%) before and after this calcination process and also its Pozzolanic Activity Index (PAI) after the calcination process. All these analyses must be correlated previously.

On this previous stage it is so important to determine the hydraulic factor contents of $Al_2O_3^{r-}$ (%) [21] and SiO_2^{r-} (%) [22] on the AC, in order to find the optimum temperature of every different clay available in the quarry.

In that sense, the activation temperature at which the highest contents of $Al_2O_3^{r-}$ (%) [21] are obtained in the AC, will be the optimum temperature. Therefore, in this way it will also be possible to determine the upper and lower activation ranges, which indicate whether this optimal thermal activation temperature is exceeded to a certain extent, in such case, a recrystallization of the *amorphous* structure of the AC obtained will be produced, losing its activation level and, therefore, pozzolanic activity. And if, on the contrary, the temperature is very low, the needed dihydroxylation will not be achieved and its pozzolanic activity will be also very poor because it still has remains of raw clay without thermal activation. Either from kaolinite and/or from illite and/or from montmorillonite or from a random mixture of all three or only two of them. This will undoubtedly result in a lower degree of replacement of Portland clinker in the cement to be designed, dosed and finally produced.

With all this information obtained through the analysis and verification tests that must necessarily be carried out at laboratory level, it is possible to clearly identify and determine the ranges in which these variables move according to the highest pozzolanic activity to be reached, since the mentioned analysis and tests must also be used in the quality control of AC at an industrial scale in the cement factory.

6. Inter-grinding

The most common operation in the cement factories is the inter grinding in a single mill, of the Portland clinker, its setting regulator (natural gypsum stone) and the active and/or non-active mineral additions incorporated in each case, where the reduction in particle size occurs. For this reason, it is especially important to know the hardness indexes of the different materials to be grinded, their humidity, their proportions and granulometric feeding, in order to, with this information, design the load of grinding balls that each grinding chamber must carry, also according to the typology and physical quality of the cement to be produced.

The AC has a very high fineness. It could be said that 85% of its mass passes through the 1 mm mesh sieve, although, this value will depend on the type of clay, its mineralogical composition, and its quartz content. As an example, we can mention that the Bond hardness index for limestone can vary from 10 to 13 Kwh/Tm, for an AC from 13 to 15 Kwh/Tm and for Portland clinker from 16 to 18 Kwh/Tm. The ranges may vary depending on the mineralogical composition, quartz content, origin, etc.

In some cases, the quartz content in the raw clayey material fed to the kiln can vary from 25 to 50%. This factor must be considered, therefore, in an inter-grinding. The AC has an intermediate hardness, although it is closer to that of limestone, having a very fine granulometric feeding so that it will be much easier to grind than limestone, leaving the first chamber of the mill quite empty. To obtain a performance of the same order of magnitude that the traditional cements, with security it will be possible to work with the specifications of a greater retained in the sieve N. ° 325, although its Blaine fineness will be also greater. As an example, for a "General Use", with a performance of ≈ 26 MPa at 28 days, it will be possible to work with a retention in screen No. 325 between 4 to 7% and a Blaine fineness between 4500 to 5500 cm^2/g.

In addition, quartz, although hard to grind, does not usually present a large size so that in this type of grinding it can play the role of "grinding admixture", also producing a cleaning effect of the balls and the lining of the mill, helping the grinding, thus being able to reduce or avoid the chemical admixture that improves the grinding itself. On the other hand, and due to the very low granulometry of the AC, the possibility of feeding it directly into the separator can also be studied. The physical aspects dealt with here make sense for replacement levels above 12%, but, however, with a low feed, its changes will not be much noticed. And as far as pozzolanic activity is concerned, this will become important with replacement levels above 8% depending on its $Al_2O_3^{r-}$ (%) content.

As for the dosage of the cements with this pozzolan, the optimal relationship between all the components, Portland clinker, AC, other SCMs and gypsum, will depend on multiple factors. Therefore, each dosage must be studied and analyzed separately and exclusively, depending on the following premises or conditions: the mineralogical composition of Portland clinker, the reactivity of the AC produced (its contents of $Al_2O_3^{r-}$ (%) and SiO_2^{r-} (%)) and the optimum content of SO_3, among others.

As an example, **Figure 6** shows the mechanical performances [23] obtained with two different types of PCs, with the same dosage of clinker, AC and limestone filler, and with the same grinding fineness, respectively. In this trial, two AC with different content of $Al_2O_3^{r-}$ (%) and different proportion of gypsum added as setting regulator were used.

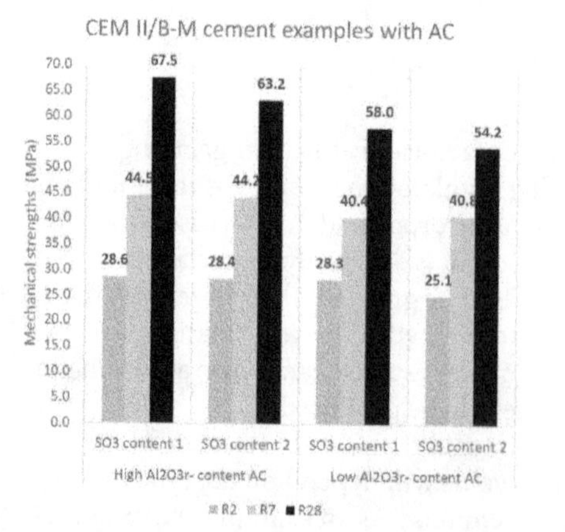

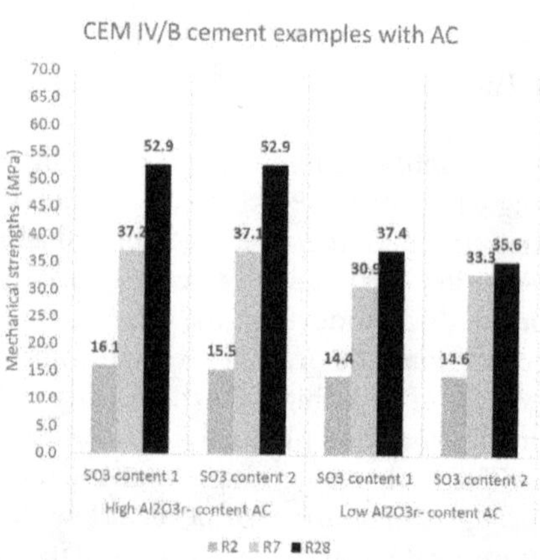

Figure 6.
Performance obtained in the dosage of different cements according to the European normativity [23].

Finally, it is also important to consider the very low granulometry of AC and its rheological behavior when it is so dry, in the transport systems, hoppers and dispensers because avalanches may occur in the hoppers and the control in the dosage may become somewhat difficult.

7. Separate grinding and blending stations

Without a doubt the best grinding option to manufacture cements with several SCMs is separate grinding. From the point of view of particle grinding, the ideal is to grind materials of similar hardness because this ensures a more controlled and efficient grinding. In a inter grinding, the grinding is conducted by the harder material and this will define the retained in the sieve No. 325 and the Blaine fineness, therefore, the softer materials will be "over grinded" and these will affect the final particle size distribution of the product. Logically, the viability of this system will depend on the availability of equipment: two mills and their production capacities.

Separate grinding offers significant savings by eliminating the time required to prepare different products when changing from one product to another. These preparation times represent economical losses and inefficiencies when having to wait for the quality conditions of the new product in the mill to be able to make the changeover to the corresponding silo. An example of this is when changing from a product with a low clinker/cement factor to one with a higher clinker/cement factor. This cement with a higher production cost is "lost" when having to go to the silo with a lower specification.

On the other hand, separate grinding allows to gain in flexibility and grinding efficiencies by specializing the mills in a base product and not a type of cement. The different types of cement will be produced in the Blending Stations. The Control Room operator will be able to specialize his mill in a single "base product" and achieve better efficiencies, stability, and productivity in the grinding process by not having to make product changes and only adjusting improve production and quality.

Another great advantage in specializing the mills is that the room operators will not have to change mill settings and their operation will be easier to perform and carry out.

Separate grinding allows you to have two "intermediate products": the first one, a "base cement" and the second one, a "mix" containing the easiest materials to be ground. The base cement can be formed by the Portland clinker and setting regulator only and/or by some additional SCM, depending on the types of cement to be produced. The mix will be formed, instead, by the AC, the rest of the SCMs and the adequate amount of setting regulator according to its composition. The mixing percentages of each of the intermediate products will depend on the quality of their components and the qualities or types of cement to be produced.

The separate grinding of the mix allows a better control in terms of the Blaine fineness and the desired retained, being in this case of the AC, materials easier to grind than Portland clinker. Depending on the materials to be ground in this mix, a "coarser" grinding can be sought in terms of the retained in sieve No. 325, which could well be in a range between 10 to 15% and the Blaine fineness would be a resultant. This physical aspect will have great importance in the final fineness and in the conformation of the pore system in the final structure of the produced cement paste which will be, with all certainty, more compact than the one reached in the inter grinding. This will undoubtedly also result in greater mechanical resistance and durability of the cements to be produced in separate grinding with blending stations.

Finally, and as we have seen, separate grinding requires the assembly of blending stations, which are simple in their operation and design but at the same time, very demanding in terms of the Dosing systems to be used, therefore that is where the success of the latter lies. A blending station is equivalent to having a new high capacity and very high efficiency mill. Moreover, it does not need preparation times and only needs to introduce the corresponding mixture of the two intermediate products mentioned: the "base cement" and the "mix". The gain in terms of operation flexibility, dispatch logistics and customer service are unquestionable. For this technology it is essential to have a high-quality dosing and mixing equipment. Its capacity design will be determined by the dispatch and storage conditions.

8. Conclusions and outlook

- Certainly, AC is just beginning to establish itself as the SCM of greater potential than fly ash and any other natural or artificial pozzolans. They are siliceous and aluminous artificial pozzolans in nature, according to the ASTM C618–19 standard [1], and *aluminous* in chemical character, according to R. Talero [3–15], from high to very high quality, according to their reactive chemical composition (SiO_2^{r-} (%) and $Al_2O_3^{r-}$ (%) contents above all and very specially controllable in their manufacture and sustainability with the environment, reducing CO_2 emissions to a 75% in their production, compared with Portland clinker.

- The clays that can be activated are not only kaolinitic but also illitic and montmorillonite (smectitic) clays. But, in any case, their viability of use depends fundamentally, as it has just been said, on the content of SiO_2^{r-} (%) and $Al_2O_3^{r-}$ (%) above all and very specially, that we are able to generate during the process of their thermal activation on an industrial scale.

- The process control of its thermal activation, in terms of maintaining the optimum temperature of calcination in the kiln, is fundamental, since it will guarantee the highest pozzolanic activity of the AC. Therefore, it is of vital importance to permanently control the process variables and the quality parameters of the recently manufactured AC in order to correlate them with the chemical and mechanical parameters of verification of best quality and with the performance variables.

- The separate grinding and blending station are the best option for grinding in terms of quality, particle size distribution, milling efficiency and economic cost.

- The use of activates clays such as SCM to reduce the clinker content in cements is one of the most innovative initiatives that is currently being implemented in the cement sector to achieve the objectives of the European Green Deal to make Europe the first continent climate neutral in 2050. This is a very ambitious goal, but reachable. Through this technology, important emission reductions that will allow the cement and concrete value chain be climate neutral by 2050. This will allow our society to have a sustainable building material.

DOI: http://dx.doi.org/10.5772/intechopen.99461

Author details

Carlos Hernando Aramburo Varela[1], Luiz Felipe de Pinho[2], César Pedrajas Nieto-Márquez[3]* and Rafael Talero Morales[4]

1 Carlos Aramburo Consultant, Cali, Colombia

2 Dynamis, Sao Paulo, Brazil

3 Cementos Argos, Medellín, Colombia

4 SACACH S.L, Madrid, Spain

*Address all correspondence to: cpedrajas@argos.com.co

References

[1] ASTM C 618-19 Standard. "Standard Specification for Coal Fly Ash and Raw or Calcined Natural Pozzolan for Use in Concrete". ANNUAL BOOK OF ASTM STANDARDS, Section 4 Construction, Vol. 04.02 Concrete and Aggregates.

[2] UNE EN 197-1:2011 Standard. "Cement -Part1: Composition, specifications and conformity criteria for common cements". AENOR. Spain.

[3] Aramburo, C., Pedrajas, C., Rahhal, V., González, M., Talero, R.: "Calcined clays for low carbon cement: Rheological behavior in fresh Portland cement pastes". Materials Letters 239, pp. 24-28, 2019.

[4] Talero R, Rahhal V "Influence of aluminic pozzolans, quartz and gypsum additions on Portland cement hydration". 12th Intern. Congress on the Chemistry of Cement, Proceedings, Montreal, Canada, 8-13 july 2007.

[5] Rahhal V, Talero R. "Calorimetry of Portland Cement with Metakaolins, Quartz and Gypsum Additions". J Therm Anal Cal, 91 (3). p. 825-834, 2008.

[6] Talero, R., Rahhal, V.: "Calorimetric comparison of Portland cement containing silica fume and metakaolin: Is silica fume, like metakaolin, characterized by pozzolanic activity that is more specific than generic?". J. Therm. Anal. Cal., 96 (2), pp. 383-93, 2009.

[7] Talero R, Bollati M.R., Hernández-Olivares F. "Manufacturing non-traditional mortars and concretes by OPC, metacaolin and gypsum (15,05%)". Mater Construcc, 49 (256). p. 29-41, 1999.

[8] Talero, R.: "Performance of metakaolin and Portland cements in ettringite formation as determined by Le Chatelier-Ansttet test: Kinetic and morphological differences and new specification". Sil. Ind. 72 (11-12), pp.191– 204, 2007.

[9] Talero R. "Expansive synergic effect of ettringite from pozzolan (metacaolin) and from OPC, co-precipitating in a common plaster-bearing solution, Part II: Fundamentals, explanation and justification". Constr Build Mater. 25, p. 1139-1158, 2011.

[10] Talero, R.: "Gypsum attack: performance of silicic pozzolans and Portland cements as determined by ASTM C 452-68". Adv.in Cem. Res. 24 (1), pp. 1-15, 2012.

[11] Arámburo C, Pedrajas C, Talero R. "Portland cements with high contents of calcined clay. Mechanical strength and sulfatic attack behaviors". Materials 2020, 13, 4206, 2020.

[12] Lannegrand R., Ramos G., Talero R. "Condition of knowledge about the Friedel's salt". Mater Construcc 51 (262), abr./may. / jun. 2001.

[13] Jones M.R., Macphee D.E., Chudek J.A., Hunter G., Lannegrand R., Talero R., Scrimeneour, S. N. "Studies using 27Al MAS RMN of AFm and AFt phases and the formation of Friedel's salt". Cem Concr Res, 33, p. 177-182 (2003).

[14] Mejía R, Delvasto S, Talero R. "Chloride diffusion measured by a modified permeability test in normal and blended cements". Adv Cem Res, Vol. 15, n°3, p. 113-118 (2003).

[15] Talero R. "Synergic effect of Friedel's salt from pozzolan and from OPC co-precipitating in a chloride solution". Constr Build Mater, 33, p. 164-180 (2012).

[16] Trusilewicz L, Fernández-Martínez F, Rahhal V,

Talero R. "TEM and SAED Characterization of Metacaolin, Pozzolanic Activity". J Amer Ceram Soc, 95 (9), p. 2989-2996, 2012.

[17] Álvarez-Pérez A, Prada-Pérez JL. "Atlas de asociaciones minerales en lámina delgada". Vol. I Caps. 12 y 29: ASOCIACIONES MINERALES EN PROCESOS CERÁMICOS". Fundación Folch. Univ. de Barcelona – España. First Edition: UB 1997.

[18] Grim R.F. "Clay Mineralogy". Mc Graw-Hill, Nueva Tork, pp. 596, 1968.

[19] Grimshaw R.W. "The Chemistry and Physics of Clays and Allied Ceramic Materials", 4th Edition Revised, Ernes Benn Limited, London. 1971.

[20] UNE-EN 196-5:2006 Standard. "Methods of testing cement. Pozzolanicity test for pozzolanic cements". AENOR.

[21] UNE 80-225:2012 Standard: "Métodos de Ensayo de Cementos. Análisis Químico: Determinación del Dioxido de Silicio (SiO_2) Reactivo en los Cementos, en las Puzolanas y en las Cenizas Volantes" AENOR.

[22] Talero, R. New method of wet chemical analysis to determine reactive alumina content in natural and artificial pozzolans. Priv. Communed. 2014.

[23] Norma UNE-EN 196-2: 2014. "Método de ensayo de cementos. Parte 2. Análisis químico de cementos". AENOR.

Chapter 10

Production of Electrical Porcelain Insulators from Local Raw Materials: A Review

Uchenna Ekpunobi, Christopher Ihueze, Philomena Igbokwe, Azubike Ekpunobi, Happiness Obiora-Ilouno, Chijioke Onu, Sunday Agbo, Samuel Ezennaya, Uzochukwu Onuigbo, Ifenyinwa Tabugbo, Arit Etukudoh, Caius Onu and Emma Amalu

Abstract

This paper reviewed the production of electric porcelain insulators utilizing from local raw materials from developing countries. The raw materials used were feldspar, quartz/silica and kaolin. The chemical composition, mineralogy, and thermal properties of the raw materials were characterized using AAS, XRD, and TGA respectively. Different weight percentage combinations of the individual raw materials were investigated by the authors. Most of the results showed relatively acceptable porcelain insulators properties such as low water absorption, porosity, high insulation resistance, dielectric strength and bulk density. The paper showed that electric porcelain insulators with good properties can be produced from available local raw materials in some developing countries using appropriate formulations. However, for production of improved porcelain insulators properties, suggestions were made on the areas for future research.

Keywords: porcelain insulator, feldspar, quartz, kaolin, electrical insulation, water absorption

1. Introduction

Since the origin of electricity generation at the Edison direct current pearl street power station, electricity industries have grown to become an essential part of human lives. The energy demand in Africa is increasing significantly due the springing up of industries and advancement in the human standards of living in the continent [1]. These have place a continuous strain on the power sectors to meet up with the consumers' demand which are increasing on daily basis. For instance, in Ethiopia the energy sector have been growing in the past two decades and reached currently electric power of 2360 MW, this would be expected to reach 10,000 MW in the next 10 years [2].

It has been estimated that more than 20% of the total outlay for a typical transmission and distribution system of electrical energy is spent on insulation alone

[3]. Nigerian electrical power holding company (PHCN) spends a lot of resources maintaining and replacing aged insulators on electric transmission lines. It imports 99% of the total insulators it uses, notably from Asian countries, of which ceramic insulators occupies a central position [3]. The high degree dependency on importation has led to the high cost of maintenance and replacement of insulators used for the transmission of the electricity. Since majority of these insulators are imported, their standard has posed a big challenge to consumers. This is due to the different environmental conditions of the countries involved in manufacturing and consumption. These varied environmental conditions affect the efficiency of insulators.

Electrical insulators help to prevent the passage of current to other areas where it is not wanted or where it can cause harm or death to the living things that come in contact with it [4]. Among the insulator materials utilized in electric power transmission and distribution systems, porcelain ceramic insulators is the most commonly used material for overhead insulators [5]. The use of ceramic porcelain as electrical insulator is unrivalled by any other materials currently. Porcelain insulators are characterized with excellent properties such as high mechanical strength, high electrical stability and corrosion resistance even in harsh environments [6]. These properties have made these insulators dominant in electrical power industries over the years, despite the emergence of new insulators made from plastics and polymer composites.

The word "porcelain" has it origin in the Italian "porcella" literally meaning "little pig", a Mediterranean sea-snail whose shell is white and translucent [7]. The first ceramic porcelain was first manufactured in China, followed by Europe during the period of industrial revolution [8]. In 1849, Werner Von Siemens adopted the traditional porcelain to produce one of the first electric insulators to insulate the telegraph cable from Frankfurt to Berlin [9]. Porcelain was believed to be the first material to be made artificially by humans, the majority of the early Chinese porcelain was called "hard paste" porcelain which was composed of: 50% Kaolinite ($Al_2O_3SiO_22H_2O$), 25% Feldspar ($K_2OAl_2O_36SiO_2$) and 25% Quartz (SiO_2) [8]. These three constituents place ceramic porcelain in the phase system in terms of oxide constituent, hence termed "Triaxial porcelain" [10]. The kaolin clay content of this porcelain gives plasticity to the ceramic mixture while quartz maintains the shape of the formed article during firing and feldspar serves as flux, which is added to decrease the required firing temperature and thus to reduce cost by saving Energy [11]. They are vitrified and fine-grained ceramic white wares, used either glazed or unglazed, baked at high temperatures to achieve vitreous, or glassy, qualities such as low porosity and translucence [5]. They are widely used in household, laboratory and industrial applications. Ceramic Porcelains are suitable for electrical, chemical, mechanical, structural and thermal wares. The versatility of porcelain makes them applicable for both low and high tension insulation in electrical transmissions. Although in electrical insulation applications, porcelains are expected to meet minimum specification of the latter two, dielectric (high resistivity, low dielectric loss) and mechanical properties [12]. They should also have low atomic mass, low defect concentration, high lattice stiffness, high purity with a minimum disorder, resistivity between $10^{12}\ \Omega$–$10^{14}\ \Omega$ and covalent [13]. Electrical porcelains have been technologically evolved regarding the design topics, manufacturing process and raw materials in order to fulfill highly demanded market requirements [14].

Over the years porcelain insulators have demonstrated numerous advantages over many insulators such as good mechanical strength, good environmental aging performance, and excellent resistance to material degradation caused by electrical stress and discharge activities [15]. Porcelain allows high surface leakage current to flow on their wetted surfaces, due to their low hydrophobic surface characteristics which permits water to form a continuous conductive film along the creepage path [16].

There is constant vandalization of ceramic porcelain insulators due to its high cost. These challenges gave rise to the introduction of polymeric insulators at distribution voltage levels, as alternative to ceramic porcelain insulators due to its low cost.

Non ceramic or polymeric insulators have good hydrophobic surface characteristics, high mechanical strength to weight ratio, resistance against vandalism and reduced maintenance costs [17]. On the other hand, polymeric insulators are easily affected by UV rays, stress due to high voltages and they also contribute to environmental pollutions [14].

1.1 Origin and functions of triaxial constituents of ceramic porcelain insulator

1.1.1 Kaolin

The major mineral constituent of the clay used in porcelain is kaolinite; rocks rich in this mineral are typically referred to as either 'china clay' of 'kaolin'. Kaolin is a soft white mineral that has a large array of uses, which, under the electronic microscope it is seen to consist of roughly hexagonal, platy crystals ranging in size from about 0.1micrometer to 10 micrometer or even larger [18, 19]. Kaolin are found in combination with other minerals such as muscovite, quartz, feldspar and anatase in nature [20]. It has always been used with other materials so as to increase it workability, and also to lower the klin temperature necessary to produce a firm product. This china clay has found extensive usage in making pharmaceuticals, paint, paper and composite materials. It is the major constituent used in manufacturing electrical porcelain. Kaolin gives the fired porcelain a soft plastic base, shape and opacity [21]. It has melting point of 1800°C, with a molecular formula $(Al_2O_3.2Si)_2\ 2H_2O$, with a highly refractory acumen [22]. Kaolinite is the main constituent of kaolin with 39.8% alumina, 46.3% Silica, 13.9% water. **Figure 1** shows the chemicals structure of kaolinite as designed by Brindley and Nakahira [23].

1.2 Quartz

Quartz or silica is a ubiquitous mineral with molecular formula SiO_2 in its purest form. It occurs in many diverse modes in nature. The name 'quartz' is an old German word of uncertain origin, first used by George Agricola in 1530 [24]. Quartz contains 99–100% silica (SiO_2) and about 0.1% impurities such as Fe_2O_3, Na_2O, CaO, MgO, Al_2O_3 and K_2O depending on its percentage purity [25]. They occur as primary and essential constituent of igneous rocks of acidic composition, such as Granite, Porphyry and Rhyolite [26]. **Figure 2** shows the schematic quartz structure showing the most intrinsic and extrinsic lattice [27].

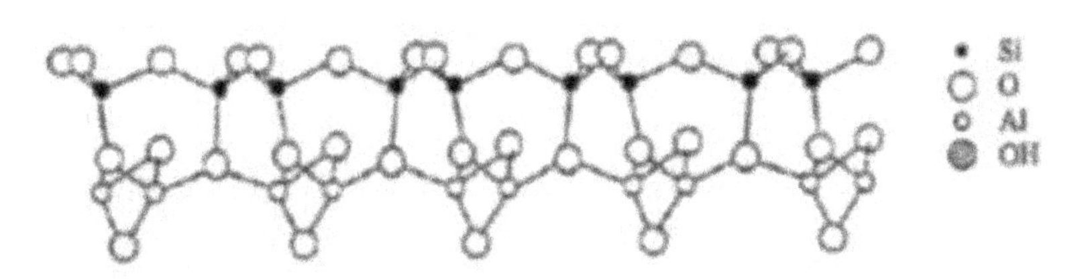

Figure 1.
Structure of kaolinite designed by Brindley and Nakahira viewed from the a-axis direction [23].

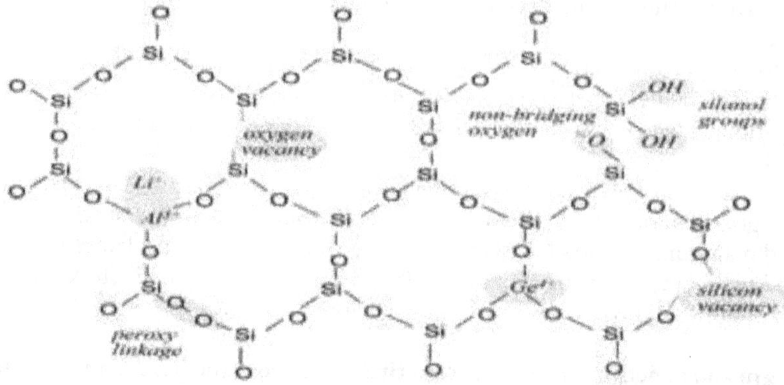

Figure 2.
Schematic structure of quartz [27].

Quartz plays a very important role in the formulation of ceramic porcelain. The fired porcelain microstructures consist mainly of glass phase, mullite and quartz as major crystalline phases. Quartz helps to maintain the shape of the ceramic porcelain during firing. Evidence have shown that under optimized conditions of firing and for particle of size of 10–30 μm, quartz has a beneficial effect on the strength of porcelain, in conformity with the matrix reinforcement and dispersion strengthening hypotheses [28]. It's evident that quartz particle size plays a vital role in controlling the mechanical strength of ceramic porcelain insulators. They also provide the refractory crystalline phase or skeleton contributing to the mechanical strength of the body.

1.3 Feldspar

The compositional and structural properties of Feldspar envisage the rich information that can be tied to their genesis. They are among the most vital minerals found in the earth crust with extensive solid solutions at temperatures higher than about 700°C and large immiscibility gaps at lower temperatures [29]. They are aluminosilicate minerals with the general molecular formula AT_4O_8 in which A = potassium, sodium, or calcium; and T = silicon and aluminum, with a Si:Al ratio ranging from 3:1 to1:1. Feldspar comes in three major formulations $NaAlSi_3O_8$, $KAlSi_3O_8$ and $CaAlSi_3O_8$ respectively [30].

The structure of feldspars is a three-diamentional framework of linked SiO_4 and AlO_4 tetrahedra, with sufficient opening in the framework to accommodate K, Na, Ca, or Ba to maintain electroneutrality as shown in **Figure 3**. In **Figure 3**, the small black circles are Si and Al, the large circles is O (oxygen) [31]. Feldspar rocks are used in the fine ceramic industry as a fluxing agent to form a glassy phase for accelerating of sintering process and, also as sources of alkalis and alumina in glazes [32]. They are the fluxing agent for the ceramic porcelains. Its selection significantly affects the properties of the fired ceramic porcelain body and optimal firing temperature or soaking time [33]. The densification of the green body and the stain resistance of polished ceramic porcelain are determined by the distribution of the particle size of feldspar [34].

Electrical ceramic porcelains are considered to be one of the most complex ceramic systems. A variation on the triaxial constituent (kaolin, feldspar and quartz) of porcelain can affect the thermal, dielectric or mechanical properties of the porcelain [5]. The effectiveness of porcelain ceramic insulator on low or high voltage transmission line is determined by its chemical constituents.

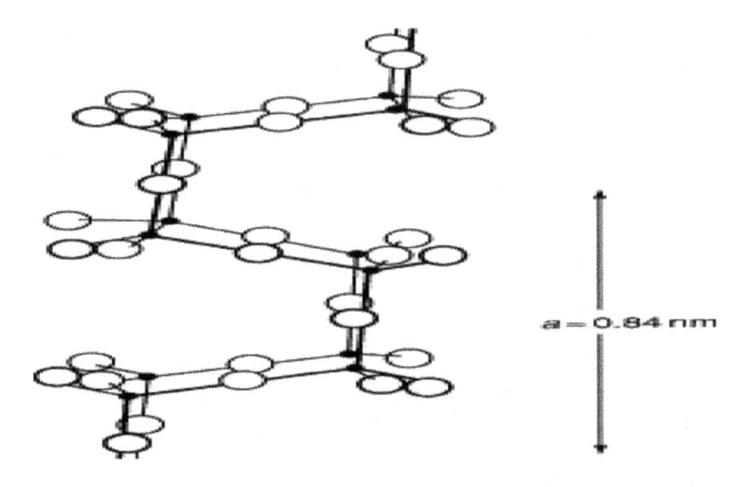

Figure 3.
The essential structural features of all feldspar projected on a plane [31].

There has been tremendous progress on the enhancement of porcelain, but challenges still remain in understanding the properties relating to the selection and investigation of its raw materials, processing, microstructure and phase evolution, all which are critical determinants for its use as electric insulation materials [35]. This research reviews the physical and chemical properties of the electrical ceramic porcelain insulators as an indication for their electrical applications.

2. Review on different materials with their percentage compositions used to produce electrical ceramic porcelain insulators (ECPI)

ECPI are made up of two major types of materials: the plastic materials and the non-plastic materials.

The plastic materials are essentially the clay materials or kaolinites, they serve as the shape makers. Plastic materials essentially give the ECPI the required shape without rupturing during forming and they also help them to retain the required shape after forming. The non-plastic materials include the quartz, feldspar and many other similar materials. These materials help to reduce the plastic nature of the ECPI so as to ameliorate cracks during drying, and also help to lower the firing temperature of ECPI [36].

Ovri and Onuoha sourced kaolin clay from Awo-omama in Oru East Local Government area of Imo state, Nigeria [5]. The clays used for the studies were called Awo-omama clay and Ibere clay located in Ikwuano Local Government Area, Abia State, while feldspar and quartz were bought locally from Umuahia in Abia State, Nigeria. The Awo-omama clay, Ibere clay, feldspar and quartz from their report showed a high level of SiO_2 and the lowest content of K_2O, with no K_2O present in quartz.

In 2018, locally sourced materials, that is, Feldspar (Kagara), Quartz (kadna) and Talc (kagara) were used for the production of ECPI by Nwachukwu and Lawal. This was to investigate their insulation strength [37]. The compositions used in the production were kaolin 28%; ball clay 10%; feldspar 35% and quartz 25% for the most potent sample as reported, the percentage composition of Talc was kept constant at 2%.

Ball clay sourced from Ise, Ikere-Ekiti, Ekiti state, Nigeria was reported as a binder in the formations of ECPI [7]. Kaolin which was the major constituent in the

ECPI was gotten from Ijapo, Akure, Ondo State, Nigeria while feldspar and quartz were sourced from Ogun state, Nigeria. In southern part of Ghana, raw kaolin, feldspar and quartz materials deposited in Assin-Fosu and Kumasi, located in central region and Ashanti region respectively were used for the manufacture of two different ECPI. Assin-fosu sample analysis showed a high level of kaolin compare to Kumasi sample, while that of Kumasi contains higher level of feldspar and quartz respectively [38].

Bamboo leaf ash was partially substituted in production of ECPI by Marimuthu in south Indian state. The combination of bamboo leaf ash gathered from the campus of Annamalai University in Chidambaram, Tamil Nadu, with clay, feldspar and quartz purchased from M/s Oriental Ceramic Industry, Viruthachalam, Tamil Nadu were employed [39].

In 2014, Olupot used ball clay from Mukono, kaolin and feldspar from Mutaka and sand from Lido beach on the shores of Lake Victoria in Entebbe, Uganda to produce ECPI [25].

The development of ECPI from local clays gotten from Ekwulobia, Iva Valley and Nawfija in Anambra state, Nigeria, were studied [40]. The study compares the physical, chemical and mechanical characteristic of these clays to obtain the unique properties that make ECPI suitable for electrical insulation in varied conditions.

Four porcelain composite comprising of kaolin (27–37%), beach sand (20–24), ball clay (13–18%) and feldspar (25–40%) were used to formulate ECPI to investigate the triaxial properties of ceramic composite [41].

2.1 Method of producing ECPI

The methods for production of ECPI are generally similar just a little alterations according the producers demand. Budnikov recommended kaolin 30%, ball clay 10%, feldspar 22% and quartz 38% as the percentage composition of the mixture used in manufacturing ECPI [42]. Although ECPI with a mixture composition of 27% kaolin, 13% ball clay, 40% feldspar and 20% sand have also been studies [39]. The basic process of production of ECPI is described in the diagram below:

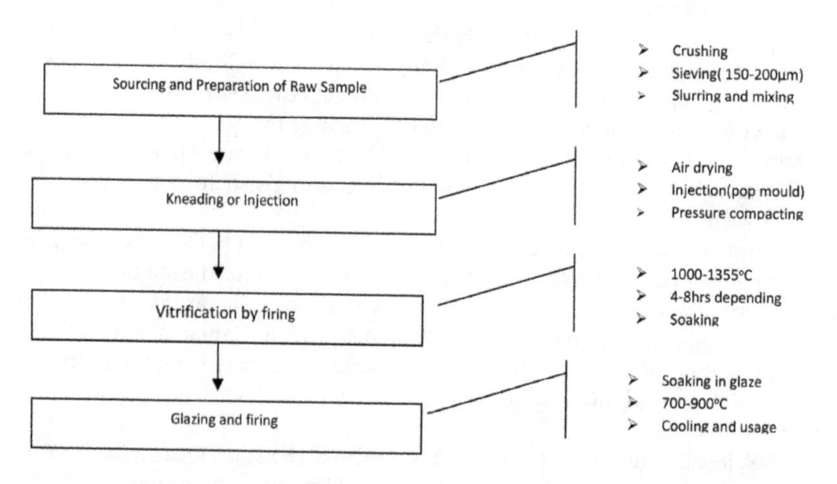

The chemical and physical properties of kaolin, feldspar and quartz were determined before the production is carried out in most of the reported previous studies [3, 7, 43]. Oladiji also used Atomic Absorption Spectroscopy (AAS) to determine the chemical composition of quartz and feldspar after the materials have been crushed and sieved properly [7]. Another study determined the physical properties of ECPI such as bulk density, moisture content, linear shrinkage and porosity using Archimedes method with water as the liquid medium as for ASTM 378–88 and universal tester (UTM) was used to determine the mechanical strength of the ECPI [39]. The morphological structure of the clay, quartz and feldspar were also determined using XRD and field emission gun scanning electron microscope (FEG-SEM) [39, 43]. The particle size and the dielectric measurements of ECPI constituents were determined using particle size distribution analyzer (Analysette 22) and a high voltage breaking voltage test machine (Terco HV-9133) [41].

3. The effect of different methods of manufacturing ECPI on its electrical, physical and mechanical properties

The chemical composition of ECPI plays an important role on the ECPI reactions to the change in environmental conditions. It's evident that the change in environmental condition such temperature and pressure can affect the life span of most chemically bonded compounds. These compounds tend to change their mode of bonding and cleavages with slight change in these environmental conditions. These changes play major roles on the physical and mechanical properties of ECPI especially on their insulation abilities.

ECPI manufactured using a dry process technique was reported [3]. The best sample of insulator produced by this method contains kaolin 30%, ball clay 10%, feldspar 22% and quartz 38%. The sample exhibited zero water absorption after immersion in water for 24 hours. This shows that the sample has very little pores or spaces which might be noticeable if the sample was allowed to stay longer in the water. Little or no water causes the ECPI to have high bulk density, high failing load and a very good resistance when use for high voltages. The breakdown voltage, dielectric constant and the two resistivity where reported as 26 kV/mm, 10.8, 7.14×10^7 Ω-m and 1.97×10^7 Ω-m respectively. The breakdown voltage suggested that the sample has high mechanical strength to withstand high voltage stress, while the dielectric constant suggests that it is a good insulating material. The dielectric constant for good insulating material should fall below 12 [44] and a breaking voltage of ≥25 kV/mm. The two resistivities were high and greater than the recommended value for a good insulator (1 x 10^6) confirming the insulation claims of the porcelain [43].

Ovri and Onuoha analyzed a locally sourced materials using AAS as shown in **Table 1** [5]. The result of **Table 1** is in agreement with previous studies [45, 46]. The two samples (Awo-omama and Ibere) with percentage composition 20–30%

Composition	Awo-omama	Ibere	Feldspar	Quartz
SiO_2	53.54	43.94	63.40	97.42
Al_2O_3	27.75	26.54	17.32	0.15
Fe_2O_3	0.92	0.48	0.83	0.46
MgO	0.93	1.61	0.24	—
CaO	1.35	3.37	0.42	—
Na_2O	0.16	0.28	1.75	—
K_2O	0.57	0.77	14.86	—
LOI (H_2O)	11.20	16.00	0.51	0.42

Table 1.
The Chemical composition of the raw materials used for the study [5].

Feldspar, 50–70% clay and 10–20% quartz exhibited high linear shrinkage of 7.27–9.24% and 8.33–9.68% when compared with other results [45]. This was suggested by Ovri and Onuoha to be due to high content of the plastic materials (clay) compared to the non-plastic content (quartz and feldspar) in the samples. ECPI showed an apparent porosity of 16.81–20.80% and 14.00–17.30% which is in agreement with the value (16.82%) obtained by Power Holding Company of Nigeria (PHCN) while the water absorptions for both clay are also high (8.9–12.15%; 8.33–10.84%). The high value of porosity and water absorption are as a result of non-plastic materials used in the production of the ECPI. These non-plastic materials create more pore or spaces which allow the trapping of moisture in ECPI. High water absorption and porosity are not beneficial for the performance ECPI, because the presence of moisture reduces the electrical resistance of the electrical porcelain. To remedy this issue, good porcelain should have high plastic content and should be glazed properly. Awo-omama and Ibere samples exhibit electrical resistivity (0.61–1.05x$10^7\Omega$-m and 0.79–1.39x$10^7\Omega$-m) that is also in agreement with the recommended PHCN resistivity (0.45x$10^7\Omega$-m). Electrical resistivity is the ability of the insulator to resist current flow.

A report on the use of Bamboo leaves ash (BLA) as a substitute for quartz in production of porcelain has provided a very important waste management strategies, and it is also a cheap readily available raw materials for ECPI production [39]. The study compares the substitution of quartz with BLA at different concentrations respectively. The properties of the specimens were compared with that of standard porcelain (SP) prepared using procedure ASTM C373, an industrial standard ceramic material. The chemical composition showed that BLA also contain high content of SiO_2 just like quartz, feldspar and kaolin. Since BLA is a product of oxidation, it contains more oxide than any of the three constituent as shown in **Table 2**. The porosity and water absorption of the BLA specimen were reported to be decreasing with increase in BLA, they were also higher than the porosity of SP. This is attributed to the fine nature of the BLA, making it easy for them to fill up the pores, therefore reducing the level of water absorption by the porcelain. Similar result have been reported [25, 47].

Low water absorption is a good quality of ECPI since high water absorption reduces the insulating abilities. The bulk density of BLA was reported to be higher than that of the SP due to the filling in of pores by BLA, thereby resulting into denser ECPI. When the bulk density is high while the porosity is low, the mechanical strength of the electrical porcelain (BLA) will be expected to be high too. The

Composition	Clay	Feldspar	Quartz	BLA
SiO_2	63.45	64.20	97.55	79.90
Al_2O_3	29.33	14.02	0.97	2.78
Fe_2O_3	3.17	0.38	0.27	0.86
K_2O	1.15	16.83	0.41	3.98
CaO	0.33	0.65	0.23	7.84
MgO	0.39	0.28	0.08	1.97
Na_2O	0.28	2.90	0.35	0.20
TiO_2	1.57	0.35	0.04	0.38
Others	0.66	0.26	0.10	2.09

Table 2.
The chemical composition of the raw materials (wt%) used [25].

linear shrinkage was also reported to increase as the BLA concentration increased. This is because significant particle occupied the inter-particle spacing as a result of the volume reduction [48]. The mechanical strength of the blended BLA insulator (3.12 MPa) was higher than the reference SP insulator (2.48 MPa). This was attributed to the pozzolanic reaction activity of the BLA insulator, the reduction of cracks and flaw. BLA exhibited higher electrical insulation resistance (21.0 GΩ) and higher flashover voltage (9.92 kV/mm) compared to standard sample (SP) (12.5 GΩ; 8.65 kV/mm) at maximum injection of 5000 DC voltage and alternative current voltage of 50 Hz frequency. The improvements in the electrical properties of BLA sample were attributed to the enhanced physical properties, the presence of fine particles and the presence of high silica content [49].

The triaxial electrical properties of ECPI were investigated by Dowuona et al. using powder XRD, SEM and particle size distribution analysis in order to determine their insulating capacity [41]. Two samples of ECPI produced comprises kaolin (27–40%), beach sand (20–24%), ball clay (13–18%) and feldspar (25–40%). SEM analysis of the materials suggested small uniform particle sizes and radial distribution for kaolin and ball clay, while sand and feldspar are relatively bigger and non-uniform in sizes. The characterization of the powder materials using XRD identified quartz as having the highest peak intensity between kaolin, sand, feldspar and ball clay. Other peaks identified are muscovite, vermiculite and mica in Kaolin; calcite and albite in sand; vermiculite and mica in ball clay; microcline and albite in feldspar. As the particle size increases the percentage shrinkages increment were reported for the different samples, this was due to a drop in the plasticity of the porcelain materials. This suggested that radial distribution of particles was the principal cause for plasticity of clay materials [50]. Larger particles have been reported previously to cause crack in vitreous phase of ECPI compare to fine particles which can easily melt and blend to the mixture [51]. The smaller the particles sizes the greater the loss on ignition (LOI). The two (A&B) samples were milled with different quantity of zirconium oxide (155.85 g and 500 g). Sample A showed bending strength less than 50% of the value of sample B. The presence of ZrO_2 helps the mechanical strength of the sample because of the fine nature of the ZrO_2 particles. The sample with the higher quantity of kaolin (37%), ball clay (18%) and ZrO_2 but low in feldspar (25%) showed highest breakage voltage of 53.4 kV with breakdown strength of 10.45 kV/mm at room temperature. It also showed a high bending strength of 71 MPa which is higher than the standard value for pin type ECPI. The same sample also portrayed very high dielectric strength when compared to the others. The report suggested that it is very important to use fine particle size distribution in order to achieve the desired result in manufacturing electrical porcelain.

Nwachukwu and Lawal used talcum powder in the preparation of ECPI to study its electrical and physical properties [37]. The talc was constant in all the samples while altering the other constituents such as kaolin, ball clay, feldspar and quartz. The constituent composition for each material used in the sample production is shown in the **Table 3**. The chemical compositions of the different materials were determined by X-ray fluorescence spectrometer. The result showed that the quartz contains 95.4% silica, the clay contains 58.75 and 27.6% of silica and alumina, while the Talc was the only constituent that contains Ta_2O_5 and NiO. **Table 4**, presents that shrinkage test, failing voltage, bulk density and water absorption. The samples with little feldspar and quartz less than 5% warped in the mold while those with less clay came out with cracks. This emphasizes the importance of the plastic (clay) and non-plastic materials (feldspar and quartz) in porcelain production. Feldspar functions as a fluxing agent allowing flow of mixtures and the formation of slags by impurities which help to reduce cracks.

Specimen	Feldspar	Quartz	Clay(Kaolin)	Plastic clay	Talc
	%	%	%	%	%
1	0	0	72.21	25.79	2
2	5	5	64.84	23.16	2
3	10	10	57.47	20.53	2
4	15	15	50.10	17.90	2
5	20	20	42.74	15.26	2
6	25	25	35.37	12.63	2
7	30	30	28.00	10.00	2
8	35	35	20.63	7.37	2
9	40	40	13.26	4.73	2
10	35	25	28.00	10.00	2

Table 3.
The percentage composition of the porcelain samples [37].

Properties	3	4	5	6	7	8	9	10
Total shrinkage (%)	8.70	4.19	3.20	3.16	3.01	2.97	5.76	2.60
Fired shrinkage (%)	0.6	0.98	1.06	0.8	0.37	0.32	1.84	0.60
Dry shrinkage (%)	8.1	3.21	2.14	2.36	2.64	2.65	3.92	2.00
Water absorption (%)	3.72	2.89	2.82	2.63	2.60	2.59	3.46	2.52
Bulk density (g/cm^3)	2.14	2.16	2.29	2.37	2.42	2.49	2.74	2.52
Failing load (kN)	1.97	2.55	2.57	2.67	2.69	2.73	1.92	3.01

Table 4.
The physical properties of produced porcelain Insulator [37].

The total shrinkage and water absorption were found to decrease as the plastic materials increases. This is because the clay helps to fill in the pore spaces in the porcelain insulator, but the samples average values are still within the accepted values for the both parameters. The increase in kaolin caused slight decrease on the bulk density even though the feldspar content was increasing. This was attributed to the different value of loss on ignition of kaolin (7.49) as against feldspar (0.73) give by the X-ray analysis [37]. The failing loads were found to be directly proportional to the kaolin content, showing that the strength of ECPI is mainly derived from the plastic materials.

The di-electric constant of the samples (8.7–11.4) showed that they will make good insulator because they fall to the recommended value for good di-electric insulator (below 12.0) [52, 53]. This suggests that the possibility of electric shock is low since the insulator has a good charge storage capacity. The samples exhibit electrical resistance that are above the recommended range $1.0x10^6$ which is a quality of a good insulator [3, 54]. Generally, this suggests that the fine nature of the talc powder helped to amplify the qualities of the other constituents in the porcelain insulators. The sample with the composition 20.63% kaolin, 7.37% plastic clay, 35.0% feldspar, 35.0% quartz and 2% talc possesses the best insulation properties for the ECPI.

The properties of ECPI fired at different temperatures (1000°C, 1100°C, 1200°C, 1300°C) with a heating and cooling rate of 6°C/min and 1-hour socking were studied [1]. The study focused on the effect of different firing temperature on the physical and mechanical properties of ECPI. **Table 5** showed the chemical composition while **Figure 1** showed the effect of temperature on the physical and mechanical properties of different ECPI samples [1].

This clay contains least quantity of SiO_2, this is uncommon for kaolin clays. The clay also has highest LOI, this was due to the loss on structural hydroxide occurred during transformation of kaolinite clay to metakaolinite phase formation around 500°C [1]. **Figure 4** shows the effect different firing temperature on the water absorption, bulk density, apparent porosity and dielectric strength. The water of absorption and apparent porosity decreased with increase in firing temperature and reaching to zero at temperature of 1300°C. This was due to the filling of spaces or pores by molten feldspar as the temperature increases. Reports have shown that the lower the absorption and apparent porosity, the better the insulation strength of ECPI [25]. The dielectric strengths of the samples were reported to reach a maximum of 13 kV/mm as the firing temperature increases. This is attributed to the increased vitrification range of the ECPI samples at the optimized firing temperature [54]. The XRD showed only feldspar and quartz peaks at 1000°C with no peak for the clay. At 1100°C a new peak appeared showing the formation of primary mullite [55]. As the firing temperatures increases beyond 1100°C, the peak for feldspar gradually disappears while that of mullite intensifies and the SEM images showed the formation of glassy phase. This variation on the XRD peaks can

Materials	Oxides (Wt %)									
	SiO_2	Al_2O_3	Fe_2O_3	CaO	MgO	Na_2O	K_2O	P_2O_5	TiO_2	LOI
Clay	46.86	36.74	0.86	0.02	0.08	0.01	1.34	0.04	0.01	13.85
Feldspar	72.50	14.55	2.40	0.52	1.00	2.95	3.68	0.09	0.16	2.08
Quartz	96.66	0.87	0.68	0.16	0.10	0.01	0.85	0.04	0.01	0.36

Table 5.
The chemical composition analysis of clay, feldspar and quartz minerals in wt% [1].

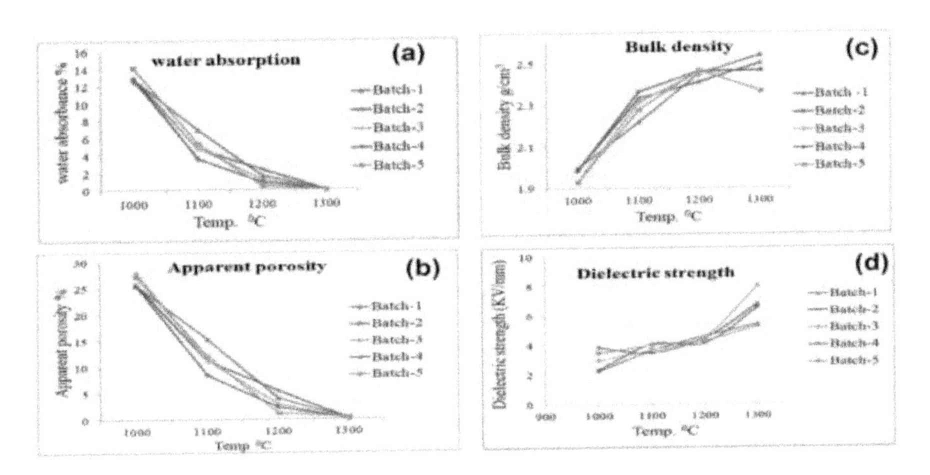

Figure 4.
Variation in (a) water absorption, (b) apparent porosity, (c) bulk density and (d) dielectric strength, of samples with temperature.

be attributed to the melting of feldspar at 1100°C and the formation of glassy phase (mullite) by the melted feldspar.

Stephy et al. reported the production of ECPI made from china clay mixed with kaolin, feldspar and quartz for use on voltage lines of 20 kV, 70 kV, and 150 kV [56]. The ECPI showed a relative permittivity (ε) of 6, with low thermal conductivity, significant heat capacity, good mechanical strength, high stability and strong resistant to corrosion. Maximum and minimum electric field of 142178 kV/cm and 30554 kV/cm respectively were obtained for the 150 kV lines. For the 70 kV lines the maximum and minimum electric field observed were 65743.3 kV/cm and 11720 kV/cm respectively, while 20000 kV/cm to 3061 kV/cm were obtained for 20 kV. Contaminants that accumulated on the porcelain insulator surface affected the distribution of the voltage and magnetic field. Voltage distribution pattern were uniform throughout the creepage distance [56].

Noori et al. monitored the effects of some design materials on properties of electrical porcelain insulators. Wet method was used to prepare the porcelain insulators with feldspar, kaolin and ball clay as the consistent raw materials [57]. The composition of quartz (silica) was varied with alumina as alumina gradually replaced silica in the mixture feed. The result indicated that the bending strength of the produced ECPI increased as the alumina content displaces the quartz in the mixture. Furthermore, the alumina content also increased the bulk density of the ECPI leading low porosity and water absorption. High voltage insulators are expected to have water absorption very close to zero to avoid current conduction. Change in dielectric loss tangent was relatively insignificant while the study on the thermal shock resistance showed that a cycle of 30 was needed before a crack was observed on the ECPI. The sintering temperature (varied between 1250°C and 1350°C) was reported to have appreciable effect on the properties of the produced ECPI. Therefore, the imperfections of quartz-based ECPI can be reduced by using alumina-based ECPI instead.

Moses and Eugene investigated the suitability of Tanzanian raw materials in ceramic porcelain insulator using Pugu kaolin, Kilimanjaro quartz and feldspar [58]. The characterization of the raw materials showed that they have the required properties for effective blending. Sintering temperature of 1300°C was utilized with one hour soaking time. Maximum bending strength of 53.525 MPa was obtained for porcelain insulator with kaolin, feldspar and quartz in the weight percentage of 48 wt%, 46 wt%, and 6.0 wt% respectively. Increase in kaolin weight content with decrease in the quartz content of the mixture significantly increased the bending strength of the ECPI. Low bending strength usually results from development of cracks. Highest ECPI insulation resistance of 42750MΩ at injection of 1000 volts was observed for a mixture of 22 wt% quartz, 64 wt% feldspar and 14 wt% kaolin. The water absorption decreased with reduction in the weight of feldspar content while increasing in the kaolin content. Furthermore, decrease in the relative weight content of feldspar led to a decrease in the bulk density of the ECPI. Linear shrinkages of the ECPI were found to decrease with increase in the kaolin content with simultaneous decrease in feldspar and quartz contents. Moses and Eugene recommended that a quality porcelain insulator should have kaolin, quartz and feldspar in the weight percentage of 48 wt%, 6 wt% and 46 wt%.

Locally sourced raw materials (kaolin, quartz, ball clay and feldspar) from Ondo and Ekiti states of Nigeria with varying compositions were used to produce and characterize porcelain insulators according to Oladiji and his research team [7]. Slip casting method was employed in producing the ECPI with sodium silicate as the deffloculant. The raw materials were separately milled and sieved at 200 μm and mixed. The mixture consists of weight percent of ball clay and quartz while kaolin and feldspar were varied. The result showed that the porcelain strength (in terms of failing load) relatively increased as the weight percent composition of kaolin increased and that of feldspar decreased. There was an insignificant reduction in bulk density of the produced ECPI as the weight of feldspar was decreased (and kaolin increased). This is as a result of high loss on ignition of kaolin compare to feldspar. Water absorption decreased from 4.58% to as low as 0.27% as the weight content of kaolin increased while feldspar decreased. This is because feldspar permits better mixture flow which subsequently increases porosity resulting to higher water absorption. Total linear shrinkage of the porcelain insulator constantly increased from 12.20% to 16.20% with increase in weight content of kaolin coupled with decrease in feldspar. This is as a result of the plastic/clay nature of kaolin. At injection of 1000 volts, the porcelain insulation resistance was relatively constant at about 50,000 MΩ. The insulation resistance gradually decreased at higher injection volts. Material mixture with composition 33 wt% kaolin, 15 wt% ball clay, 32 wt feldspar and 20 wt% quartz was recommended for best ECPI.

Okolo et al. reported on the use of Nigerian clays from different clay deposits in Anambra State in producing ECPI with major objective of determining the insulation resistance of the insulator. Mixtures of the clay, feldspar and quartz of varying composition were used to produce the porcelain insulator [40]. The mixed samples were fired at 900°C after glazing, before sintering at 1250°C. The porcelain insulation resistance was found to increase up to 1.13 GΩ ohms as the clay content reduced at injection of 5000 volts. The best porcelain insulators was found to consist of a combination of 50 wt% clay, 30 wt% feldspar and 20 wt% quartz for Nwafija clay mixture and 60 wt% clay, 25 wt% feldspar and 15 wt% wt% clay for Ekwulobia and Iva valley clays. The work concluded that very low content of non-plastic material led to distortion and high firing shrinkage while very high content resulted to disintegration of the porcelain insulators and vitrification leading to cracking.

Andualem et al. investigated the suitability of local raw materials available in Ethiopia for ECPI production [1]. The quantity of quartz was kept at constant weight of 10 wt% while the weight of feldspar and clay were varied. XRD, AAS, and TGA were used to characterize the individual materials. The materials were mixed, ground and sieved at about 45 to 75 micro meters. Different firing temperatures of 1000°C, 1100°C, 1200°C and 1300°C were utilized. The result indicated that water absorption (and consequently corrosion) decreased as firing temperature increased reaching almost zero at 1300°C. This was as a result of the melting of feldspar at higher temperature. Expectedly, increase in temperature resulted to an increase in the bulk density of the ECPI since water absorption has an inverse relation with bulk density. However, increase in feldspar to clay ratio led to a decrease in the bulk density due to the large amount of viscous liquid phase from the melted feldspar. The dielectric strength of the porcelain insulator increased with increasing firing temperature with maximum of 8 kV/mm attained at 1300°C. This was due to increased vitrification range at higher temperature. The mixture analysis showed that relatively equal proportion of feldspar and kaolin/clay showed better dielectric strength.

4. Indication for use

Low voltages (500 V to 2000 V): Electrical ceramic porcelain insulator with percentage composition ranges of kaolin 30–50%, feldspar 20–30% and quartz 25–35% at firing temperature of up to 1300°C can be suggested for low voltages.

High voltages (˃2000 V): Electrical ceramic porcelain insulator with the percentage composition ranges kaolin 20–25%, plastic clay 7–10%, feldspar 30–35%, quartz 30–35% and talc 2% at a firing temperature of up to 1250°C can be suggested for high voltages.

Humid geographical locations: The porcelain with percentage composition of kaolin 30%, ball clay 10%, feldspar 22% and quartz 38% with firing temperature of 1300°C. This porcelain will have the least moisture absorption in a humid environment.

5. Conclusion and recommendation

The present paper reviewed the production and characterization of electric porcelain insulators reported by authors using local raw materials. The three major factors for good electrical ceramic porcelain insulators are the percentage composition of the raw materials, the fine nature of the raw materials and the firing temperature. The best percentage composition of porcelain is that which allows minimal water absorption and apparent porosity (kaolin 30%; feldspar 22%; quartz 38%). The fine nature of the porcelain plays a major role in improving the bulk density, total shrinkage, mechanical strength and electrical resistance. The firing temperature of up 1300°C is very good for the vitirification of electrical porcelain. It is important to note the chemical composition of the raw materials differs, so the need to access it is vital to obtaining a quality product. The study concludes that standard and acceptable electric porcelain insulators can be produced from the local raw materials.

Future research suggestions for improved standard porcelain insulators,

- The use of local materials for the production of high voltage ECPI should be investigated.
- Further research should be channeled towards possible full/partial substitution of feldspar by recyclable and economic material with high alkaline content which may increase the glassy phase at reduced firing temperature.
- The potentials of replacing silica with alumina in the feed mixture should be investigated for better quality porcelain insulator.
- The chemical structure of the mixtures before and after firing should be investigated to provide more insight into their effect on the properties/thermal properties of the produced porcelain insulators.

Acknowledgements

The authors are grateful to TETFund Nigeria and hereby acknowledge the body for the award of NRF grant in 2019 which enabled the research on electrical Porcelain.

Abbreviations

AAS	Atomic Adsorption spectroscopy
ECPI	Electrical ceramic porcelain insulator
FEG-SEM	Field emission gun scanning electron microscope
PHCN	Power holding company of Nigeria
MW	Megawatts
SEM	Scanning electron microscope

TGA	Thermogravimetric Analysis
UTM	Universal testing machine
UV-Ray	Ultra violet ray
XRD	X-ray diffraction

Author details

Uchenna Ekpunobi[1*], Christopher Ihueze[2], Philomena Igbokwe[3], Azubike Ekpunobi[4], Happiness Obiora-Ilouno[5], Chijioke Onu[3], Sunday Agbo[1,6], Samuel Ezennaya[7,8], Uzochukwu Onuigbo[1], Ifenyinwa Tabugbo[1], Arit Etukudoh[6], Caius Onu[6] and Emma Amalu[1]

1 Pure and Industrial Chemistry Department, Faculty of Physical Sciences, Nnamdi Azikiwe University, Awka, Anambra State, Nigeria

2 Industrial and Production Engineering Department, Faculty of Engineering, Nnamdi Azikiwe University, Awka, Anambra State, Nigeria

3 Chemical Engineering Department, Faculty of Engineering, Nnamdi Azikiwe University, Awka, Anambra State, Nigeria

4 Physics and Industrial Physics Department, Faculty of Physical Sciences, Nnamdi Azikiwe University, Awka, Anambra State, Nigeria

5 Statistics Department, Faculty of Physical Sciences, Nnamdi Azikiwe University, Awka, Anambra State, Nigeria

6 Project Development Institute (PRODA), Enugu, Enugu State, Nigeria

7 Electrical Engineering Department, Faculty of Engineering, Nnamdi Azikiwe University, Awka, Anambra State, Nigeria

8 Electric Energy Storage Technology Unity, Faculty of Electrical Engineering and Computer Science, TU Berlin, Germany

*Address all correspondence to: ue.ekpunobi@unizik.edu.ng

References

[1] Merga A., Ananda H.C., Murthy E.A., Kalid A., and Eshetu B. (2019). Fabrication of Electrical Porcelain Insulator from Ceramic Raw Materials of Oromia Region, Ethiopia. *Heliyon* 5, no. 02327.

[2] Mondal M.A.H., Bryan E., Ringler C., Mekonnen D., and Mark R. (2018). Ethiopian Energy Status and Demand Scenarios: Prospects to Improve Energy Efficiency and Mitigate GHG Emissions. Energy 149.161-72.

[3] Anih L.U. (2005). Indigenous manufacturer and Characterization of Electrical Porcelain Insulator" Nigerian Journal of Technology, 24 (1).

[4] Porcelain (2009). [online], Accessed 11th August 2009, Available from World Wide Web: http://en.wikipedia.org/wiki/Porcelain.

[5] Ovri J.E. and Onuoha C. (2015). Characterization of Some Nigerian Local Clays for Electrical Porcelain Applications. Int. J. Appl. Math. Res 1(3), 113-119.

[6] Dana K., Das S., and Das K.S.(2004). Effect of Substitution of Fly Ash for Quartz in Triaxial Kaolin–Quartz–Feldspar System.Journal of the European Ceramic Society 24, pp 3169-75.

[7] Oladiji, A.O., Borode J.O., Adewuyi B.O, and Ohijeagbon I.O. (2010). Development of Porcelain Insulators from Locally Sourced Materials. Journal of Research Information in Civil Engineering, 2010; 7(1), 47 – 58.

[8] Jones D.w.(1985). Development of dental ceramic and historical perspective. Dent Clin North Am.1985:29: 621-645.

[9] Lieberman J. (2003). New effective ways toward solving the pronlem of contamination of porcelain insulator. Refrat.Ind. Ceram. 43, 55-64.

[10] Buchanan R.C. (1991). Ceramic Material for Electronics, Dekker, New York.

[11] Olupot P.W. (2006). Assessment of Ceramic Raw Materials in Uganda for Electrical Porcelain. Licentiate Thesis in Materials Science, Department of material Science and Engineering, Royal Institute of Technology(KTH) Stockholm, Sweden.

[12] Barsoum M.W. (1997). Fundamentals of Ceramic New York. McGraw-Hill pp.89, 74-79.

[13] Liu J., Yan H., Reece J.M and Jiang K. (2012). Toughening of zirconia/alumina composites by the addition of grapheme platelets.j. Eur. Ceram Soc., no.16, pp.4185-4193.

[14] Contreras J. E. and Edén A.R.(2017). Nanostructured Insulators – A Review of Nanotechnology Concepts for Outdoor Ceramic Insulators.*Ceramics International* 43, no. 12 8545-50.

[15] Mishra A.P, Gorur R.S, Venkataraman S. (2008). Evaluation of porcelain and toughened glass suspension insulators removed from service. IEEE Trans. Dielectr. Electr. Insul., 467-475

[16] Braini S.M. (2013). Coatings for Outdoor High Voltag Insulators (Ph.D thesis). School of Engineering Cardiff University, Wales

[17] Hackam R. (1999). Outdoor HV composite polymeric insulators. IEEE Trans. Dielectr. Electr.Insul., vol6 557-585.

[18] Ciullo P.A. (1996). Industrial Minerals and their uses: a handbook and formulary, William Andrew, Pp 647.

[19] Aleanizy F.S., Alqahtani, F., Gohary, O.A., Tahir, E.E. and Shalabi, R.A. (2014). Determination and characterization of metronidazole-kaolin interaction.Saudi pharmaceutical Journal.

[20] Richerson.D.(2005). Modern ceramic engineering: properties, processing and use in design.CRC press.

[21] Eke H.O. (2006). Electrical Porcelain Insulators.NIRAN publications, Owerri, Nigeria. ISBN: 978-38215-2-0

[22] Jamo H.U.(2017). Structural Analysis and Surface Morphology of Quartz.Bayero Journal of Pure and Applied Sciences 9, no. 2, 230.

[23] Gabriel V. (2007). The structure of kaolinite and metakaolinite. Epitoanyag-journal of silicate based and composite materials, vol. 59, pg 6-9

[24] Ralph K. and Kinf Z. (1952). Chemical encyclopedia, 8th edition.

[25] Onaji, P. B. and Usman M, (1988), Development of Slip Cast Electrical Porcelain Body: Bomo Plastic Clay, Nigeria Journal of Engineering (NJE), Vol. 5, No.2, pp.89-96

[26] Madugu C.H. and Labaran A. M.(2011). The chemical analysis and composition of kanyi quartz for glassmaking, 6.

[27] Aasly K.(2008). Properties and behavior of quartz for silicon process. Researchgate.net/publication/265414932

[28] Olupot P.W., Jonsson S. and Byaruhanga J.K. (2014). Development of Electrical Porcelain Insulators from Ceramic Minerals in Uganda. In *Ceramic Engineering and Science Proceedings*, edited by Dileep Singh and Jonathan Salem. Hoboken, NJ, USA. John Wiley 25-113.

[29] Balic-Zunic T., S. Piazolo S., Katerinopoulou A., and Schmith J.H.(2013). Full Analysis of Feldspar Texture and Crystal Structure by Combining X-Ray and Electron Techniques.American Mineralogist 98, no. 1 41-52

[30] Dietrich R.V. (2018). identification of specific feldspars. Encyclopaedia Britannica.

[31] Haung P.M and Wang M.K (2005). Encyclopedia of soil in the environment, Columbic University, New York USA

[32] Schairer J.F. (1950). The Alkali-Feldspar join in the system $NaAlSiO_4$-$KAlSiO_4$-SiO_2. Journal of Geology, vol. 58 pp.512-516

[33] Das S.K. and Dana K. (2003). Differences in Densification Behaviour of K- and Na-Feldspar-Containing Porcelain Bodies. Thermochimica Acta 406, no.1, pp199-206.

[34] Alves H. J., Melchiades F.G., and Boschi A.O.(2012). Effect of Feldspar Particle Size on the Porous Microstructure and Stain Resistance of Polished Porcelain Tiles. Journal of the European Ceramic Society 32, no. 10 2095-2102.

[35] Choudhary R.N.P. and Patri S.K.(2009). Dielectric Materials. Introduction, Research and applications. Nova Science Publishers, Hauppauge, N.Y. pp152.

[36] Rado P. (1969). An introduction to the technology of pottery, first Edition Oxford: Pergamon.

[37] Nwachukwu, V.C. and Lawal.S.A.(2018). Investigating the Production Quality of Electrical Porcelain Insulators from Local Materials. *IOP Conference Series: Materials Science and Engineering* 413012076. https://doi.org/10.1088/1757-899X/413/1/012076

[38] Yaya A., Tiburu E.K., Vickers M.E., Efavi J.K., Onwona-Agyeman B. and Knowles K.M. (2017). Characterisation and Identification of Local Kaolin Clay from Ghana. A Potential Material for Electroporcelain Insulator Fabrication. Journal of *Applied Clay Science* 150, pp125-30. https://doi.org/10.1016/j.clay.2017.09.015

[39] Marimuthu S., Sivakumar G., and Mohanraj K.(2017). Estimation of Bamboo Leaf Ash Waste as Partially Substitution in Ceramic Electrical Insulator. International Journal of Waste Resources 07, no. 04.

[40] Okolo C.C., Ifeagwu E.N., Ezechukwu O.A. and Unegbu, R.C. (2014). Development of electrical porcelain insulator from local clays. Int. J. Eng Innov Res. 3,2394-3694.

[41] Dowuona A. N., Yaya A., Nyankson E., Efavi J.K., L N W Damoah L.N.W., Dodoo-Arhin D., Apalangya V.(2018). Investigating Triaxial Electrical Properties of Ceramic Composites for Electroporcelain Insulators. Journal of Ceramic Processing Research 19.

[42] Budnikov, P.P.(1964). The technology of ceramics and the refractoriness London, Edward Arnold Ltd.

[43] Anih, L.U. (1997). Characterization of kaolin-feldspar-quartz triaxial porcelain for insulator application. Proceedings of Electric Power Engineering Conference University of Nigeria, Nsukka.

[44] Briks, J.B.(1960). Modern dielectric materials London, Heywood and Company Ltd.

[45] Chester J. H. (1973). Refractories, Production and Properties. The Iron and Steel Institute London, pp. 4-13,295-315

[46] Grimshaw R. W. (1971). The Chemistry and Physics of Clay and Allied Ceramic Materials. Wiley Interscience, 4th Edition Revised New York, p. 15.

[47] Sivakumar G., Hariharan V., Shanmugam M., Mohanraj K. and Corres Author C.(2014). Fabrication and Properties of Bagasse Ash Blended Ceramic Tiles 4.

[48] Mostafa N. Y., Abdallah A.S., Mohamed S. A., and El-maghraby A.(2010). Sintering Mechanism of Blast Furnace Slag–Kaolin Ceramics. Materials & Design 31, no. 8 3677-82.

[49] Moyo M.G. and Park E. (2014). Ceramic raw materials in Tanzania – structure and properties for electrical insulation application. International Journal of Engineering Research & Technology 3, 1015-1020.

[50] Nkoumbou C., Njoya A., Njoya D., Grosbois C., Njopwouo D., Yvon J. and Martin F. (2009). Applied Clay Science 43. vol.1, pp. 118-24.

[51] Ece O.I. and Nakagawa Z. (2002). Bending strength of Porcelains, Ceramics International 28, pp. 131-140.

[52] Anih L.U. (1988). Characterization of Kaolin-Quartz-Feldspar Triaxial Porcelain for Insulation Application (Msc). Obafemi Awolowo University, Ile-Ife.

[53] Azeta J., Okokpujie K. O., Okokpujie I. P., Osemwegie O., and Chibuzor A. (2016). A Plan for Igniting Nigeria's Industrial Revolution. International Journal of Scientific & Engineering Research, 7(11), 489.

[54] Ngayakamo B. and Park S.E. (2018). Effect of firing temperature on triaxial electrical porcelain properties made from Tanzania locally sourced ceramic raw materials. J. silic. Compos. Mater. 70(4).

[55] Islam R.A., Chan, Y.C. and Fakhrul Islam M.d., (2004). Structure property

relationship in high tension ceramic insulator fired at high temperature. Mater. Sci. Eng. B-Soild. 106, 132-140.

[56] Stephy B. W., Salama M., Zahir .Z., and Faizal A.S. (2018). Design analysis of ceramic and polymer 150kV insulators for tropical condition using quickfield software. Engineering International Conference (EIC2017). AIP Conference Proceedings 1941, 020048 (2018); https://doi.org/10.1063/1.5028106

[57] Noori .R.N., SarrafMamoory R. and Mehraeen S.(2007). Effect of Materials Design on Properties of Porcelain Insulators, American Ceramic Society Bulletin, Vol. 86, No. 3. 9201-9203

[58] Moses G. M. and Eugene P. (2014). Ceramic Raw Materials in Tanzania – Structure and Properties for Electrical Insulation Application.International Journal of Engineering Research & Technology (IJERT). 3: (10): 1015 – 1020.

Chapter 11

Clay Hybrid Membranes in Wastewater Treatment

Tanushree Choudhury

Abstract

Most of NF membranes which are developed recently are composite membranes, whose support layer is covered with an active layer. Among different ceramic support materials that are currently used as support layer, α-alumina supports are integral part of the membrane which is made of artificial materials like alumina and thus adds to the high price of the membrane. This draws our attention in making low cost support material of natural clay which aims to be an excellent membrane support as it possesses high mechanical strength, high permeability, narrow pore size distribution and low manufacturing cost. Titania as active layer for ceramic membrane is preferred over Al_2O_3 membranes. One of the problems encountered when photocatalysts are immobilized on support is the detachment of the micro particles from the support for high flow rates of liquid effluent. This can be overcome by using Montmorillonite clay as support material as it is a great binder.

Keywords: pillared clay, Titania, photocatalysis, dye removal, wastewater treatment, regeneration

1. Introduction

Wastewater encompasses potential contaminants from toxic wastes to natural organic matter and minerals that augurs for a definite treatment and reuse method so as to make water available for the ever increasing population. Some of the typical methods include adsorption, electrocoagulation, sedimentation, chemical oxidation and biological digestion. Each of these processes has its own advantages and disadvantages. Thus the search is on to find effective nanomaterials/technology for the remediation/purification of contaminated water [1–9]. Though titania is an important solid acid photocatalyst, the use of titania pillared clay membranes for wastewater treatment finds less mention in the literature. As a consequence, catalyst screening and design are imperative for efficient wastewater treatment [10]. The integration between catalysis and membrane is a very relevant area to mention for the development of a sustainable novel water treatment technology [11].

Titania as an active layer for ceramic membrane is preferred to Al_2O_3 membranes because of the following reasons such as (a) no neurological toxicity (b) high chemical stability in organic solvents and caustic soda (c) high material purity (d) small crystallite size (e) high surface area and porosity (f) narrow pore size distribution (g) low cost of crystalline anatase form and (h) extreme photostability and (i) extremely amphoteric character [12–14]. Moreover if the TiO_2 material (active layer) is immobilized onto porous support (clay), the photocatalytic membrane

IntechOpen

reactor renders immense advantage due to the multiple functions ranging from decomposition of organic pollutants to self antibiofouling action [15].

2. National and international status of the work

Membrane separation processes have attracted the attention of researchers of late due to its manifold advantages such as cost effectiveness, ease in material recovery, and environmental impact reduction as compared to other separation techniques [16]. The performance of such a system can be further enhanced by the incorporation of nanomaterials and nanotechnology. Composite materials of polymers and ceramics can be used to synthesize membranes with increased permeability, selectivity, and resistance to fouling. Nanofiltration membranes are thus finding applications in wastewater treatment processes too.

Nanofiltration membranes are widely classified into i) organic polymeric membranes and ii) inorganic polymeric membranes. Polymers such as polysulfone, cellulose acetate, polyamide, etc. are commercially used to make polymeric nanofiltration membranes. Conventionally cellulose membranes are used in ultrafiltration and reverse osmosis membrane process. The performance of cellulose acetate membranes can be improved by blending it with appropriate polymers in view of the fact that polymers in view of the fact polymer blends have provided an efficient way to fulfill new requirements for material property. Cellulose acetate/sulfonated Polyethyl ether ketone blend ultrafiltration membranes have been used for separating Cr (III) ions [17].

Phenol is a potential human carcinogen and is of considerable health concern, even at low concentration. A. Bodalo et al. studied the behavior of different nanofiltartion membranes of polyamide thin film composite membranes to remove phenol in wastewater in different operating conditions [18]. It has been observed that the concentration of As in drinking water can be considerable reduced by nanofiltration and reverse osmosis techniques. Literature finds mention of these methods in abundance, but they are not cost effective.

Membrane based separation separation techniques have been widely employed in different countries for treating a wide variety of industrial effluents. The effectiveness of nanofiltration membrane processes in water and wastewater treatment has now become one of the most reliable standard techniques to obtain good drinking water. Harisha et al. investigated the feasibility of arsenic removal from simulated arsenic contaminated water by an indigenously built nanofiltration plant with commercial thin film composite membrane of polyamide [19]. The potential use of nano filtration polyamide membrane for removing Co and Pb ions from wastewater was investigated by Saliha et al. [20]. Polyaniline because of its high degree of solvent resistance is employed to be used as an ultrafiltration membrane by Jinwen Wang et al. [21].

Cr, a typical example of class of pollutant, is generated in aircraft maintenance, electroplating, dye, textile and leather industries. Cr is highly toxic and traditional techniques for Cr removal include adsorption, precipitation, and extraction using aliquat 336 solvents. The membranes used for Cr separation are mostly organic polymer (for example cellulose acetate, polyaniline, etc). The major drawback is that the chemical stability of conventional polymeric membranes is limited with respect to corrosive media like strong acids and organic solvents. Therefore research focuses on ceramic nanofiltration membranes, though only few studies exist on use of ceramic membranes for Cr removal. A novel separation scheme for the removal of As and Cr from water based on adsorption and ultrafiltration processes using porous ceramic membranes has been proposed by A. E. Pagana et al. [22]. In recent years, great advances were made regarding the development of non-silicate ceramic membranes as these membranes have a high selectivity against small macro molecules, drugs, hormones and antibodies. ZrO_2/TiO_2 microporous ceramic membranes were developed by U. Aust et al. for gas separation applications [23].

Ceramic nanofiltration membranes can be used to separate solvents from multivalent ions and small organic molecules. Promising membrane materials for separation of highly charged molecules are Nafion, Nafion/silica hybrid membranes, supported γ-alumina membranes and mesostructured silica layers supported on porous α-alumina. Sandwich type ceramic composite membranes with NF characteristics became available having pore size in the range 0.5–2 nm which can be used efficiently for large ion recovery. Chowdhury. S et al. studied the transport and retention properties of potentially suitable membranes for recovery of highly charged large polyoxomethylate (POM) catalyst molecules from aqueous solution [24].

Wastewater in petrochemical industry is currently treated by activated sludge process with pretreatment of oil/water separation. Tightening efficient regulation and increasing need for reuse of treated water have generated interest in the treatment of petrochemical wastewater by membrane bio-reactor process [25]. Ceramic membranes under micro, ultra and nanofiltration conditions have proven to be economically attractive for the removal of oil from oil produced water [26]. Of all ceramic NF membranes in literature, sol–gel derived γ-Al_2O_3 membranes have emerged as perhaps the most intensively studied inorganic membrane system, because of their unique surface charge characteristics. γ-Al_2O_3 membranes may acquire either a positive or negative charge due to their amphoteric behavior of their surface sites (-OH groups). This allows controlling the sign and charge of the membrane through pH of the solution [27]. Majority of the reported γ-Al_2O_3 membranes were derived from the expensive Al alkoxides that makes them very costly. Hence, research should be focused on the development of an alternative cost effective membrane material.

Clay minerals find potential application as a choice for membrane support material due to its low cost, environmentally benign, good rheological, barrier, adsorption, and binding properties. Though not much work has been done in this regard, development of clay based membrane material would usher in a new technological advancement in the field of Clay Science.

Utilization of clay minerals is now of growing interest. Unmodified and modified UF zeolite clay composite membranes (pore size of the order 10–30 nm) have been used for the separation of Cr by A. Shukla and A. Kumar [28]. Low cost γ-Al_2O_3 composite membrane on clay support has been prepared by Abhijit et.al for the separation of electrolytes from its aqueous solutions [29]. Removal of phenol and o-cresol from water by a combined process of clay adsorption and ultrafiltration was investigated by Liu. S. Hsia et al. [30]. Low cost γ-Al_2O_3 clay composite membrane on a clay support has been prepared using local available cheap clays by Abhijit et al. for the separation of Bovine Serum albumin [31].

However, membrane fouling is still a critical problem of NF plants, which results in flux decline with operating time. TiO_2 has received much attention because of its important role in various applications such as photocatalysts, oxygen sensors, antimicrobial coatings, pigments etc. Among them, the photocatalytic properties to decompose organic compounds can be used in filtration membranes which possibly overcome fouling phenomenon [32]. Zhang. H et al. prepared TiO_2/Al_2O_3 composite membranes with photocatalytic ability by sol–gel technique which has the multi-function of separation and photocatalysis simultaneously [33].

Going by the literature, there are many reports about the preparation of TiO_2 composite membranes, especially using Al_2O_3 as support, but work needs to be done using clay as support material. Development of such low cost membranes shall offer to remove heavy metal ions from industrial wastewater and thus provide a sustainable solution.

2.1 Methods of preparation

2.1.1 Preparation of titania pillared clay membranes

Scientific description of the process **Figure 1**:

Preparation of asymmetric membranes: The development of such a configuration includes shaping of an appropriate support material and formation of mesoporous interlayers with a cut off value less than 1000 Da.

Preparation of flat disk support: Montmorillonite (Mt) was fabricated into flat disks of 25 mm diameter and 2 mm thickness, and was sintered at 600°C in a temperature controlled muffle furnace with a heating and cooling rate of 2°C/min with a hold time of 30 minutes. Mechanical hardness of such membranes was analyzed using Micro vickor, Shimadzu, Model No HMVG20S (load range of 10 g to 2 kg) in Mechanical Workshop in VIT Chennai. It was found to be 26.4 Hv.

Preparation of interlayer Titania sol by colloidal sol–gel process: The precursor for the colloidal sol–gel process was Ti (IV) isopropoxide, common titanium based organometallic compound, purchased from Avra chemicals, India, and was

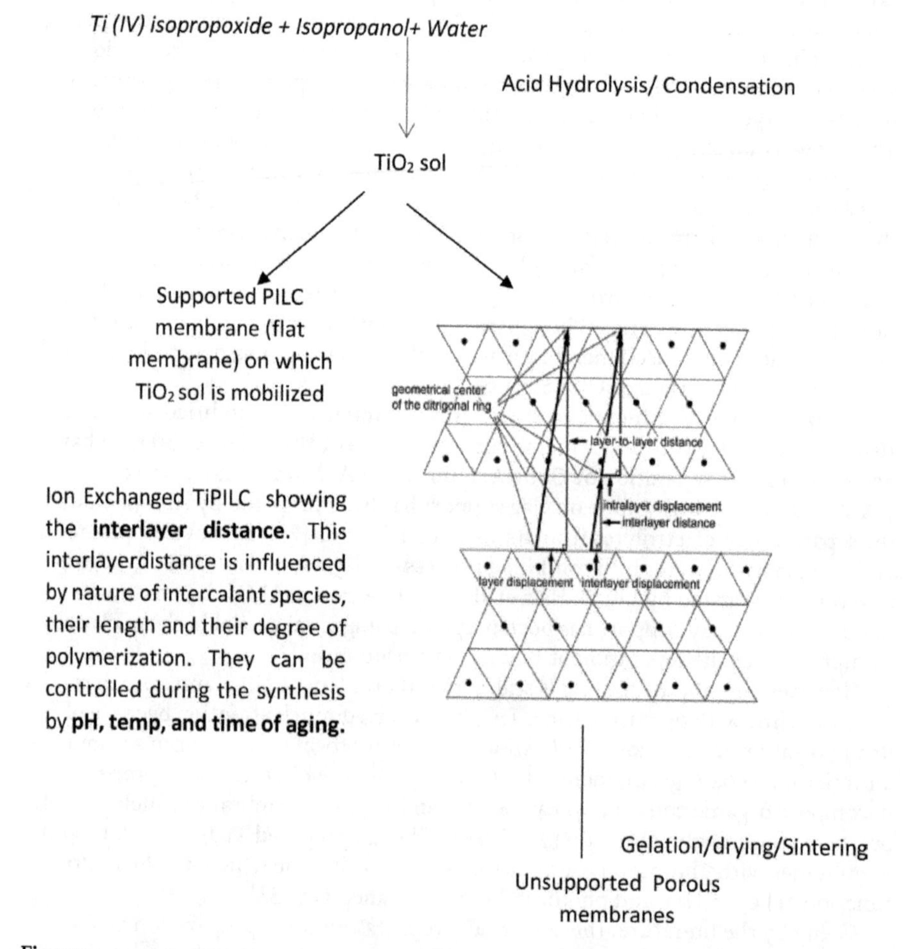

Figure 1.
The flat disk TiPILC membranes prepared at pH 2 and pH 3.5 and sintered at 300°C can be used for filtration of organic contaminants, over a wide range of pH (1–11), with a MW less than 1000 Da. The direct beneficiaries include textile industries (to remove coloring agents), food and pharmaceutical industries (small organic molecules), and wastewater recycling.

hydrolysed by adding excess water. The sol was then stirred at room temperature for 3 hrs after which it was peptized by the addition of glacial acetic acid (99%, Sigma Aldrich, USA) to attain pH 2 and pH 3.5 respectively.

Preparation of interlayer binary (Titania and clay) sol: 0.1 g of Mt. (Montmorillonite K10 with CEC of 80–100 meq/g, Himedia) was dispersed in 10 mL deionized water and was kept for stirring for 3 hrs. 0.1 wt% of cetyl trimethyl ammonium bromide (CTAB, Himedia) solution was added to the clay sol as an organic modifier. The resulting clay sol was then added dropwise to titania sol prepared at pH 2 and pH 3.5 respectively and was stirred overnight for complete intercalation of Ti^{4+} ions into the interlayer spaces of Mt. [34].

Preparation of TiPILC membranes: The interlayer sols thus prepared were immobilized on the flat disk supports by a dip coater with a withdrawal rate of 25 mm/sec. 5 wt% of binder carboxymethyl cellulose (CMC, Avra chemicals, India) was added to the sol as pore directing agent. After uniform coating, the membranes were dried at room temperature and then in air oven at 40°C for few hours. They were then sintered in programmable temperature controlled muffle furnace at 300°C, 500°C, 600°C, which was ramped at a heating/cooling rate of 2°C/min and was kept for hold time of 1 hour. The excess drained from supports were poured onto petri dishes, dried in oven and sintered at same temperatures as above for characterization by Fourier Transform-Infra Red Spectrocopy (FT-IR), X-Ray Diffraction (XRD), Brunnauer Emmett Teller specific surface area (BET), Zeta Potential analysis and Scanning Electron Microscope (SEM).

Number of samples prepared: 24 (12 supported membranes and 12 unsupported ones).

Nomenclature (Supported Membranes).

S1, S6, S10 - Membranes with TiO_2 interlayer at pH 2 sintered at 300°C, 500°C, and 600°C.

S2, S5, S11 - Membranes with binary interlayer of TiO_2 and clay at pH 2 sintered at 300°C, 500°C, and 600°C respectively.

S3, S4, S12 - Membranes with TiO_2 interlayer at pH 3.5 sintered at 300°C, 500°C, and 600°C respectively.

S8, S9, S13 - Membranes with binary interlayer of TiO_2 and clay at pH 3.5 sintered at 300°C, 500°C, and 600°C respectively.

Unsupported Membranes.

PS1, PS6, PS10 - Powder membrane materials with TiO_2 interlayer at pH 2 sintered at 300°C, 500°C, and 600°C respectively.

PS2, PS5, PS11 - Powder membrane materials with TiO_2 and clay binary interlayer at pH 2 sintered at 300°C, 500°C, and 600°C respectively.

PS3, PS4, PS12 - Powder membrane materials with TiO_2 interlayer at pH 3.5 sintered at 300°C, 500°C, and 600°C respectively.

PS8, PS9, PS13 - Powder membrane materials with binary interlayer of TiO_2 and clay at pH 3.5 sintered at 300°C, 500°C, and 600°C respectively.

2.1.2 Instrumentation

XRD was done using Bruker AXS D8 advance powder diffractometer equipped with Cu-Kα generator (λ= 1.5405600 A°). The generator tension was 35 kV. IR was done on Thermo Nicolet Avatar 370 in the spectral range of 4000–400 cm^{-1}. Zeta potential was measured using Horiba Scientific Nano Partica Nano Particle Analyzer SZ-100. SEM of cross section of membranes was taken using High Resolution Hitachi S-4800 Scanning Electron Microscope. BET surface area of samples was characterized by Nova 1000 Quantachrome Instrument by N_2 sorption at 77.35 K. The concentration of the permeate samples from filtration experiment was measured using Thermoscientific UV–Vis Spectrophotometer in the visible range of 200–800 nm. The membrane filtration unit consisted of a cylindrical chamber with a membrane adapter connected to a pressure gauge of 2 Pa and a peristaltic pump Model No RH-P120 VS [34].

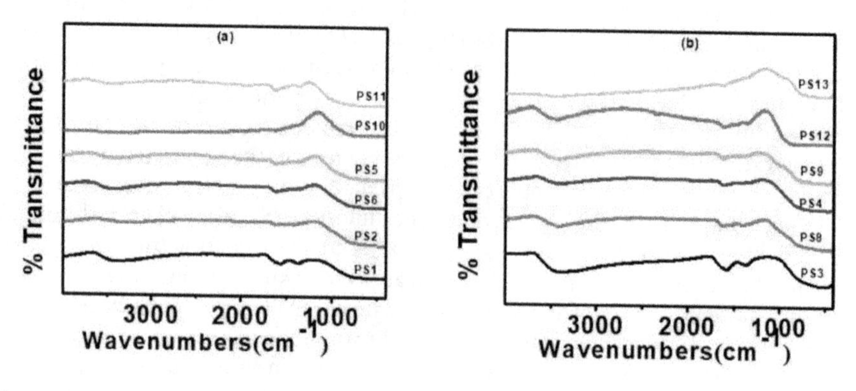

Figure 2.
(a) And (b) FT-IR spectra of unsupported membrane materials at pH 2 and pH 3.5 respectively.

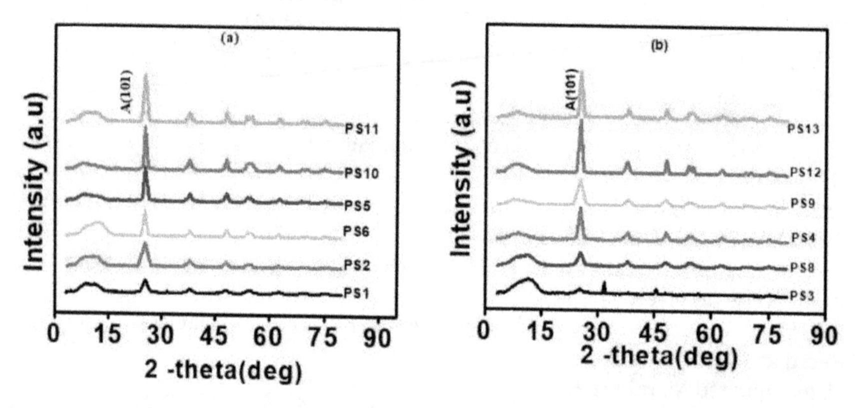

Figure 3.
(a) And (b) XRD diffractograms of unsupported membrane materials at pH 2 and pH 3.5 respectively.

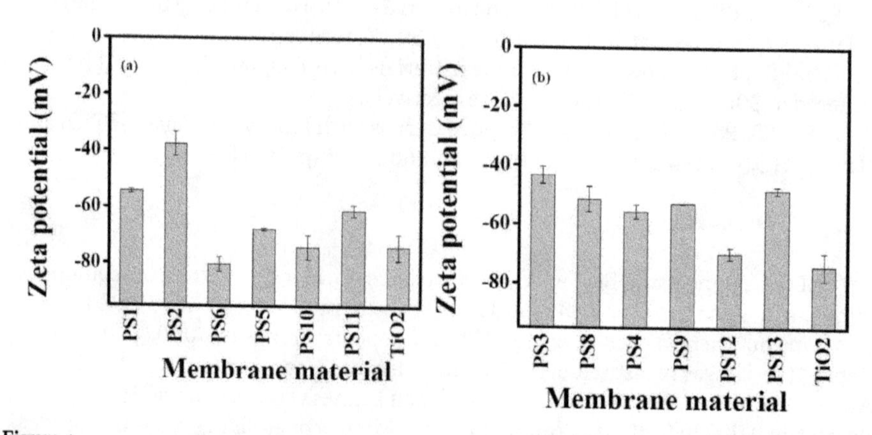

Figure 4.
(a) And (b) zeta potential values of unsupported membrane materials prepared at a) pH 2 and b) pH 3.5 respectively.

2.1.3 Characterization

FT-IR (**Figure 2**)
XRD (**Figure 3**)
Zeta potential analysis (**Figure 4**)
Pore size distribution (**Figure 5**)
SEM (**Figures 6** and 7)
Figures 2–7

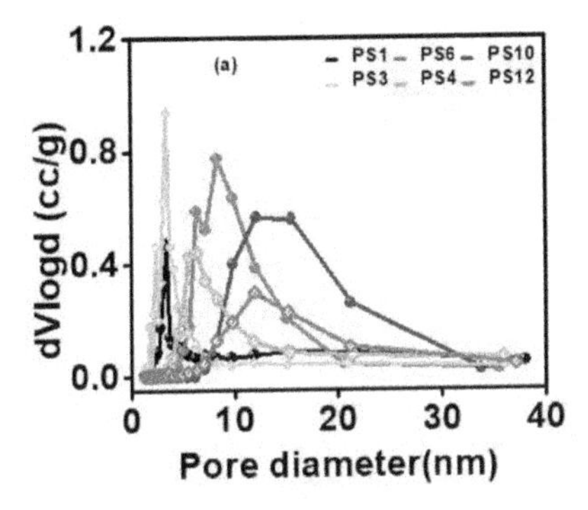

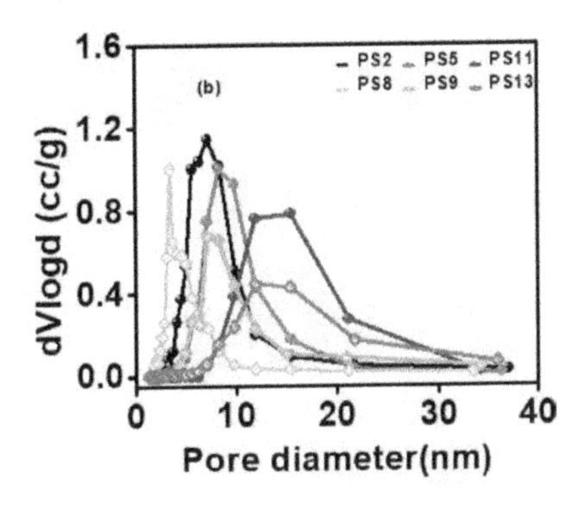

Figure 5.
(a) And (b) pore size distribution curves of TiO_2 interlayer and binary interlayer of TiO_2 and clay respectively.

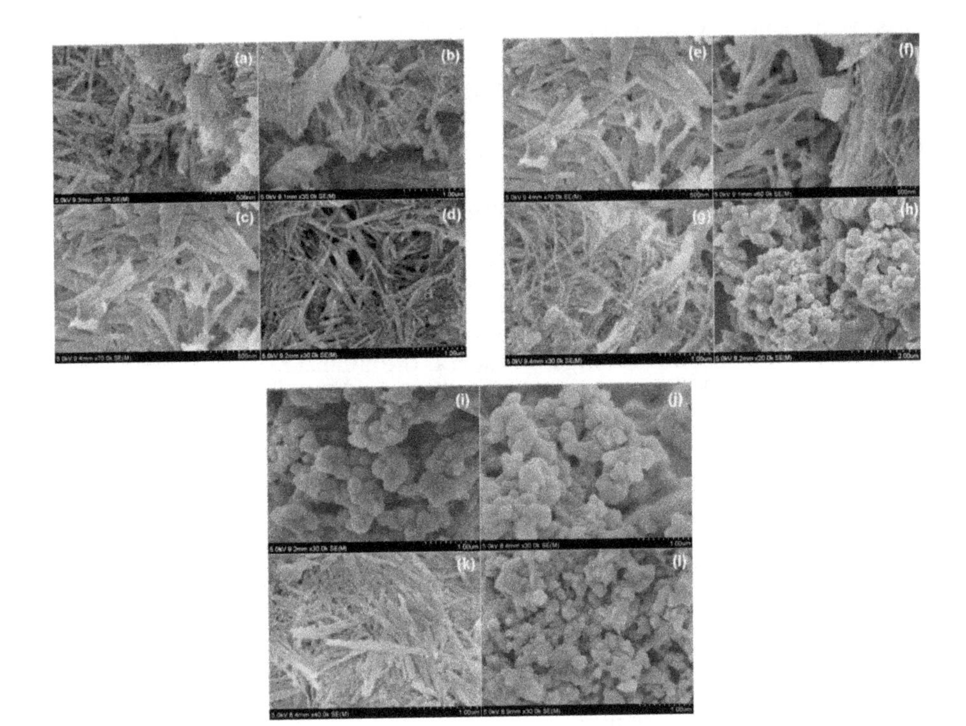

Figure 6.
(a) To (d) SEM of membranes S1, S2, S3, and S8 sintered at 300°C respectively. (e) To (h) SEM of membranes S6, S5, S4, and S9 sintered at 500°C respectively. (i) To (l) SEM of membranes S10, S11, S12, and S13 sintered at 600°C respectively.

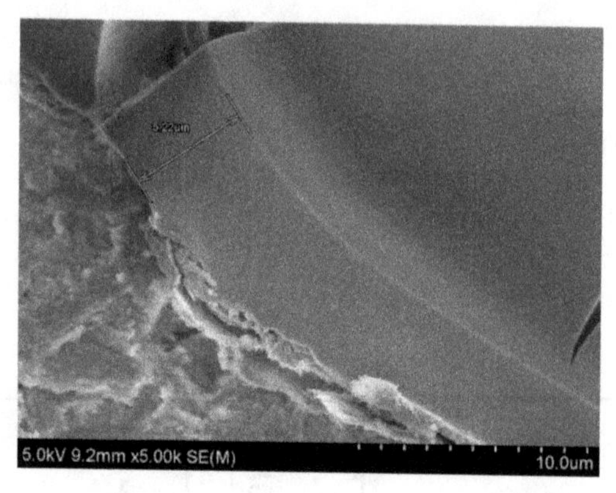

Figure 7.
SEM of asymmetric membrane showing the interlayer of thickness 5.2 μm on the support.

3. Result and discussion

Temperature affects the pore size distribution pattern as can be clearly seen from **Figure 5(a)** and **(b)**. It can be clearly observed that a narrow pore size distribution is observed at a sintering temperature 300°C for membrane materials with interlayer of TiO_2 and binary interlayer of TiO_2 and clay. Addition of clay to TiO_2 alters its pore size distribution facilitating removal of organic dye molecules. XRD diffractograms show the presence of single phase of anatase TiO_2 at temperature 300°C. As the temperature increases to 500°C and 600°C, the anatase phase is the major crystal type which is very efficient for photocatalytic degradation of organic pollutants. FT-IR spectra show the presence of strong bands at 3399.03 cm^{-1} and 1621.55 cm^{-1} due to bonded –OH stretching and bending vibrations of water, thus indicating the formation of anatase phase. Characteristic bands at 1049.31 cm^{-1} and 523.68 cm^{-1} which correspond to Si-O-Si stretch and Si-O stretch respectively are lost completely, indicating complete intercalation of Ti^{4+} ions into the interlayer space resulting in formation of a delaminated and homogeneous TiPILC material [34]. **Figure 4** shows the results for the zeta potential of powder suspensions of membrane materials and model TiO_2 obtained from measurements of the electrophoretic mobility in an aqueous medium. Zeta potential values obtained for membrane materials at pH 2 and sintered at a lower temperature show more negative value as the number of hydroxyl groups in the anatase phase is higher than that of rutile obtained at higher sintering temperature.

3.1 Determination of membrane cut off through filtration with methylene blue (MB) dye

30 ppm of 30 mL MB (Sigma Aldrich, USA) dye solution was prepared. Filtration test was carried by using a peristaltic pump and a cylindrical membrane adapter fitted with a pressure gauge. An average flux rate of 70–110 $L/m^2/h$ was obtained at a constant pressure of 1.2–1.7 Pa. Permeates from the separation experiments were collected and their concentrations were measured by Uv–vis spectrophotometer using the equation:

$$\% \text{ Removal} = (C_0 - C_r / C_0) \times 100 \tag{1}$$

As can be seen from **Figures 8–10** which correspond to percentage removal of MB dyes by membranes sintered at 300°C, 500°C, and 600°C respectively in 3 cycles of filtration, around ~100% removal is achieved. This retention can be explained by high polarity of compounds which causes interactions with the charged membrane.

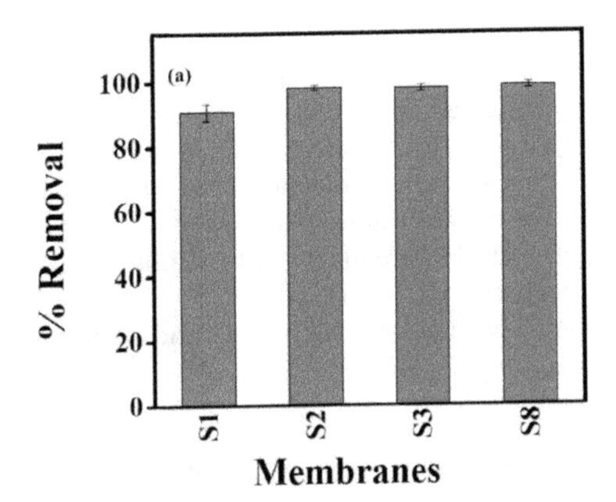

Figure 8.
% removal of MB dye by membranes sintered at 300°C.

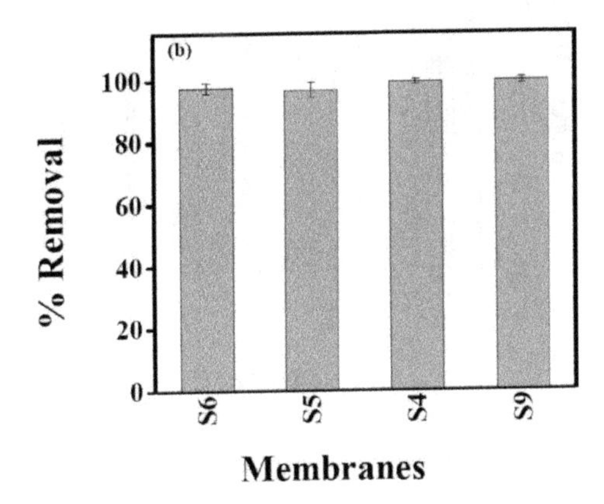

Figure 9.
% removal of MB dye by membranes sintered at 500°C.

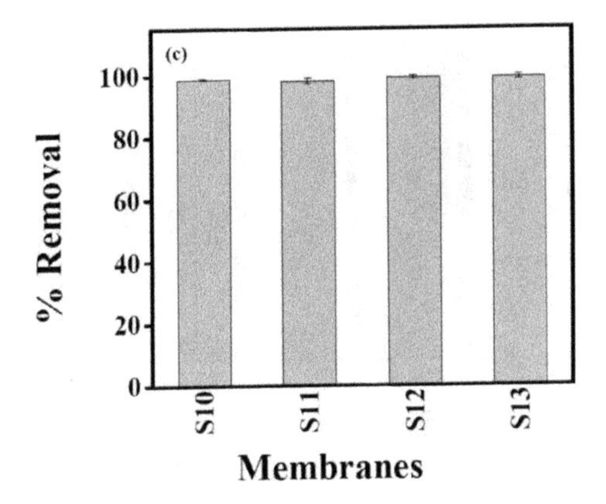

Figure 10.
% removal of MB dye by membranes sintered at 600°C.

Thus the feed solution pH can be considered one of the most important parameters influencing hydrophobicity, the adsorption, and the chemical separation of dissociable organic compounds as well as the membrane surface charge during the experiment.

3.2 Static corrosion test

The corrosion test was performed by dipping the membranes in 50 mL of four different pH solutions i. e pH 1, pH 3, pH 11, and pH 13 for 24 hours followed by drying in oven at 100°C for 4 hours. These membranes were then studied for MB dye rejection test. Corrosion measurements as that of **Figures 11** and **12** indicate that membranes prepared at pH 2 are most stable in mild aqueous media (pH 3–11) as compared to those prepared at pH 3.5.

Thus in aqueous media with a lower/higher pH, the membrane configuration composed of anatase at pH 2 with a MW cut off <1000 Da on Mt. support is preferred.

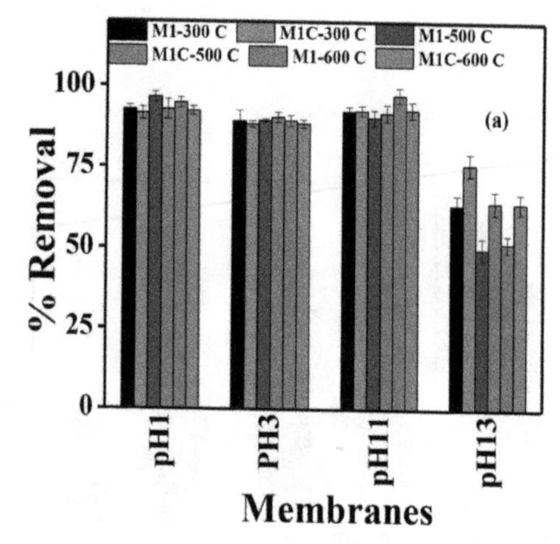

Figure 11.
% removal of MB dye by membranes prepared at pH 2 after corrosion.

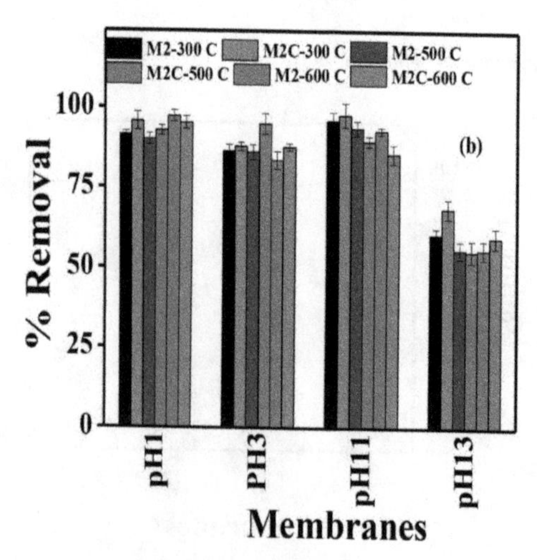

Figure 12.
% removal of MB dye by membranes prepared at pH 3.5 after corrosion.

DOI: http://dx.doi.org/10.5772/intechopen.99075

4. Conclusion and outlook

Titania pillared clay membranes are amphoteric membranes, whose surface charge depends on the pH of the solution. It is a hybrid membrane reactor which integrates the functions of both separations with photocatalysis. These hybrid membranes are characterized by their asymmetric configuration, i. e a top layer of titania in nanometer range immobilized on a porous ceramic support. The separation depends on the thickness of the top layer deposited on the base membrane. The pore size, and the microstructure of the membranes can be governed by choosing the right solvent, suitable pH, temperature of the reaction and peptization during the sol–gel process that governs the key to fine separation. Sintering temperature is a function of the porosity developed in the membranes. TiPILC membranes sintered at 300°C yielded only anatase phase with a narrow pore size distribution for effective separation of organic contaminants. It has been observed during the treatment of such membranes with synthetic dyes such as Methylene Blue (MB), a thin cake is adsorbed on the surface which decreases the flux rate with time thus resulting in the loss of efficiency of the membrane. Titania immobilized on clay support not only increases the hydrophilicity and the flux rate, but also helps in self-cleaning mechanism of the membrane for prolonged use.

Development of field membrane out of that developed in the laboratory is desired for complete utilization. The developed membranes can also be used for removal of heavy metal ions from wastewater followed by their recovery from the membranes would yield the maximum benefit. The product developed can best treat textile effluent from dye industry with concentration in the range of 50 ppm.

Author details

Tanushree Choudhury
VIT Chennai, Chennai, India

*Address all correspondence to: tanushree.c@vit.ac.in

References

[1] Theron. J, Walker. J. A, Cloete. T. E. Nanotechnology and water treatment: application and emerging opportunities. Crit Rev Microbiol, 2008; 34: 43-69.

[2] Busca. G, Berardinelli. S, Resini. C, Arrighi. L. Technologies for the removal of phenol from fluid streams: a short review of recent developments. J. Hazard Mater, 2008; 160: 265-288.

[3] Liotta. L. F et al. Heterogeneous catalytic degradation of phenolic substartes, J. Hazard Mater, 2009; 162: 588-606.

[4] Kwon. S et al. Photocatalytic applications of micro and nano TiO_2 in environmental engineering. Crit Rev Environ Sci Tech, 2008; 38: 197-226.

[5] Bhargava. S. K et al. Wet oxidation and catalytic wet oxidation. Ind Eng Chem res, 2006; 45: 1221-1258.

[6] Centi. G, Perathoner. S. Use of solid catalysts in promoting water treatment and remediation technologies. In: Spivey J J, editor. Catalysis: Royal Society of Chemistry Publishing, Cambridge; 2005 (18). p. 46-71.

[7] Gogate. P. R, Pandit. A. B. A review of imperative technologies for wastewater treatment II: hybrid methods. Adv Environ Res, 2004; 8: 553-597.

[8] Oliviero. L et al. Wet air oxidation of nitrogen containing organic compounds and ammonia in aqueous media. Appl Catal B: Environ, 2003; 40: 163-184.

[9] Imamura. S. Catalytic and non-catalytic wet oxidation. Ind Eng Chem Res, 1999; 38: 1743-1753.

[10] Centi. G, Perathoner. S. Novel catalyst design for multiphase reactions. Catal Today, 2003; 79-80: 3-13.

[11] Rios. G. M et al. Membrane technologies at the service of sustainable development through process intensification. In: Centi. G, Trifiro. F, Perathoner. S, Cavani. F, editors. Sustainable industrial processes, Wiley; 2009. p. 257-278

[12] Hong Wang. Y et al. Titania membrane preparation with chemical stability for very harsh environmental applications. J. Membr. Sci, 2006; 280: 261-269.

[13] Molinari. R et al. Study on a photocatalytic membrane reactor for water purification. Catal Today, 2000; 55: 71-78.

[14] Chin. S., Chiang. K., Fane. A. G. The stability of polymeric membranes in a TiO_2 photocatalysis process. J. Membr. Sci, 2006; 275: 202-211.

[15] Choi. H., Statathos. E., Diaonysiour. D. D. Photocatalytic TiO_2 films and membranes for the development of efficient wastewater treatment and reuse systems. Desalination, 2007; 202: 199-206.

[16] Tarabara. V. V. Multifunctional Nanomaterial Enabled Membranes for water Treatment. In: Nanotechnology Applications: Solutions for Clean Water. Diallo M, Duncan J, Savage N, Sustich R, Street A; 2009. p. 59-75.

[17] Nagendran. A et al. Toxic metal ion separation by cellulose acetate/ sulfonated poly (ether imide) blend membranes: Effect of Polymer Compositions and additive. Journal of Hazardous Materials, 2008; 155: 477-485.

[18] Bodalo. A et al. Nanofiltration membranes to reduce phenol concentration in wastewater. Desalination, 2009; 245: 680-686.

[19] Harisha. R. S. Arsenic removal from drinking water using thin film composite NF membrane. Desalination, 2010; 252: 75-80.

[20] Bouranene. S et al. Influence of operating conditions on the rejection of Co and Pb ions in aqueous solutions by a NF polyamide membrane. J. Membr. Sci, 2008; 325: 150-157

[21] Wang. J et al. Preparation of NF membranes from polyacrylonitrile UF membranes. J. Membr. Sci, 2006; 286: 333-341.

[22] Pagana. A. E et al. Microporous ceramic membrane technology for the removal of As and Cr ions from contaminated water, Microporous and Mesoporous Materials. 2008; 110: 150-156.

[23] Aust. U et al. Development of microporous ceramic membranes in the system TiO_2/ZrO_2. J. Membr. Sci, 2006; 281: 463-471.

[24] Chowdhury. S. Roy., Elshoften. J. E., Benes. N. E., Keizer. K. Development and comparative study of different nanofiltration membranes for recovery of highly charged large ions. Desalination, 2002; 144: 41-46.

[25] Ravanchi. M. Taht., Kaghazchi. T., Kargair. A. Application of membrane separation processes in petrochemical industry: A Review. Desalination, 2009; 235: 199-244.

[26] Ebrahimi et al. Characterization and application of different ceramic membranes for oil-field produced water treatment. Desalination, 2009; 245: 533-540.

[27] Schaep et al. Modelling the retention of ionic compounds for different nanofiltration membranes, SEP PURIF TECHNOL, 2001; 22-23: 169-179.

[28] Shukla. A., Kumar. A. Separation of Cr (VI) by zeolite-clay composite membranes modified by reaction with NO_x. SEP PURIF TECHNOL, 2007; 52: 423-429.

[29] Majhi, M., Monash, P., Pugazhenthi. G. Fabrication and characterization of γ-Al_2O_3 clay composite UF membrane for the separation of electrolytes from aqueous solution. J. Membr. Sci, 2009; 340: 181-191.

[30] Liu. S. Hsia et al. Removal of soluble organics from water by a hybrid process of clay adsorption and membrane filtration. Journal of Hazardous Materials, 2006; B135: 134-140.

[31] Monash. P., Majhi. A., Pugazhenthi. G. Separation of bovine serum albumin (BSA) using γ-Al_2O_3 clay composite UF membrane. J Chem Technol Biotechnol, 2010; 85: 545-554.

[32] Lee. H. S. et al. Polyamide thin film NF membranes containing TiO_2 nanoparticles. Desalination, 2008; 219: 48-56.

[33] Zhang. H et al. Fabrication of photocatalytic membrane and evaluation its efficiency in removal of organic pollutants from water. SEP PURIF TECHNOL, 2006; 50: 147-155.

[34] Neethu. N., Choudhury, T. Treatment of Methylene Blue and Methyl Orange Dyes in Wastewater by Grafted Titania Pillared Clay Membranes. Recent Patents on Nanotechnology, 2018; 12:200-207

Printed in the USA
CPSIA information can be obtained
at www.ICGtesting.com
LVHW051931290923
759510LV00027B/40